Discontinuous and Optimal Control

McGRAW-HILL SERIES IN
MODERN APPLIED MATHEMATICS

Menahem M. Schiffer: Consulting Editor

Flügge-Lotz: DISCONTINUOUS AND OPTIMAL CONTROL
Leitmann: AN INTRODUCTION TO OPTIMAL CONTROL

Discontinuous and Optimal Control

IRMGARD FLÜGGE-LOTZ
Professor of Engineering Mechanics
Stanford University

McGRAW-HILL BOOK COMPANY

New York   San Francisco   St. Louis   Toronto   London   Sydney

Preface

The study of systems with relay control began in this country in 1934 with the publication of H. L. Hazen's paper in vol. 218 of the *Journal of the Franklin Institute*. Ja. S. Tsypkin (Ref. 1.2) has given a rather extensive description of the historical development, and an annotated collection of references up to 1955 can be found in the interesting report by R. W. Bass (Ref. 1.3). During World War II a need for a deeper study of relay controls developed, and it was at this time that the author became interested in a field which has become increasingly important.

Today discontinuously working elements (on-off controls) are widely used in automatic control systems. Their principal advantage is their simple construction, but they may produce complicated phenomena in the controlled system. Since the publication in 1953 of the author's *Discontinuous Automatic Control* (Princeton University Press), which presented numerous results on linear second-order systems, third-order systems, and some fourth-order systems, automatic control has attracted more attention, and the concept of designing optimal controls has appeared. Pontryagin's maximum principle, which opened the way to computing optimal controls, showed that in many technically interesting cases optimal controls are discontinuous controls if the controls are bounded. For instance, optimal controls are discontinuous, *if the plant and the performance criteria are linear* and the controls are bounded.

It soon became apparent that although optimal controls are not always easy to realize, discontinuous suboptimal controls can still be profitable.

As interest in optimal controls increased, the practicing engineer was confronted with a new literature that was hard reading for him because of its enormous emphasis on mathematical formulation, generality, existence theorems, etc. The purpose of this book is to acquaint the reader with the problem of discontinuous control by presenting the essential phenomena in simple examples before guiding him to an understanding of systems of higher order, both linear and nonlinear. The references at the end of each chapter allow a deeper mathematical penetration if desired.

The author has had ample opportunity to teach this subject to first-year graduate students and to study specific problems with more advanced students. Such experience has been a great help in preparing this book, and the author wants to express her thanks to all those who have been exploring with her new ways to handle specific engineering problems of discontinuous controls.

Irmgard Flügge-Lotz

Contents

Discontinuous and Optimal Control

1
Introduction

1.1 GENERAL REMARKS

The study of dynamic systems is usually based on the well-known laws of dynamics. Depending on the number of degrees of freedom, one or more ordinary differential equations will describe the behavior of such a system as an airplane, a rocket, or a satellite. If linear differential equations are used, it is mostly possible to replace the system by one differential equation of, say, nth order for one variable. However, this may not be the best way of studying the behavior of such a system when its equilibrium is disturbed. With nonlinear equations it may be necessary to cope with a system of second-order equations, which can, of course, easily be reduced to a larger system of first-order differential equations.

There are different ways, both mechanically and conceptually, to influence the behavior of dynamic systems. For example, for fast damping of a disturbance in the desired path of a rocket we might apply the continuous control of watching for undesirable deviations and correcting for them by adjusting flaps, or we might apply the discontinuous control

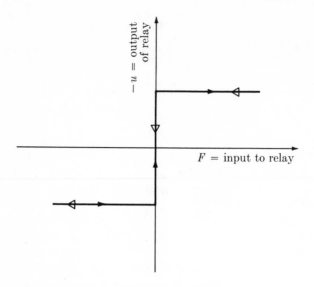

Fig. 1.1 Ideal relay, input-output relation.

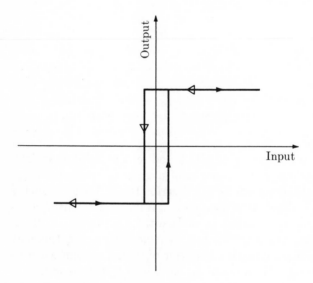

Fig. 1.2 Relay with delayed action.

of using only two flap settings in opposite directions and choosing favorable instances of change in direction. There are other systems which for simplicity of design are controlled discontinuously. For instance, in controlling the temperature of a building it is much easier to heat or not to heat (either electrically or by gas) than to heat with varying intensity.

It is thus obvious that discontinuous control is an important design concept. Its importance has been recognized for some time, but theoretical development was slow because discontinuous control is nonlinear. In a linear system (plant) discontinuous control leads to a description by linear differential equation between switchings, but this is not much help; it is certainly easier to view the behavior of the system as a whole than to follow up the behavior from one interval to another.

It was natural to try to apply methods successful in linear systems to systems with relay control. One of the most powerful of these methods was the study of the response of a system to sinusoidal inputs of different frequencies. The introduction of the "describing function" for the relay action (see p. 566 of Truxal's book, Ref. 1.1) raised the hope of achieving some insight into the behavior of systems with relays. However, certain essential features of behavior could not be studied in this way. In a system with relays *transients* play a strong role; at every switching a new transient state begins, and when the switching instances follow one another closely, new phenomena arise which were not observed in linear systems. This fact raises the question of whether it is even possible to describe the action of a relay adequately in a simple mathematical manner. Relays are not perfect; that is, a relay does not act as described in Fig. 1.1 but may act as described in Fig. 1.2, where there is a delay in action. Or it may even work as described in Figs. 1.3 and 1.4. If time delay and the dead zone are construed as imperfections which need to be taken into account, the mathematical description becomes much more complicated. If we were to consider only the case described in Fig. 1.2, we would have to work with differential-difference equations instead of simple ordinary differential equations.

In this book we shall consider relay imperfections but avoid the use of differential-difference equations. Instead, the modifications necessary to accommodate imperfections will be discussed in terms of the action of perfect relays and a description of imperfections that influence them, particularly those imperfections that influence steady-state behavior after a disturbance is nearly zeroed. It will also be made apparent that an oversimplification (the introduction of a "perfect" relay) leads to strange mathematical consequences which contradict experience, an interesting example of what can or cannot be considered an "adequate" mathematical description of a physical event.

We shall examine all the new features of systems with relay controls;

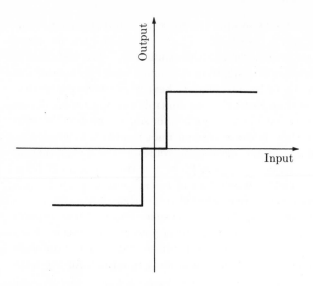

Fig. 1.3 Relay with dead or neutral zone.

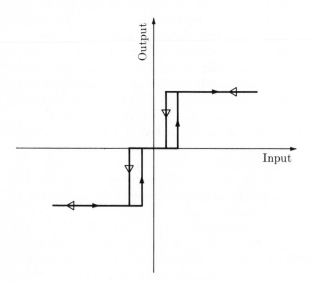

Fig. 1.4 Relay with dead zone and delayed action.

i.e., features which do not occur in systems with continuous control elements. The many examples in Chap. 2 of discontinuous control in second-order plants are chosen because they allow a simple graphical description of the behavior. This description may be in the form of simple drawings or in the form of recordings of systems simulated on the analog computer. Note that simulation of ordinary differential equations on the analog computer is not unique; the simulation must be chosen to avoid differentiation of the output of a relay. Otherwise there is certain to be difficulty in trying to handle infinitely large derivatives, which would overload the computer.

Many results for second-order systems have been obtained graphically and then checked by analog computer simulation.[1] Graphical methods are still possible for third-order systems, and perhaps even for fourth-order systems, but for higher-order systems the graphical methods should really be discarded as too unwieldy. Some play with simple second-order systems, however, is a substantial aid to understanding higher-order systems and developing easy recognition of the essentials in handling of them.

Studies with a digital computer may also be made, but it should be kept in mind that a digital computer practically replaces a differential equation by a difference equation. Switching cannot be expected to coincide with a time instance that corresponds to an instance $t_0 + n(\delta t)$. An integration scheme that automatically reduces integration steps when singular events occur may cause trouble if the program is not adapted to the fact that discontinuous functions have to be handled. With such an adaptation there is no real obstacle to studying relay systems by this means. However, the analog computer or the hybrid computer is preferable because its elements closely resemble the hardware that will actually be used for building a relay control system.

We shall not go into systems with delays in the feedback path, which (if linear) might be written as

$$\sum_{n=0}^{N} a_n x^{(n)}(t) + b_n x^{(n)}(t - \theta_n) = u(t)$$

where $x(t)$ = the output variable
    (n) = the derivatives
    θ_n = a time delay
    $u(t)$ = the controlling function, not further specified at this moment [$u(t)$ may be equal to $u^*(x^{(i)})$]

The system input is assumed to be $r(t) \equiv 0$ for $t > 0$; that is, only initial disturbances are investigated. In addition, the behavior of $x^{(n)}$ for

---

[1] This is much easier today than it was in the early 1950s because of a substantial improvement in analog computers.

$-\theta_n < t < 0$ must be specified.   There has been some theoretical treatment of this problem (Ref. 1.4), and there is currently an interest in practical solutions.   However the few problems that have been solved indicate that presentation of this subject should await further experience (Ref. 1.4).

1.2 SPECIAL REMARKS

Since backgrounds of the readers may vary widely, from aeronautical, mechanical, or electrical engineering to applied mathematics, a word should be said about notation.   The electrical engineer will have a thorough background in linear control theory.   He will be familiar with the use of Laplace transforms and will feel at home with block diagrams; he may find it difficult to describe a system instead by differential equations.   Conversely, engineers from other fields will be accustomed to differential equations and may have only a slight acquaintance with a representation by block diagrams.

In this book both block diagrams and Laplace transforms will be used, but only as a kind of shorthand, because the block diagram is based essentially on the Laplace transform, and the Laplace transform is practically useless in treating nonlinear problems.

No special preparation should be required for the reader with an average engineering background.   However, some readers may find useful Sec. 1.1, "The differential equation of control systems and block diagrams," of the book by D. Graham and D. McRuer (Ref. 1.5); figs. 1.8 and 1.9 of that section will be helpful to those who are not familiar with block diagrams.

REFERENCES

1.1   Truxal, J. G.: *Automatic Feedback Control System Synthesis*, McGraw-Hill Book Company, New York, 1955.

1.2   Zypkin, Ja. S.: *Theorie der Relaissysteme der automatischen Regelung* (*Theory of Automatic Contact Control*), translated from the Russian into German by W. Hahn and R. Herschel, R. Oldenbourg KG, Munich, 1958.   (The Russian original appeared in 1955 in Moscow; transliteration of the author's Russian name varies.)

1.3   Bass, R. W.: The Analysis and Synthesis of Relay and Nonlinear Servosystems, *Johns Hopkins Inst. Cooperative Res., Final Rept. Contract* DA-36-034-ORD-1273 RD, sec. III, 1955.   (Microfilms available; gives 188 references in the bibliography.)

1.4   Oguztöreli, M. Namik: *Time-lag Control Systems*, University of Queensland, Australia, Academic Press Inc., New York, 1966.

1.5   Graham, Dunstan, and Duane McRuer: *Analysis of Nonlinear Control Systems*, John Wiley & Sons, Inc., New York, 1961.

2

Discontinuous control of second-order systems

2.1 REACTION TO INITIAL DISTURBANCES AND TO STEP INPUTS: LINEAR SWITCHING FUNCTIONS

In this chapter we shall examine systems whose behavior can be easily visualized.

2.1.1 Simple systems with one control input

2.1.1a *Plant with a transfer function* $1/(s^2 + 1)$. Before we go into the matter of even one control, let us look at a very simple dynamic system with no controls.

Consider a spring-mass system described by

$$m\ddot{x} + nx = 0 \tag{2.1}$$

which undergoes an initial disturbance $(x(0) = x_0, \; \dot{x}(0) = x_0)$. The behavior of this system can be described by plotting $x(t)$ and $\dot{x}(t)$, and also by plotting x as a function of $\dot{x}$, with t as parameter.

For convenience the dimensionless time $\tau = \sqrt{n/m}\, t = \omega_0 t$ is introduced[1] in Eq. (2.1). If derivatives with respect to τ are denoted by primes, Eq. (2.1) yields

$$x'' + x = 0 \tag{2.2}$$

The solution of Eq. (2.2) is given by

$$
\begin{aligned}
x &= C \cos (\tau + \phi) \\
x' &= -C \sin (\tau + \phi)
\end{aligned}
\tag{2.3}
$$

That is, x is a harmonic function or an undamped oscillation. In an x,x' plane (see Fig. 2.1) the behavior of the system is described by the motion of the *phase point* (x,x'). The phase point moves on a circle with radius C, which is determined by the initial values x_0 and x_0'. The time $\Delta\tau$ for going from a point P_1 to a point P_2 can easily be measured by the subtended angle $\Delta\psi$.

This system has no damping force, so the motion produced by the initial disturbance cannot be zeroed. The next task is to employ a simple control for zeroing the motion resulting from this initial disturbance. A *block diagram* describes the controlled system (see Fig. 2.2) with input $r(\tau)$ and output $c(\tau)$. If the input $r(\tau) \equiv 0$ for $\tau > 0$—that is, if only the reaction of the system to an initial disturbance is considered—the error $e(\tau) = -c(\tau)$.

[1] Dimensionless time is also used in later examples. Its relation to real time is indicated only where relevant to the discussion.

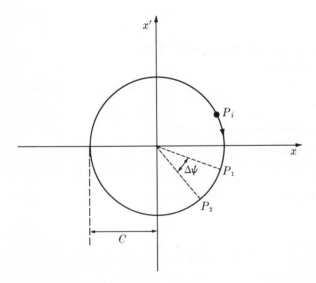

Fig. 2.1 Phase-plane diagram; plant $1/(s^2 + 1)$.

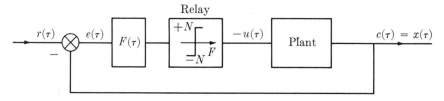

Fig. 2.2 Block diagram of controlled plant.

In block diagrams of linear systems with linear control the Laplace transform is often used to characterize a plant (in this case the spring-mass system) by its transfer function [in this case $1/(s^2 + 1)$]. Laplace transforms cannot be used in dealing with nonlinear systems, but the shorthand notation $d/d\tau = s$ is often used. Figure 2.2 shows that a function of $e(\tau)$ governs the relay. $F(\tau) = e + ke'$ will be chosen. Then the controlled-system equations are

$$r(\tau) - c(\tau) = e(\tau) \tag{2.4}$$

and, with $r(\tau) \equiv 0$ for $\tau > 0$,

$$e(\tau) = -c(\tau) \tag{2.5}$$

$$F(\tau) = e + k\frac{de}{d\tau} = e + ke' \tag{2.6}$$

$$u(\tau) = -N\frac{F(\tau)}{|F(\tau)|} \equiv -N \operatorname{sgn} F(\tau) \tag{2.7}$$

$$c'' + c = N \operatorname{sgn} F \tag{2.8a}$$

or $\quad e'' + e = u(\tau) = -N \operatorname{sgn} F \tag{2.8b}$

N is called the *control effort*. The function[1] sgn F can accept only two values, $+1$ or -1. It changes from one value to the other when $e + ke'$ passes zero and changes sign. The point in the phase plane at which this happens is called the *switching point*. Between two switching instances Eq. (2.8b) is a linear equation

$$e'' + (e \mp N) = 0 \tag{2.9}$$

In other words, the phase point (e, e') passes along the portion of a circle whose center is either at $+N$ or at $-N$. Since the chosen function F is a linear function of the phase variables e and e', the locus of all switching points is a straight line through the origin of the phase plane.

The next problem is the choice of k. Let us first consider $k = 0$. In this case the switching line coincides with the e' axis. We see immediately from Fig. 2.3 that the motion remains undamped; only the period of the motion has been changed.

[1] The notation sgn stands for *signum*, the Latin word for "sign."

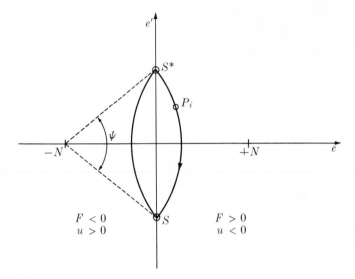

Fig. 2.3 Plant $1/(s^2 + 1)$; phase diagram; switching on $e = 0$.

There are two switching points, S and S^*, in which the slope de'/de is discontinuous.   This is understandable, since

$$\frac{de'}{de} = \frac{de'/d\tau}{de/d\tau} = \frac{e''}{e'} \tag{2.10}$$

and e'' changes discontinuously at switching.

Without control the period (measured in τ) was 2π, and now it is 2ψ; it has become shorter.

If we choose $k > 0$ there is a possibility of coming closer to the origin (see Fig. 2.4).   However, a peculiar situation arises at switching point S_2.   At this point the function $F(\tau)$ reaches zero.   The slope of $F(\tau)$, given by

$$F'(\tau) = e' + ke'' = e' + k(-N \operatorname{sgn} F - e) \tag{2.11}$$

changes discontinuously at switching points (see Fig. 2.5).   However, if switching were to take place at S_2, the function $F(\tau)$ for $\tau > \tau(S_2)$ would have the same sign as for $\tau < \tau(S_2)$; switching has been ordered but has not been allowed to take place.   Hence S_2 is not a switching point but is instead a *point of indecision*.   The behavior of the system described by Eq. (2.8b) with $F = e + ke'$ and $k > 0$ has no solution for $\tau > \tau(S_2)$.

S_2 would be an endpoint[1] of the motion with ideal relays, but fortunately there are no ideal relays.   Switching is actually done with a delay

[1] See also Fig. 2.32 and the accompanying text.

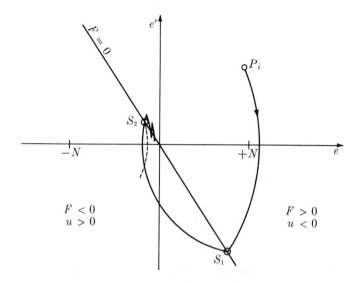

Fig. 2.4   Plant $1/(s^2 + 1)$; occurrence of chatter.

$\Delta\tau$ after the command has been given at $\tau(S_2)$, although this delay is very small in modern relays.[1]   If the delay $\Delta\tau$ exists (see Fig. 2.6), F becomes positive after S_2, and at S_2' the change in slope can take place.   Naturally, this event will repeat.   The phase-point motion after S_2 (indicated in Fig. 2.4) is a high-frequency motion which takes the phase point closer

[1] There are other imperfections, as described in the introduction.   They will be treated in Sec. 3.2.

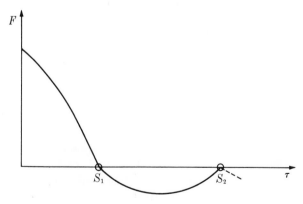

Fig. 2.5   Switching function versus time; S_2 = point of indecision (ideal relay).

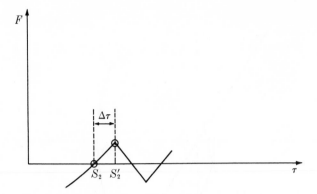

Fig. 2.6 Switching function versus time; delayed switching
(S_2 = switching command, S_2' = actual switching).

and closer to the origin. If $\Delta\tau$ is very small, the motion is practically
described by

$$e + ke' = 0 \tag{2.12a}$$

$$\text{or} \quad e = D \exp\left\{-\frac{1}{k}[\tau - \tau(S_2)]\right\} \tag{2.12b}$$

with the factor D determined by

$$e(S_2) = D \tag{2.12c}$$

This high-frequency motion is called a *chatter motion* arising from the
imperfection of the relay. Such motions will be studied in greater detail
in Sec. 3.3; at this point it is important to realize that systems with
idealized relays may have solutions that are limited to certain regions of
the phase plane. Thus "idealization" may lead to results that do not
come close to those obtained for real plants.

It is interesting to attempt a solution for $k < 0$. Figure 2.7 shows
that the solution will diverge.

The only case still to be considered is $k \to \pm\infty$; $k \to \infty$ is equivalent
to

$$u = \text{sgn } e' \tag{2.13}$$

Figure 2.8 shows the result for this case, a highly undesirable periodic
motion with a finite average value of e. The period is determined by the
imperfection of the relay. The limit $k \to -\infty$ naturally leads to a
divergent motion (Fig. 2.9).

Figure 2.10 shows a special case in which the phase point reaches
zero without chatter; that is, k has been incidentally chosen such that the

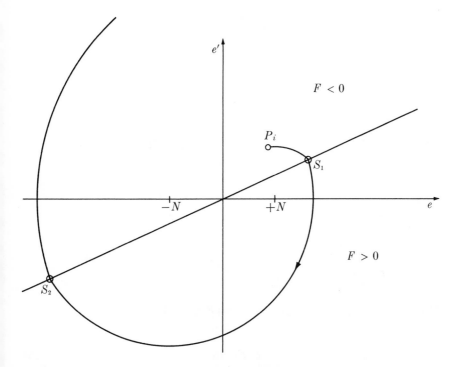

Fig. 2.7   Plant $1/(s^2 + 1)$; control leading to divergent motion; $k < 0$.

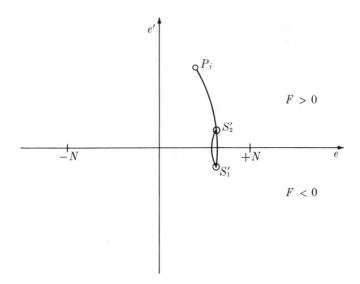

Fig. 2.8   Plant $1/(s^2 + 1)$; badly chosen switching line; $k \to +\infty$.

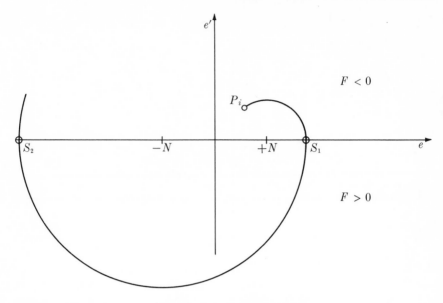

Fig. 2.9   Plant $1/(s^2 + 1)$; divergent motion; $F = e + ke'$; $k \to -\infty$.

last switching point lies on the circle around $-N$.   If linear switching is used, only a limited set of initial conditions leads to such motions.   They will be studied in detail in Chap. 4.   In this case the disturbance is zeroed in finite time.

The final result of the investigation of the system

$$e'' + e = -N \,\mathrm{sgn}\,(e + ke')$$

shows that a positive k [that is, a lead term in the control function $F(\tau)$] allows a disturbance to be zeroed.   This zeroing takes infinite time in general, and to be exact, the phase point does not reach zero in this time, but rather reaches a very small limit cycle of the form shown in Fig. 2.3 and shown in detail in Fig. 2.11.   The magnitude of the limit cycle depends on k and $\Delta\tau$.   A simple but tedious computation can be based on the following relations:

$$
\begin{aligned}
e'_s &= r_s \sin \phi \qquad N - e_s = r_s \cos \phi \\
e'_m &= r_s \sin (\phi + \Delta\tau) \\
\text{and}\quad (e'_m)^2 + N^2 &= (e'_s)^2 + (e_s - N)^2 \\
e_s + ke'_s &= 0
\end{aligned}
\tag{2.14}
$$

This gives

$$e'_s = \frac{N(1 - \cos \Delta\tau)}{k \cos \Delta\tau - \sin \Delta\tau} \tag{2.15a}$$

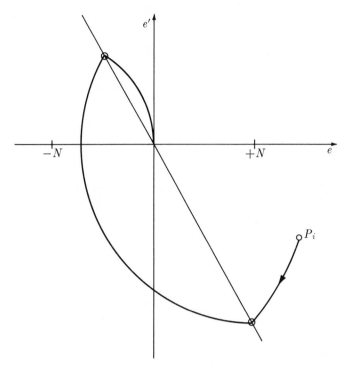

Fig. 2.10   Plant $1/(s^2 + 1)$; zeroing of disturbance without chatter; ideal relay.

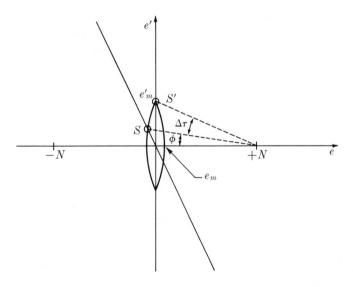

Fig. 2.11   Plant $1/(s^2 + 1)$; small limit cycle due to imperfection of a relay.

and, for small $\Delta\tau$,

$$e'_s = \frac{N\,\Delta\tau^2/2}{k} = \frac{N\,\Delta\tau^2}{2k} \tag{2.15b}$$

The last simplified formula is based on the assumption that $k \gg \Delta\tau$. From Eqs. (2.14) and (2.15b),

$$e'_m = N\,\Delta\tau \tag{2.16a}$$

$$|e_m| = N\,\frac{\Delta\tau^2}{2} \tag{2.16b}$$

That is, for larger k the limit cycle depends essentially on $\Delta\tau$. If k is smaller, but still larger than $\Delta\tau$, we obtain the approximate formulas[1]

$$e'_m = N\,\Delta\tau\left(1 + \frac{\Delta\tau}{2k}\right) \tag{2.16c}$$

$$|e_m| = N\,\frac{\Delta\tau^2}{2} \tag{2.16d}$$

It should be kept in mind that this derivation is based on Fig. 2.11. If a very small k is chosen, however, and the relay is bad, with a comparatively large $\Delta\tau$, a motion results that is equivalent to one that would occur in an ideal system with slightly negative k; that is, the motion diverges (see Fig. 2.12).

It can be shown that for a switching command on the line

$$e_c + ke'_c = 0 \tag{2.17}$$

actual switching occurs on another straight line which forms an angle with the command line. To compute this relation for e_s and e'_s we use the general solution

$$\begin{aligned} e &= -N\,\text{sgn}\,F + C\cos(\tau + \delta) \\ e' &= -C\sin(\tau + \delta) \end{aligned} \tag{2.18}$$

We must further observe the command relation of Eq. (2.17) and the fact that the actual switching occurs with a delay $\Delta\tau$ at (e_s, e'_s). Thus

$$\begin{aligned} e_s &= -N\,\text{sgn}\,F + C\cos(\tau_c + \delta + \Delta\tau) \\ e'_s &= -C\sin(\tau_c + \delta + \Delta\tau) \end{aligned} \tag{2.19}$$

Expressing e_c and e'_c with the help of e_s and e'_s (only first-order terms in $\Delta\tau$ are retained) gives

$$e_s(1 + k\,\Delta\tau) + e'_s(k - \Delta\tau) = (-N\,\text{sgn}\,F)k\,\Delta\tau \tag{2.20}$$

---

[1] Terms of third and higher order in $\Delta\tau$ are neglected.

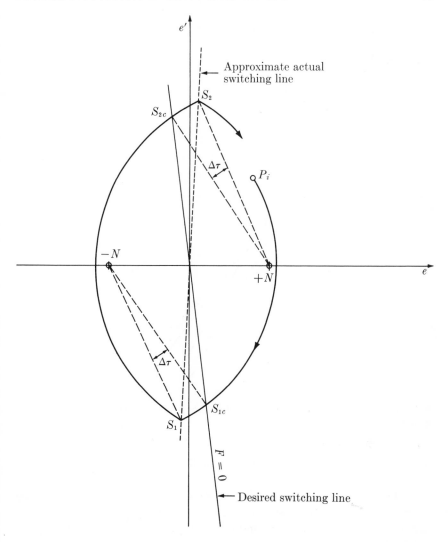

Fig. 2.12 Plant $1/(s^2 + 1)$; delayed action of relay causes divergent motion for very small positive k.

which is the relation for two straight lines (see Fig. 2.13). For $e_s = 0$ Eq. (2.20) yields[1]

$$e_s' = \frac{(-N \operatorname{sgn} F) \, k \, \Delta\tau}{k - \Delta\tau} \rightarrow (-N \operatorname{sgn} F) \, \Delta\tau \qquad (2.21)$$

[1] In Fig. 2.12 these two lines lie so close together that they appear to be one line.

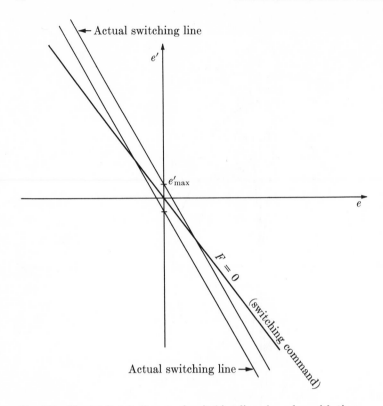

Fig. 2.13   Plant $1/(s^2 + 1)$; actual switching lines for relay with time delay.

This value is exactly e'_{max} of the small limit cycle which is reached in after-endpoint chattering.

The plant with the transfer function $1/(s^2 + 1)$ was chosen as first example because of the ease with which phase curves can be traced; they are composed of circular arcs, and the transfer function has two imaginary poles, $+i$ and $-i$.

So far only motions produced by initial disturbances have been considered. If $r(\tau)$ is a step input—that is, if $r(\tau) \equiv 0$ for $\tau < 0$ and $r(\tau) \equiv r_0$ for $\tau > 0$—the output of the system will be different from that of the response to an initial disturbance only. For this case Eq. (2.5) must be replaced by

$$e(\tau) = r_0 - c(\tau) \qquad \tau > 0 \tag{2.5*}$$

and Eq. (2.8b) changes to

$$e'' + e = r_0 - N \operatorname{sgn} F \tag{2.8b*}$$

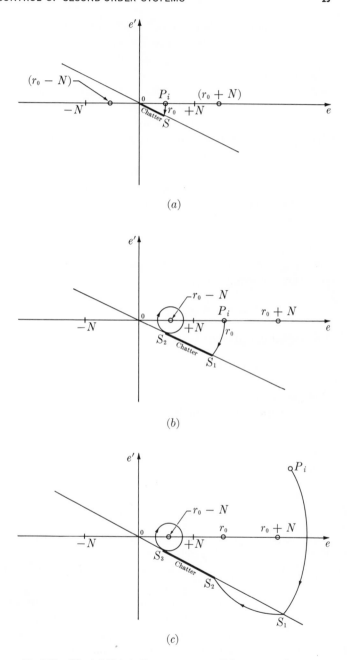

Fig. 2.14 Plant $1/(s^2 + 1)$; responses to different step inputs r_0.

The meaning of this is evident.   The center of the circles which are used for constructing the trajectories are now at $r_0 - N$ and $r_0 + N$.   Figure 2.14a shows the case for $r_0 - N < 0$, and Fig. 2.14b shows the case for $r_0 - N > 0$; in the latter case the centers of the circles generating regular portions of trajectories both lie to the right of the phase-plane origin. The case for $r_0 - N < 0$ is not essentially different from that for $r_0 \equiv 0$, but that for $r_0 - N > 0$ shows an undesirable reaction to the step input. The system does not approach zero error or a very small limit cycle around $(e = 0, e' = 0)$; instead it approaches a limit cycle with a finite radius $(r_0 - N)/\sqrt{1 + k^2}$ about the center $r_0 - N$.   Figure 2.14c shows a similar undesirable response to too large a step input if $c(0) \neq 0$ and $c'(0) \neq 0$.   Thus for a satisfactory approach of a step input r_0 the control effort N must be larger than r_0.

   2.1.1b   *Plant with a transfer function $1/s^2$.*   A plant without restoring force and with one control input is described by the differential equation (after normalization)

$$c'' = -u(\tau) = N \operatorname{sgn} F \tag{2.22a}$$

For initial disturbances only, $c = -e$ and Eq. (2.22a) yields

$$e'' = +u(\tau) = -N \operatorname{sgn} F \tag{2.22b}$$

Between two switching points u is constant, so an integration is possible. After integration the equation

$$e'e'' = ue'$$

yields

$$\frac{e'^2}{2} = u(e - e_v) \tag{2.23}$$

which is the equation of a parabola (see Fig. 2.15).   It will open to the right or the left, depending on the sign of u.   Figure 2.16a shows a trajectory for $F = e + ke'$, with $k > 0$.   It is evident that points of indecision (the endpoints of an ideal relay control) can occur.   Hence chatter occurs between S_1 and zero.   The steady state is a limit cycle around $(0,0)$ whose magnitude depends strongly on the switching delay $\Delta\tau$.

   The choice $k = 0$ leads to a finite limit cycle (Fig. 2.16b); that is, the error cannot be zeroed.   Infinitely large positive k is also undesirable, as Fig. 2.16c illustrates.   An infinitely small limit cycle around a finite value of e marks the steady state of the system.   Trajectories for negative k, including $k \to -\infty$, are given in Figs. 2.16d and e.

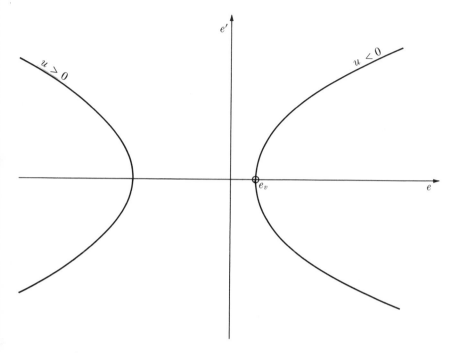

Fig. 2.15 Plant $1/s^2$; basic trajectories.

Figure 2.16f shows a very interesting case. The chosen switching function F is

$$F = \frac{e'|e'|}{2} + e \tag{2.24}$$

That is, the switching curve is composed of branches of trajectories which go through the origin of the phase plane. In this case every possible trajectory will lead to zero after at most one switching. If the initial point P_i incidentally lies on a zero branch, no switching will be required to reach the zero point.

For this system, which has two real poles at zero, the time for passing from one point on a phase trajectory to another can easily be measured by

$$\Delta e' = u\,\Delta\tau \tag{2.25}$$

Hence the time T^* for reaching zero without chatter can be determined easily.

In all cases where chatter occurs (the majority of cases if $F = e + ke'$ is chosen) the time for reaching zero will be longer. Since T^* is given by

$$T^* = e_i' + 2|e_{s*}'|$$

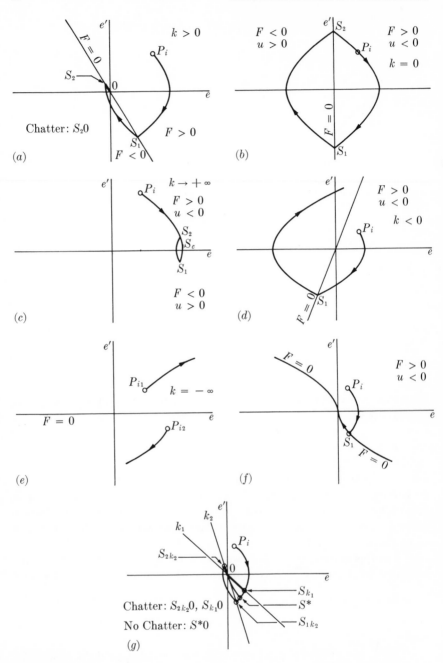

Fig. 2.16 Plant $1/s^2$; examples of controlled motion.   (a) $k > 0$; (b) $k = 0$; (c) $k \to \infty$; (d) $k < 0$; (e) $k \to -\infty$; (f) switching on zero trajectory; (g) comparison of switching on straight lines and on zero trajectory.

it is obvious without considering the time spent in chatter that $T(k_2)$ is a longer period (see Fig. 2.16g). The fact that $T(k_1) > T^*$ is evident on reflecting that during chatter

$$e = C \exp \left[-\frac{1}{k}(\tau - \tau_s) \right] \qquad C = e(\tau_s)$$

or $\quad \tau - \tau_s = -k \ln \dfrac{e}{C}$

For $e \to 0$ the time $\tau - \tau_s \to \infty$. Even if we were to compare times for reaching $e = \epsilon$, the result $T(k_1) > T^*$ would hold as long as $\epsilon > e_m$ of the limit cycle. It may now be more apparent that the switching function Eq. (2.24) leads to a minimum-settling-time control; a proof is given in Chap. 4.

If we consider the response of the system $e'' = u$ to a step input instead of to an initial disturbance ($e(0) = e_0$, $e'(0) = 0$), we find immediately that there is no difference in the behavior of the system. This is because the error e is not a factor in the differential equation.

2.1.1c *Plant with a transfer function* $1/s(s + a)$. The differential equation describing the controlled system[1] is

$$e'' + ae' = u(\tau) \qquad a > 0 \tag{2.26}$$

It is immediately apparent that for this system the response to an initial disturbance ($e_0 \neq 0$, $e_0' = 0$) is also identical to the response to a step input, because there is still one pole at zero. The solution to Eq. (2.26) is given by

$$e_1(\tau) = e(\tau) = C_1 e^{-a\tau} + \frac{u}{a}\tau + C_2 \tag{2.27a}$$

$$e_2(\tau) = e'(\tau) = -C_1 a e^{-a\tau} + \frac{u}{a} \tag{2.27b}$$

The phase plot for this system can be greatly simplified by introducing the new variables

$$\begin{aligned} y_1 &= e' \\ y_2 &= e' + ae \end{aligned} \tag{2.28}$$

Then the differential equation (2.26) yields the system

$$\begin{aligned} y_1' &= u - ay_1 \\ y_2' &= u \end{aligned} \tag{2.29}$$

---

[1] In general the uncontrolled system does not allow the motion following a disturbance to be zeroed.

with the solutions

$$y_1 = \frac{u}{a} - \beta e^{-a\tau}$$

$$(2.30)$$

$$y_2 = u\tau + \alpha$$

The constants α and β depend on the initial state. y_1 and y_2 will be called *state variables*.[1]

In the y_1y_2 plane the trajectories can be plotted easily because

$$y_1 = \frac{u}{a} - \beta e^{-ay_2/u}$$

$$(2.31a)$$

where β is a constant that depends on the initial state. Reaching the origin ($e = 0$, $e' = 0$) from an initial state (e_0, e_0') is equivalent to going from (y_{10}, y_{20}) to ($y_1 = 0$, $y_2 = 0$), because the transformation, Eq. (2.28), is linear and homogeneous.

Figure 2.17a shows possible trajectories in the y_1y_2 plane. Figure 2.17b shows (dashed lines) two zero trajectories that could be used as a switching curve. In this case the origin would be reached from any point in the y_1y_2 plane with at most one switching. The equation of this switching line is

$$y_1 = - (\text{sgn } y_2) \frac{N}{a} [1 - e^{(a/N)y_2 \text{ sgn } y_2}]$$

$$(2.31b)$$

This is rather complicated, and in general a simpler switching curve is preferable. Let us therefore investigate $F = e + ke'$ again. First, the function F must be expressed by the new state variables:

$$F = \frac{1}{a}(y_2 - y_1) + ky_1 = y_1\left(k - \frac{1}{a}\right) + \frac{y_2}{a}$$

$$(2.32)$$

That is, the linear switching function is a straight line in the y_1y_2 plane through its origin. Since we expect chatter to occur with an average motion toward the origin, k should be positive. Figure 2.17a shows a trajectory with regular motion from P_i to $\hat{S}$ and chatter from $\hat{S}$ to 0.

The motion for negative k is best investigated by first studying the possibility of a *periodic motion* of finite amplitude. Figure 2.17c shows a periodic motion characterized by

$$y_1(S) = -y_1(S^*)$$

$$(2.33)$$

$$y_2(S) = -y_2(S^*)$$

[1] They differ from the phase variables $e = e_1$ and $e' = e_2 = e_1'$ in that y_2 is not simply a derivative of y_1 [see Eq. (2.28)].

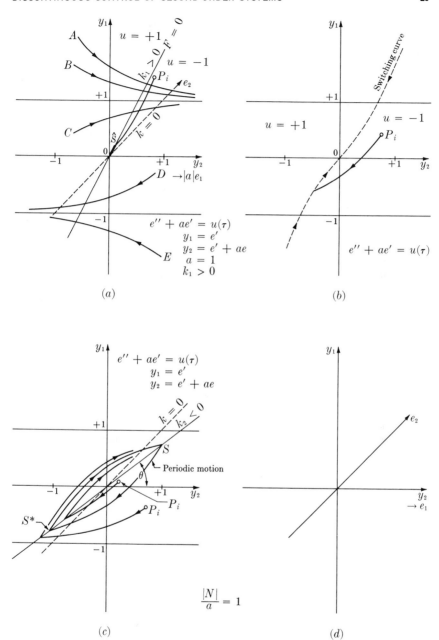

Fig. 2.17 Plant $1/[s(s+a)]$; $a > 0$. (a) $P_i\hat{S}$ regular motion, chatter from $\hat{S}$ to 0 (curves A through E show the form of possible trajectories, $a = 1$, $k > 0$); (b) zero-trajectory branches (dashed lines) used as switching curve; (c) $F = e + ke'$; (d) relation of coordinate systems y_1, y_2 and e_1, e_2.

The length of the period is denoted by $2T$.   If we count $\tau(S) = 0$, these conditions yield

$$y_{1s} = -\frac{N}{a} - \beta^* = -\left(-\frac{N}{a} - \beta^* e^{-aT}\right)$$

$$y_{2s} = \alpha = -(-NT + \alpha)$$

$$\tag{2.34a}$$

Therefore

$$2\alpha = NT \qquad \text{or} \qquad T = \frac{2\alpha}{N} \tag{2.34b}$$

and $\beta^* = \dfrac{-2N/a}{1 + e^{-aT}}$ $\tag{2.34c}$

In other words,

$$-\frac{N}{a} \geq \beta^* \geq -\frac{2N}{a}$$

The ratio y_{1s}/y_{2s} determines the slope of the switching line [see Eq. (2.32)]; hence

$$\frac{y_{1s}}{y_{2s}} = \frac{-1/a}{k - 1/a} = \frac{-(N/a) + (2N/a)/(1 + e^{-aT})}{NT/2} = \frac{\tanh aT/2}{aT/2}$$

$$\tag{2.35}$$

We immediately find the limiting case for $T \to 0$ as

$$\frac{y_{1s}}{y_{2s}} \to 1$$

with $y_{1s} \to 0$ and $y_{2s} \to 0$ [see Eq. (2.35)], and the limiting case for $T \to \infty$ as

$$\frac{y_{1s}}{y_{2s}} \to 0$$

with $y_{1s} \to N/a$ and $y_{2s} \to \infty$.
Equation (2.35) yields

$$k = \frac{1}{a}\left(1 - a\frac{T}{2}\coth\frac{aT}{2}\right)$$

or for small $T \;\cdot\;\cdot\;\cdot$

$$k = -\frac{1}{3a}\left(a\frac{T}{2}\right)^2 \cdots$$

and for large $T \;\cdot\;\cdot\;\cdot$

$$k \to -\infty$$

Thus $0 \geq k \geq -\infty$ allows periodic motions; or the slope of the switching line in the y_1y_2 plane must be such that $0 \leq \theta \leq 45°$ (see Fig. 2.17c).

The design of phase curves for control with negative k shows immediately that for initial points lying within the region limited by the periodic motion for the chosen k_1 the phase point will move toward this periodic motion, or limit cycle; for initial points lying outside this region it will also move toward the limit cycle. In no case is it possible to reach the origin with negative k; this is possible only for $k = 0$, because the limit cycle has zero amplitude.

To read e and e' directly from trajectories drawn in the y_1y_2 plane we can enter the lines $e' = 0$ and $e = 0$ in this plane (see Fig. 2.17d). The elapsed time between two phase-point locations can be measured easily by y_2, because, from Eq. (2.30), $\Delta y_2 = u\,\Delta\tau$.

If a is negative, then e and e' grow indefinitely with time in an uncontrolled system

$$e'' + ae' = 0 \tag{2.36}$$

It is interesting to investigate whether or not a relay control would allow a disturbance in this system to be zeroed. The following observations can be made:

1. The basic curves for constructing the trajectories are the same, but the phase point runs in the opposite direction (compare Fig. 2.18a with Fig. 2.17a).

2. The zero trajectories are given in Fig. 2.18b; they lie inside the strip

$$-\frac{N}{|a|} \leq y_1 \leq \frac{N}{|a|}$$

3. If the zero trajectories are chosen as switching curves, motions starting at initial points outside the strip

$$-\frac{N}{|a|} < y_1 < \frac{N}{|a|}$$

diverge and cannot be controlled. Motions inside this strip will zero after one switching (or no switching, if the initial point lies incidentally on a zero trajectory.)

4. Periodic motions are of the same type as shown in Fig. 2.17c, but they proceed in opposite directions; that is (see Fig. 2.18c), motions starting inside the cycle go toward the origin and those starting outside the cycle go toward infinity (they diverge). The limit cycle is unstable. For $k \to \infty$ the limit cycle becomes very large; it approaches the strip boundaries.

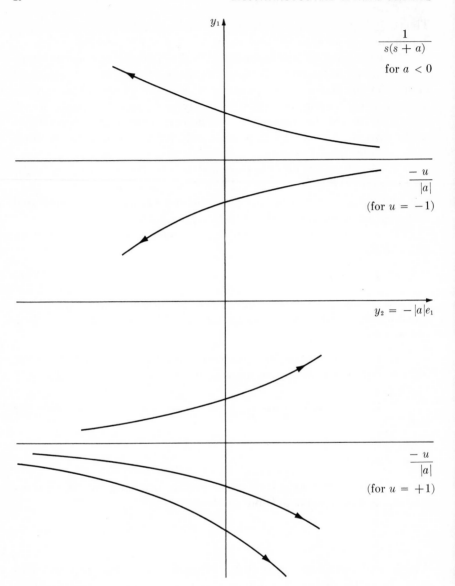

$$\frac{1}{s(s+a)}$$

for $a < 0$

$$\frac{-u}{|a|}$$

(for $u = -1$)

$$y_2 = -|a|e_1$$

$$\frac{-u}{|a|}$$

(for $u = +1$)

Fig. 2.18   Plant $1/[s(s+a)]$, with $a < 0$.   (a) Basic trajectories.

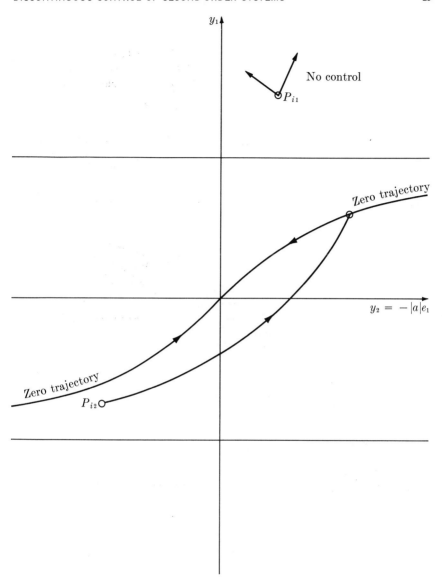

Fig. 2.18 Plant $1/[s(s + a)]$, with $a < 0$. (b) Switching on zero trajectories.

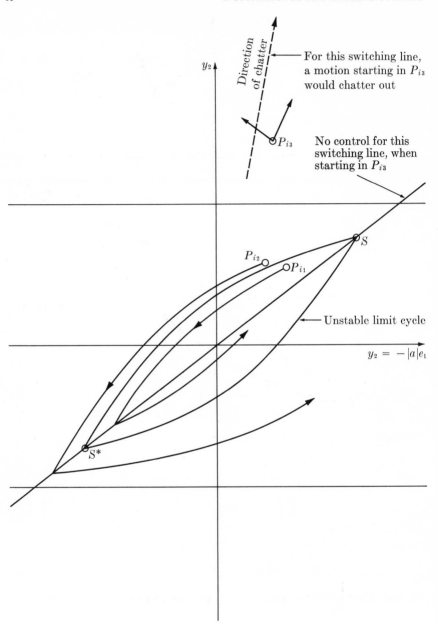

Fig. 2.18 Plant $1/[s(s + a)]$, with $a < 0$. (c) Occurrence of periodic motions.

5. With linear switching and rather large k we can control a rather large region, but the phase point will approach zero very slowly. With a k of moderate size the controllable region is smaller than for switching on zero trajectories.

The important conclusion from the case of negative a is that it seems possible to control systems with negative real poles, but that only limited regions of the phase plane can be controlled. This point will be discussed further in later chapters.

2.1.1d *Plant with a transfer function* $1/[(s + a)(s + b)]$. The constants a and b are assumed to be real. They can be both positive, both negative, or of opposite sign. The differential equation for a controlled system is given by

$$e'' + (a + b)e' + abe = u \tag{2.37}$$

The solution between two switchings is

$$e_1 = e = \frac{u}{ab} + Ae^{-a\tau} + Be^{-b\tau} \tag{2.38a}$$

with the derivative

$$e_2 = e' = -Aae^{-a\tau} - Bbe^{-b\tau} \tag{2.38b}$$

when A and B are integration constants. The time τ can be eliminated by combining Eqs. (2.38a) and (2.38b) to obtain the relation

$$\frac{[(e_1 - u/ab)a + e_2]^a}{[(e_1 - u/ab)b + e_2]^b} = M \tag{2.39a}$$

or
$$\left[\left(e_1 - \frac{u}{ab}\right)a + e_2\right]^a = \left[\left(e_1 - \frac{u}{ab}\right)b + e_2\right]^b M \tag{2.39b}$$

where the constant M represents the former constants A and B and depends on the initial values of e_1 and e_2 at the beginning of the interval under consideration.[1] If new coordinates

$$y_1 = \left(e_1 - \frac{u}{ab}\right)a + e_2 = B(a - b)e^{-b\tau}$$
$$y_2 = \left(e_1 - \frac{u}{ab}\right)b + e_2 = A(b - a)e^{-a\tau} \tag{2.40}$$

are introduced, the trajectories are composed of curves

$$y_1{}^a = My_2{}^b \tag{2.41}$$

[1] It is obvious that for $a = -b = i$ the system $1/(s^2 + 1)$ would evolve, and Eq. (2.39a) would be the equation of a circle.

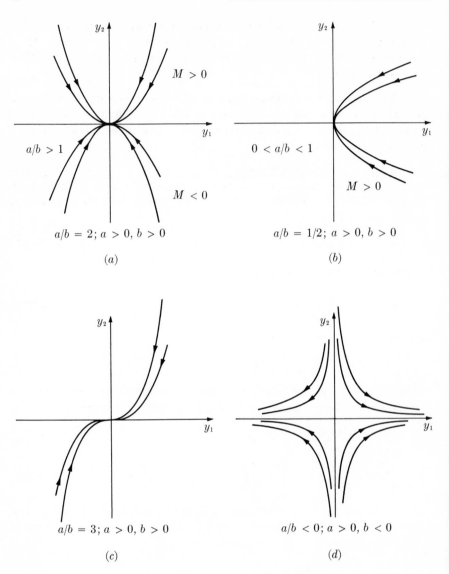

Fig. 2.19 Curves $y_1{}^a = My_2{}^b$.

These well-known curves are treated in many books (see Fig. 2.19).
From Eq. (2.40) it is obvious that for positive a and b the phase point will
travel with increasing time toward the origin of the y_1y_2 plane; if a and b
are both negative, the opposite is true.   If a and b are of opposite sign,
the trajectories in the y_1y_2 plane show that the origin is a saddle point of

the system and can never be reached (Fig. 2.19d). The trajectories in the phase plane (that is, the e_1e_2 plane) can be obtained from the y_1y_2 plots rather easily. The position on the e_1 axis of the center of the trajectory system will vary with the value of u.

It may be argued that in systems of this type with positive a and b any single disturbance will be zeroed and there is no reason to use a control. However, there may be cases with small values of a or b in which the uncontrolled system is too slow and some control is desirable. If a linear switching function $F = e_1 + ke_2$, with $k > 0$, is chosen, chatter is expected. Motion in the chatter region is governed by $e = Ce^{-(\tau-\tau_s)/k}$, which may be preferable to $e = Ae^{-a\tau} + Be^{-b\tau}$ for a choice of $k < b < a$. Therefore let us consider the case of positive real a and b.[1] We shall, in fact, examine not only linear switching, but switching on zero trajectories. This latter case requires a rather complicated switching function when a and b are not integers, but it does permit zeroing of a disturbance in finite time.

Figure 2.20a shows possible trajectories in the y_1y_2 plane and the e_1e_2 plane. In Fig. 2.20b linear switching is compared with switching on zero trajectories for two initial conditions, P_{i1} and P_{i2}. The chosen k does not satisfy the condition $k < b < a$; a well-chosen k would have made the drawing of the figure too difficult, but the influence of decreasing k can easily be inferred. Figure 2.20c shows periodic motions for negative k. A negative k should never be chosen, because for initial points outside and inside a limit cycle the motion tends toward the limit cycle, which is stable. It is obvious that in using very small positive k time delays in control must be kept to a minimum in order to avoid an effective[2] negative k, which would allow a limit cycle to appear.

The periodic motions can be computed easily as follows: Counting of time is started at a corner point of a cycle; the length of the period is called $2T$. The two portions between the corner points have u values of opposite sign, with $u_1 = -u_2$. The corner points are *images* of each

---

[1] It is interesting to note the influence of linear feedback of error only on the response of systems with small positive a and b. In this case the controlled system is described by

$$e'' + (a + b)e' + abe = Ke$$

and the poles are located at

$$\lambda_{1,2} = -\frac{a + b}{2} \pm \sqrt{\frac{(a + b)^2}{4} - ab + K}$$

That is, instead of poles at $-a$ and $-b$, we obtain poles at $-b + \Delta$ and $-a - \Delta$. Hence discontinuous control is preferable.

[2] See the discussion relating to Fig. 2.12.

$$\frac{1}{(s + a)(s + b)}$$

$$a = 2, b = 1, |u| = 1$$

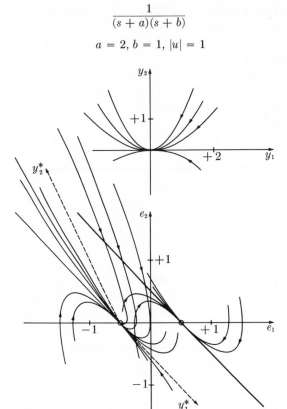

(a)

Fig. 2.20 Plant $1/[(s + a)(s + b)]$, with $a > 0, b > 0$.
(a) Trajectories in the $e_1 e_2$ planes obtained from the
$y_1 y_2$ plane. (b) Comparison of linear switching to
switching on zero trajectories. (c) Periodic motions
for negative k (linear switching). For P_i outside limit
cycle, motion tends toward limit cycle; for P_i inside
limit cycle, motion tends toward limit cycle.

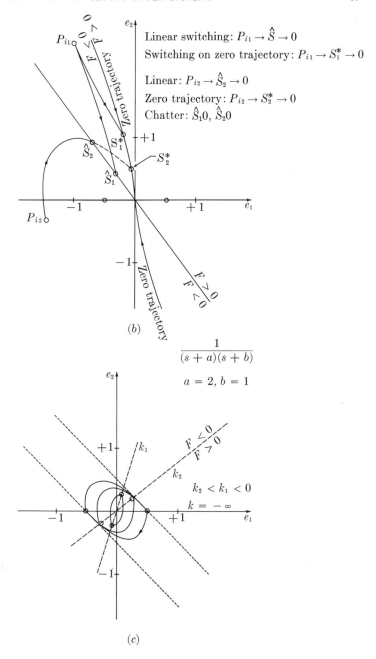

Linear switching: $P_{i1} \to \hat{S} \to 0$

Switching on zero trajectory: $P_{i1} \to S_1^* \to 0$

Linear: $P_{i2} \to \hat{S}_2 \to 0$

Zero trajectory: $P_{i2} \to S_2^* \to 0$

Chatter: $\hat{S}_1 0, \hat{S}_2 0$

(b)

$$\frac{1}{(s+a)(s+b)}$$

$$a = 2, b = 1$$

$k_2 < k_1 < 0$

$k = -\infty$

(c)

other with respect to the coordinate origin.   Hence

$$e_{1s} = \frac{u_1}{ab} + A + B = -\left(\frac{u_1}{ab} + Ae^{-aT} + Be^{-bT}\right)$$

$$e_{2s} = -Aa - bB = -(-Aae^{-aT} - Bbe^{-bT})$$

$$(2.42)$$

and $A = \dfrac{2u_1/a}{(a - b)(1 + e^{-aT})}$

$$B = \dfrac{-2u_1/b}{(a - b)(1 + e^{-bT})}$$

$$(2.43)$$

Since the corner point lies on the switching line,

$$k = \frac{1}{ab} \frac{(a - b)(e^{-(a+b)T} - 1) + (a + b)(e^{-bT} - e^{-aT})}{2(e^{-bT} - e^{-aT})} \qquad (2.44)$$

For small T

$$k = -\frac{a + b}{12} T^2 \cdot \cdot \cdot$$

For large T the coefficient k approaches a negative infinite value.   For infinite T the corner points of the cycle are the singular points u/ab of the system; that is, the cycle has limited amplitude and velocity.

Trajectories for systems with negative real a and b should now be easy to visualize.   The basic forms of the trajectories in the y_1y_2 plane are the same as those shown in Fig. 2.20a, except the direction of the arrows is reversed.   In transferring these trajectories to the e_1e_2 plane, it is immediately apparent that the y_1 and y_2 axes in the e_1e_2 plane are the images of those we obtained for positive a and b (compare Figs. 2.21a and 2.20a).   The system without control would let most disturbances grow; however, in the controlled system there exist periodic motions and hence the possibility of controlling disturbances of limited magnitude.

Let us consider switching on the zero trajectories for the system with negative real values a and b (see Fig. 2.21b).   In this case all disturbances in the region bounded by the limit cycle for $k \to \infty$ (that is, $T \to \infty$) can be zeroed.   If linear switching is applied, the controllable region shrinks, since the limit cycle for $0 < k < \infty$ encloses a smaller region than that for $k \to \infty$ (see Fig. 2.21c).   This example shows a motion which goes into chatter after the trajectory intersects the switching line. It is possible that for an initial point P_i farther to the left the trajectory will have one regular switching point and then approach the switching line again on the same side of the origin.   At this second intersection chatter motion will start toward the origin.

We can now turn to the most interesting case, systems with one negative and one positive real pole.   Figure 2.22a shows possible trajectories for a controlled system with $a = 2$ and $b = -1$.   Figure 2.22b

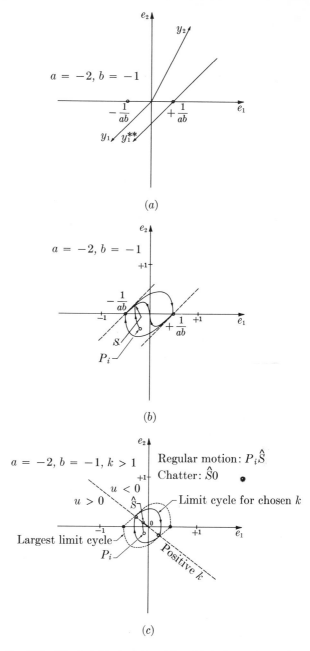

Fig. 2.21 Plant $1/[(s + a)(s + b)]$. (a) Relation between y_1, y_2 coordinates and e_1, e_2 coordinates [compare to Fig. 2.20a; the y_1 and y_2 axes in Fig. 2.21a are the images of those in Fig. 2.20a with respect to the e_2 axis; note that the y_1 and y_2 axes in Fig. 2.20a are parallel to y_1^* and y_2^* and pass through the origin]. (b) $a = -2$; $b = -1$; control with switching on zero trajectory; the limit cycle through the points ($\pm 1/ab$) encloses the controllable region. (c) Limit cycle for chosen k bounds the "controllable" region.

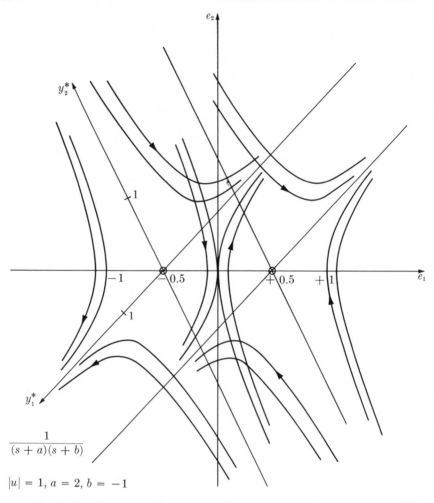

Fig. 2.22   Plant $1/[(s + a)(s + b)]$; $a > 0$, $b < 0$.   (a) Samples of basic curves used for constructing trajectories.

shows the zero trajectories and the largest limiting cycle, which is in the form of a parallelogram.   Also shown is the zeroing of initial disturbances for switching on zero trajectories.   From P_{i1} and P_{i2} the phase point moves toward the origin of the phase plane.   However, a disturbance at point P_{i3} cannot be zeroed.   We recognize immediately that only a strip of the e_1e_2 plane is controllable—that bounded by two asymptotes through the points u/ab (compare Figs. 2.22a and b).   An investigation of the limiting cycles shows that the corner points lie, as usual, on straight lines through the coordinate origin, but that the slope of these lines is limited to

$$\frac{a + b}{2ab} \leq k \leq 0 \qquad |a| > |b|$$

and $\frac{a + b}{2ab} \geq k \geq 0 \qquad |a| < |b|$ (2.45)

where $a > 0$ and $b < 0$ are assumed.

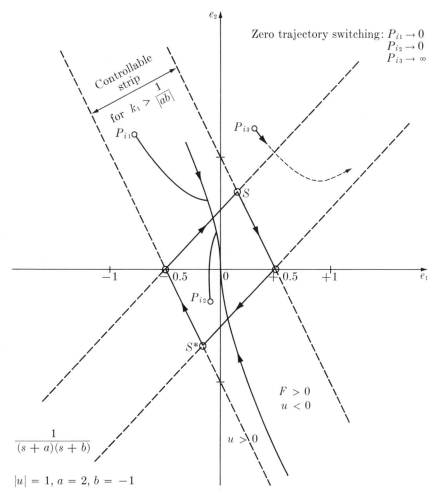

Fig. 2.22 Plant $1/[(s + a)(s + b)]$; $a > 0$, $b < 0$. (*b*) Zero trajectories and largest limit cycle $[2T \to \infty]$; corner points S and S^* lie on a straight line through the origin with $k = -\frac{1}{4}$.

In Fig. 2.22c some limit cycles are indicated.   All k for which limit
cycles exist should be avoided if linear switching functions are chosen.
Initial disturbances that lie inside a limit cycle will lead to a motion on the
limit cycle.   Disturbances lying outside the cycle but inside the strip will
also cause a motion toward the limit cycle.   Motions starting outside the
limit cycle and outside the strip diverge.   For a choice of $k_1 < |N/ab|$
only disturbances in a "narrowed" strip can be zeroed (see Fig. 2.22d).
In the presented example a choice of $k < -\frac{1}{4}$ would show divergent
motion for any initial disturbance.

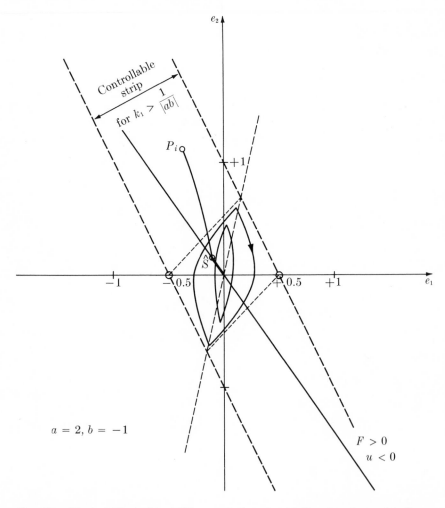

Fig. 2.22   Plant $1/[(s + a)(s + b)]$; $a > 0$, $b < 0$.   (c) For $0 > k > -\frac{1}{4}$, linear
switching leads to limit cycle; for $k \leq -\frac{1}{4}$, linear switching leads to divergent motion.

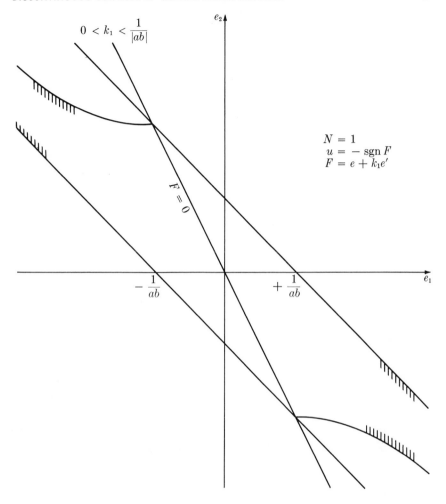

$$0 < k_1 < \frac{1}{|ab|}$$

$$-\frac{1}{ab} \qquad +\frac{1}{ab}$$

$$N = 1$$
$$u = -\operatorname{sgn} F$$
$$F = e + k_1 e'$$

$F = 0$

e_2

e_1

Fig. 2.22 Plant $1/[(s + a)(s + b)]$; $a > 0$, $b < 0$. (d) Narrowing of the strip for stable motions if $0 < k_1 < N/|ab|$.

2.1.1e *Plant with a transfer function* $1/(s^2 + 2\zeta s + 1)$ *with* $0 < |\zeta| < 1$. The uncontrolled system is described by the differential equations

$$e'' + 2\zeta e' + e = 0 \qquad (2.46)$$

The solution is

$$e = A e^{-\zeta \tau} \cos (\nu t + \delta) \qquad (2.47a)$$

where $\nu = \sqrt{1 - \zeta^2}$ and A and δ are integration constants. The deriva-

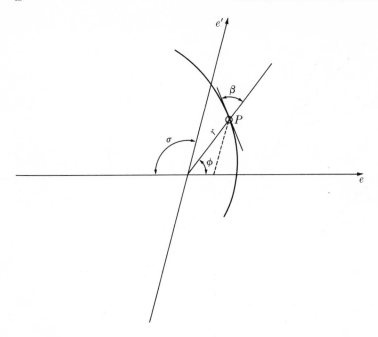

Fig. 2.23   Plant $1/(s^2 + 2\zeta s + 1)$; phase plane with oblique coordinates.

tive e' is given by

$$e' = Ae^{-\zeta\tau} \cos(\nu\tau + \delta + \sigma) \qquad \cos\sigma = -\zeta \tag{2.47b}$$

Hence only a phase shift is needed to obtain e' from e.   This fact allows us to show that in an oblique system ee' (see Fig. 2.23) the radius vector is given by

$$r = A \sin\sigma\, e^{-\zeta\tau} \tag{2.48}$$

[This can be proved by using $r^2 = e^2 + e'^2 - 2ee' \cos\sigma$ and the relation $\cos(\nu\tau + \delta + \sigma) = \cos(\nu\tau + \delta)\cos\sigma - \sin(\nu\tau + \delta)\sin\sigma$.]   In addition, the relation

$$\frac{e'}{r} = \frac{\sin\phi}{\sin\sigma} = \frac{Ae^{-\zeta\tau}\cos(\nu\tau + \sigma + \delta)}{Ae^{-\zeta\tau}\sin\sigma}$$

shows that

$$\sin\phi = \sin\left(\frac{\pi}{2} - \nu\tau - \sigma - \delta\right)$$

or $$\Delta\phi = -\nu\,\Delta\tau \tag{2.49}$$

The motion of system (2.46) is thus described by a logarithmic spiral around the origin.   At each point of the spiral the tangent forms the angle β with the radius vector (see Fig. 2.23):

$$\tan \beta = \frac{r\,d\phi}{dr} = -\frac{r\nu\,d\tau}{dr} = \frac{\nu}{\zeta} = -\cot\sigma$$

or
$$\beta = \pi - \sigma \tag{2.50}$$

The trajectories of the controlled system

$$e'' + 2\zeta e' + e = u = -N \operatorname{sgn} F \tag{2.51}$$

would be composed of portions of spirals around $e = \pm N$.

Logarithmic spirals can easily be drawn, particularly with the approximate (but rather accurate) design suggested by L. S. Jacobsen (see App. 2.1 at the end of the chapter). However, oblique coordinates can be avoided by introducing the coordinates

$$
\begin{aligned}
y_1 &= e - e' \cos \sigma \\
y_2 &= e' \sin \sigma
\end{aligned}
\tag{2.52}
$$

(see Fig. 2.24), which form a rectangular system.

Now let us examine the behavior of the system for positive ζ with a linear switching function $F = e + k_1 e'$. The straight line $e_s + k_1 e_s' = 0$ forms the angle η with the e' axis (see Fig. 2.25):

$$-\frac{1}{k_1} = \frac{e_s'}{e_s} = \frac{\sin(\sigma - \eta)}{\sin \eta} = \sin \sigma \cot \eta - \cos \sigma$$

or
$$\tan \eta = \frac{k_1 \sin \sigma}{1 + k_1 \cos \sigma} = \frac{k_1 \nu}{1 - k_1 \zeta} \tag{2.53}$$

For positive k_1 we obtain $0 \leq \eta \leq \sigma$.

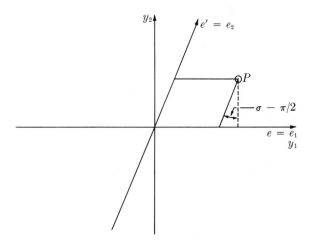

Fig. 2.24 Relation between oblique and orthogonal coordinates.

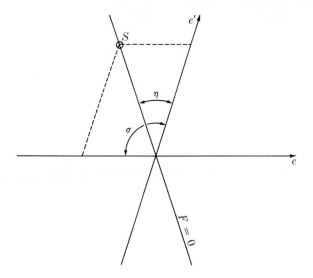

Fig. 2.25   Location of switching line in oblique system.

Figure 2.26a shows a trajectory for positive k_1, and Fig. 2.26b shows the approach of zero in a similar case. S_3 is a point of indecision (the endpoint of regular motion).   Because of infinitesimal imperfections, the motion from S_3 to the origin will be governed by

$$e + k_1 e' = 0$$

that is, in the limit

$$e = \exp\left(-\frac{\tau - \tau_{S_3}}{k_1}\right)$$

Note that, just as in the case of the system with the transfer function $1/(s^2 + 1)$, the trajectory may have numerous switching points, depending on the magnitude of the initial disturbance.

Figure 2.27 depicts a periodic motion for negative k_1, and Fig. 2.28 shows that for negative k_1 every trajectory approaches a limit cycle (periodic motion).   If the initial disturbance lies outside the limit cycle the cycle is approached from the outside; if the disturbance lies inside it is approached from the inside.   Hence the periodic motion is a stable limit cycle.

Figure 2.29 shows the final state of a motion which has a relay with threshold imperfection.   The motion is a limit cycle around the origin, and its magnitude depends on the value of the threshold.   In Fig. 2.30 a trajectory for a relay with a dead zone is shown; here the final motion is a spiral around the origin.

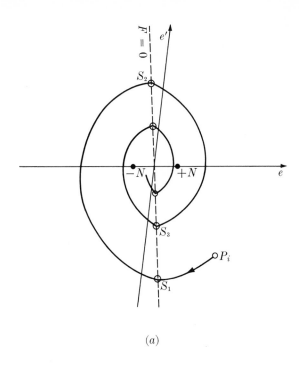

(a)

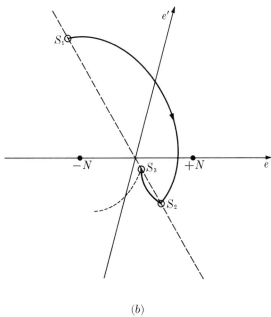

(b)

Fig. 2.26 Plant $1/(s^2 + 2\zeta s + 1)$. (a) Trajectory for positive k; (b) trajectory approaches point of indecision.

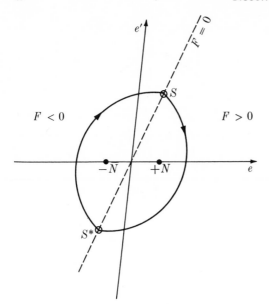

Fig. 2.27 Plant $1/(s^2 + 2\varsigma s + 1)$; periodic motion for $k < 0$.

For relays with a time delay actual switching will take place on two straight lines inclined toward the line $F = 0$. This fact was discussed in detail for the system $1/(s^2 + 1)$, which is a special case of the systems group $1/(s^2 + 2\varsigma s + 1)$.

The periodic solutions play an important role in determining the steady state of a system with imperfect relays that has been subjected to a single disturbance; hence we shall examine the equations for such solutions. With a time of zero assigned to the corner point S (Fig. 2.27) and the length of period denoted as $2T$, the coordinates of the corner points and the value of k_1 are determined by

$$e_{sp}(0) = -e_{sp}(T)$$
$$e'_{sp}(0) = -e'_{sp}(T)$$

Upon application of the general solution

$$e = u + Ae^{-\varsigma\tau} \cos(\nu\tau + \delta)$$

in the form

$$e = u + A_1 e^{\lambda_1\tau} + A_2 e^{\lambda_2\tau}$$

where $\lambda_{1,2} = -\varsigma \pm i\nu$, a simple but tedious computation yields

$$e_{sp}(0) = -\operatorname{sgn} F \frac{(\varsigma/\nu) \sin \nu T - \sinh \varsigma T}{\cos \nu T + \cosh \varsigma T} \qquad (2.54a)$$

$$e'_{sp}(0) = \frac{\operatorname{sgn} F}{\nu} \frac{\sin \nu T}{\cos \nu T + \cosh \varsigma T} \qquad (2.54b)$$

In Fig. 2.31 $e'_{sp}(0)$ is plotted as a function of $e_{sp}(0)$ for various values of ζ, with T as a parameter.

To determine the steady-state limit cycle it is convenient to know e'_{sp} and e_{sp} for small T:

$$e_{sp} = \operatorname{sgn} F \frac{\zeta T^3}{12} \cdots$$

$$e'_{sp} = \operatorname{sgn} F \left(\frac{T}{2}\right) \cdots$$

(2.55)

Equations (2.54) yield

$$\frac{e_{sp}}{e'_{sp}} = -\zeta + \nu \frac{\sinh \zeta T}{\sin \nu T} = -\zeta + \zeta \left(1 + \frac{T^2}{6} + \cdots\right) = \zeta \frac{T^2}{6} + \cdots$$

and $k_{1p} = -\zeta \dfrac{T^2}{6} \cdots$

(2.56)

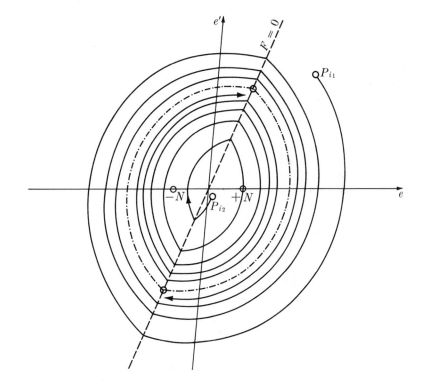

—··—··—··—
limit cycle

Fig. 2.28 Plant $1/(s^2 + 2\zeta s + 1)$; trajectories approaching stable limit cycle.

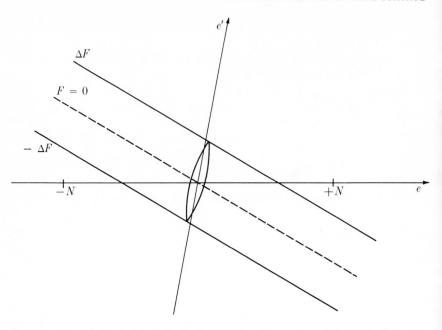

Fig. 2.29 Plant $1/(s^2 + 2\zeta s + 1)$; final state of motion; relay with threshold imperfection.

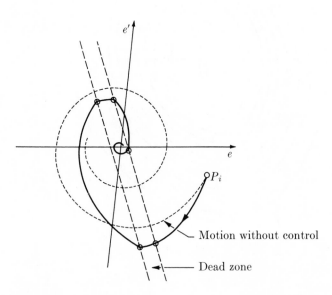

Fig. 2.30 Plant $1/(s^2 + 2\zeta s + 1)$; trajectory for relay with dead zone.

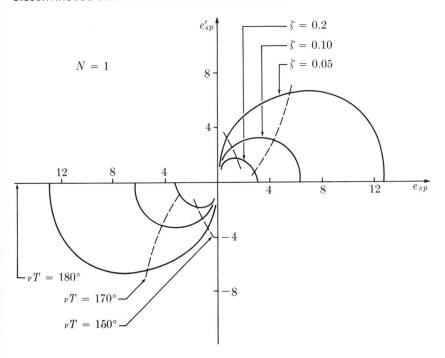

Fig. 2.31 Locus of cornerpoints for the periodic motions of plants $1/(s^2 + 2\zeta s + 1)$.

For instance, to determine the period of the limit cycle depicted in Fig. 2.29, we can write

$$e_{sp} + k_1 e'_{sp} = (\text{sgn } F)\, \Delta F = (\text{sgn } F) \left(\frac{\zeta T^3}{12} + \cdots + k_1 \frac{T}{2} \cdots \right)$$

which yields

$$T = \frac{2\, \Delta F}{k_1} \cdots \tag{2.57}$$

(accurate to first order for not too small k_1), with $e_{sp} \approx 0$ and

$$e'_{sp} = \left(\frac{\Delta F}{k_1} \right) \text{sgn } F$$

It is obvious that the behavior of a system with positive ζ can be improved by a control with $u = -\text{sgn }(e + k_1 e')$ only if a positive k_1 is chosen. In this case the origin is approached with a chatter motion. During this chatter motion the system behaves as a linear system, and

$$e = e^{-(\tau - \tau_s)/k_1}$$

where τ_s indicates the time in which the endpoint of the regular motion was reached. So far it seems desirable to choose a small k_1 so that the origin will be approached quickly. However, a few examples will show that the region of possible endpoints on a switching line also depends very strongly on k_1. Computation of the region of endpoints in the ee' plane will serve to illustrate the importance of the choice of k_1.

To determine the location of endpoints it is necessary first to study the behavior of a phase-point trajectory in the neighborhood of a switching point. Since

$$e'' + 2\zeta e' + e = u = - \operatorname{sgn} F$$

the second derivative e'' is discontinuous at switching points. The slope of a trajectory in the phase plane is given by

$$\frac{de'}{de} = \frac{e''}{e'} = \frac{u - 2\zeta e' - e}{e'} = -2\zeta + \frac{u - e}{e'} \tag{2.58}$$

It is obvious that at a switching point, where u changes sign, the derivative de'/de experiences a jump. This fact has been observed in many figures. The linear switching function $F = e + k_1 e'$ is continuous at switching points, but its derivative is discontinuous (see Fig. 2.32). Figure 2.32b indicates that regular switching is impossible and only chatter can ensue (Fig. 2.32d). Figure 2.32c shows the limiting case between regular motion and chatter motion which determines the chatter region on a switching line:[1]

$$F(t_s) = e_E + k_1 e'_E = 0$$
$$F'(t_{s+}) = e'_E + k_1 e''_E = 0 = e'_E + k_1(- \operatorname{sgn} F_+ - 2\zeta e'_E - e_E)$$
$$= 0 \quad (2.59)$$

Equations (2.59) yield the coordinates of that endpoint which has the largest distance from the origin:

$$
\begin{aligned}
e'_E &= \frac{k_1 \operatorname{sgn} F_+}{1 - 2\zeta k_1 + k_1{}^2} \\
e_E &= \frac{-k_1{}^2 \operatorname{sgn} F_+}{1 - 2\zeta k_1 + k_1{}^2}
\end{aligned}
\tag{2.60}
$$

Upon eliminating the parameter k_1 from Eqs. (2.59) we obtain

$$e'^2 + 2\zeta ee' + e^2 + e \operatorname{sgn} F_+ = 0 \tag{2.61}$$

This is the equation of a circle, as can easily be shown by introducing the rectangular coordinates y_1 and y_2 [see Eq. (2.52)]. In these coordinates

---

[1] In the following equations the subscript $s+$ means immediately after switching and $s-$ means immediately before switching.

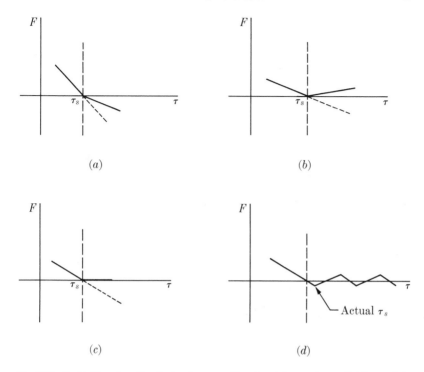

Fig. 2.32   Switching-function behavior near $F = 0$.   (a) regular switching point; (b) switching impossible; (c) limiting case; (d) chatter.

Eq. (2.61) yields

$$y_1{}^2 + y_2{}^2 + (\text{sgn } F)(y_1 + \cot \sigma \cdot y_2) = 0$$

That is, the center lies at $(y_1 = -\tfrac{1}{2}\text{ sgn } F, \; y_2 = -\tfrac{1}{2}\cot \sigma \text{ sgn } F)$. Because of sgn F, the two circles pass through the points

$$(e,e') = \begin{cases} (0,0) \\ (-\text{ sgn } F_+, 0) \end{cases}$$

(see Fig. 2.33).

Since endpoints occur only for positive k_1, the meaning of those points on the circle for which k_1 is negative must still be explained.   In Fig. 2.34 an attempt is made to start a trajectory on a switching line with negative k_1 in the interior of one of the circles.   It is obvious that two trajectories can be started at the point P_{st} but that P_{st} cannot be reached in any way other than by a chatter along the line $e + k_1e' = 0$. Figure 2.35 shows the behavior of $F(t)$ in the neighborhood of a "starting" point P_{st}.   If we replace F_+ by F_- in Eq. (2.59), we can determine the

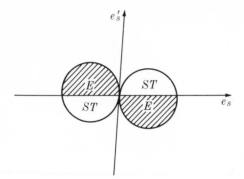

Fig. 2.33 Plant $1/(s^2 + 2\zeta s + 1)$; regions for endpoints and for starting points; $0 < \zeta < 1$.

starting points. Since sgn F already comprises positive and negative values, the final result, Eq. (2.61), is not changed. In Fig. 2.33 endpoint and starting-point regions are marked.

We are now prepared to choose a positive k_1 for reaching the origin (or, strictly speaking, the small limit cycle around the origin) as fast as

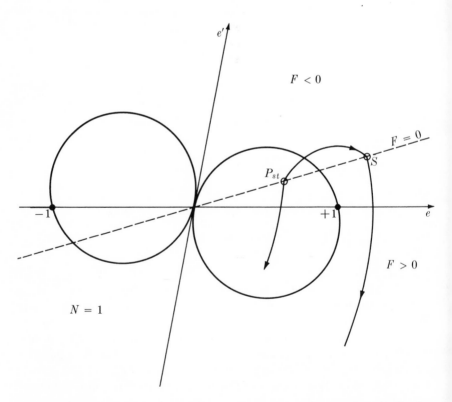

Fig. 2.34 Plant $1/(s^2 + 2\zeta s + 1)$; two phase-point trajectories in a "starting" point; $0 < \zeta < 1$.

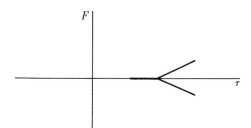

Fig. 2.35 Behavior of the switching function $F(\tau)$ in the neighborhood of a starting point.

desired. If a very small k_1 is chosen, as in Fig. 2.26a, the trajectory will oscillate for a long time, because the region of possible endpoints on the switching line is very small. Thus k_1 should not be chosen too small. In addition, recall from the system $1/(s^2 + 1)$ that time delay in the relay might turn the lines of actual switching so much that the effective k_1 becomes slightly negative. In this case the motion becomes divergent, and the zero point or its neighborhood will never be reached.

So far we have considered only positive values of ζ. With negative values of ζ an uncontrolled system will diverge. From experience with other systems, however, we might expect such a system to be controllable if the disturbances are limited. In fact there are nondivergent motions. A look at Eqs. (2.54) indicates that there are periodic motions for negative ζ.

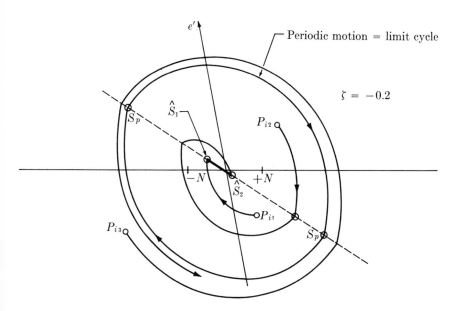

Fig. 2.36 Plant $1/(s^2 + 2\zeta s + 1)$ with negative ζ; $|\zeta| < 1$. Limit cycle for $k_1 > 0$; motion inside tends toward zero, motion outside tends toward the limit cycle.

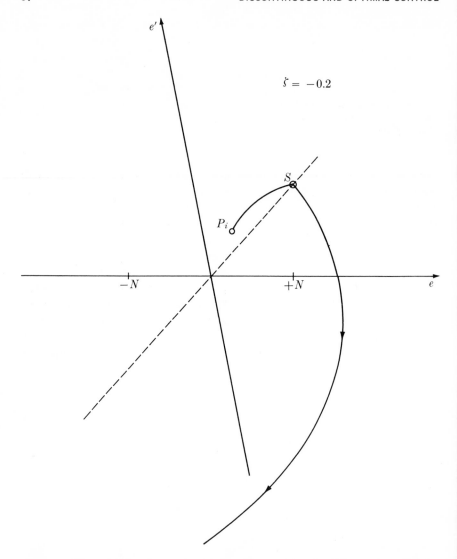

Fig. 2.37 Plant $1/(s^2 + 2\zeta s + 1)$ with negative ζ; $|\zeta| < 1$. Divergent motion for negative k_1.

For a better idea of this, observe that in Fig. 2.36 σ is an acute angle. This figure traces the periodic motion for the chosen positive k_1 in $F = e + k_1 e'$ and, in addition, shows three trajectories. Those which start inside the limit cycle proceed toward the origin. In each case ($\hat{S}_1 0$ and $\hat{S}_2 0$) a chatter motion occurs after a regular motion. If the initial point lies outside the limit cycle, the phase point moves away from it; that is, the motion is divergent. The limit cycle is termed unstable because any slight deviation from it will cause the phase point to go either toward the origin or toward infinity. Figure 2.37 presents a trajectory for a system with $\zeta = -0.2$ and $F = e + k_1 e'$, with $k_1 < 0$. This example shows that for negative k_1 only divergent solutions exist.

It is also interesting to examine the response to step inputs of different magnitude. In this case (see Fig. 2.2) the error $e(t) = r_0(t) - c(t)$, and the system behavior is governed by the differential equation

$$e'' + 2\zeta e' + e = r_0 - N \operatorname{sgn} F \tag{2.62}$$

This can be considered a system with a *biased* relay. In general, if $F > 0$ the restoring force is $r_0 - N$, and if $F < 0$ the restoring force is $r_0 + N$. It will become apparent that the behavior of the system is very different for $|r_0| < N$ and $|r_0| > N$. It is important to become familiar with this response to a step input, because this study is the basis for a first evaluation of the response of the system to a time-varying input. We shall assume initial values $c(0) = 0$ and $c'(0) = 0$; that is, $e(0) = r_0$ and $e'(0) = 0$. Let us first consider systems with $1 > \zeta > 0$, and then systems with $-1 < \zeta < 0$.

Figure 2.38 shows the phase-point trajectory for positive ζ, positive k_1, and $|r_0| < N$. The phase point moves toward the origin. From P_{i1}

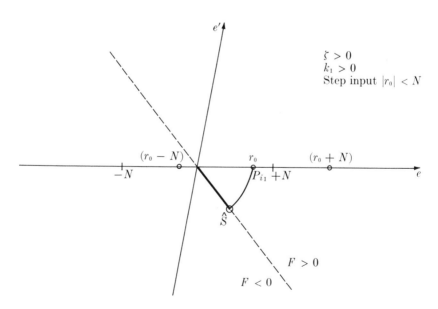

Fig. 2.38 Plant $1/(s^2 + 2\zeta s + 1)$; response to step input.

to $\hat{S}$ the motion is regular; at $\hat{S}$ chatter motion starts.   Figure 2.39 illustrates the case for $|r_0| > N$.   After a regular motion from P_i to $\hat{S}_1$, chatter occurs from $\hat{S}_1$ to $\hat{S}_2$.   Then the phase point moves again in a regular way, approaching the point $e = r_0 - N$ after infinite time in a spiral motion.[1]

Figure 2.40 shows the trajectory for $\zeta < 0$, $k_1 > 0$, and $|r_0| < N$. The behavior is what might be expected.   Of much more interest is the case for $\zeta < 0$, $k_1 > 0$, and $|r_0| > N$ (Fig. 2.41).   We see immediately that a phase point starting at P_i will go to $\hat{S}_1$, where chatter starts, and then to $\hat{S}_2$, where chatter ends.   From $\hat{S}_2$ it will move in a regular motion to $\hat{S}_0$; then chatter starts again, and after $\hat{S}_1$ the process repeats.   Thus the steady state is a limit cycle around $r_0 - N$ which consists of regular and chatter motion.   If the initial values are something other than $c(0) = 0$ and $c'(0)$, this difference is important.   As long as P_i lies inside limit cycle I, the final state is as described, namely, limit cycle I.   If point P_{i2} lies outside cycle I, the phase point will move toward cycle I as long as P_{i2} lies inside limit cycle II.   All motions starting outside limit cycle II are divergent.   This fact may be considered practically unimportant, because in most cases $c(0)$ and $c'(0)$ will not be that large.   Note that limit cycles I and II are both asymmetric, and limit cycle I contains a

[1] At $\hat{S}_2$ the spiral around $r_0 - N$ is tangent to the line $e + k_1 e' = 0$.

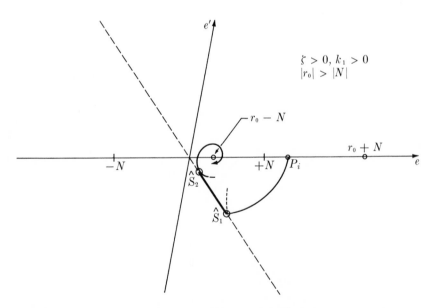

Fig. 2.39   Plant $1/(s^2 + 2\zeta s + 1)$; response to step input.

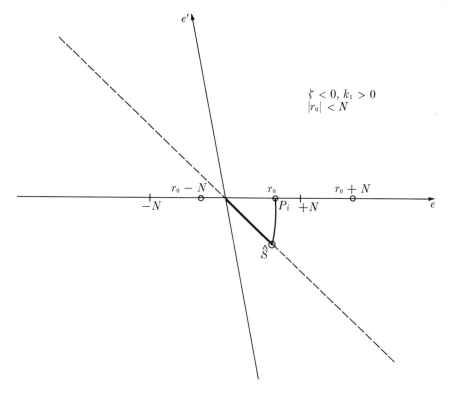

Fig. 2.40   Plant $1/(s^2 + 2\zeta s + 1)$; response to step input.

chatter region.   In systems with asymmetric relays a response to initial disturbances will create only asymmetric limit cycles.

2.1.2 Systems with one zero and one control input

In the simple system $(b_1 s + 1)/s^2$ the strong influence of a zero in the transfer function becomes evident immediately.   The differential equation of the system is

$$e'' = b_1 u' + u \qquad (2.63)$$

where $u = -N \operatorname{sgn} F = -N \operatorname{sgn} (e + k_1 e')$

Since $u(t)$ is discontinuous, $u'(t)$ is a δ function.   Integration of Eq. (2.63) in the neighborhood of a switching point at t_0 over an interval $t_0 - \epsilon \le t \le t_0 + \epsilon$ gives

$$\int_{t_0-\epsilon}^{t_0+\epsilon} e'' \, dt = b_1 \int_{t_0-\epsilon}^{t_0+\epsilon} u' \, dt + \int_{t_0-\epsilon}^{t_0+\epsilon} u \, dt \qquad (2.64)$$

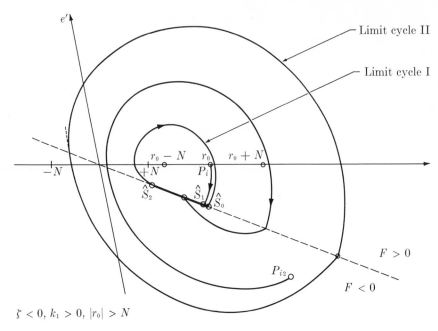

$\zeta < 0,\ k_1 > 0,\ |r_0| > N$

Fig. 2.41   Plant $1/(s^2 + 2\zeta s + 1)$; combination of ζ, k_1, and $|r_0|$ which generates two limit cycles.

or, in the limit with $\Delta_1 u = \lim\limits_{\epsilon \to 0} [u(t_0 + \epsilon) - u(t_0 - \epsilon)]$,

$$\Delta_1 e' = b_1 \Delta_1 u + 0 = 2(\pm N)b_1 \tag{2.65}$$

Therefore the derivative e' is discontinuous at switching. This means that the switching function F is also discontinuous at switching.

In Figs. 2.42 and 2.43 two different types of switching-function behavior are exhibited. Figure 2.42 shows a *noncontrolling* chatter. The function F reaches zero and passes a threshold θ. Actual switching occurs τ_d sec after F passes $-\theta$. Then F jumps by $k_1 b_1 \Delta_1 u = 2N b_1 k_1$, and during the jump passes zero and the threshold θ; hence another switching must occur τ_d sec later. This behavior will be repeated. The corresponding behavior of $u = -\operatorname{sgn} F$ is traced in the same figure (lower part). Observe that u_{av} of a "cycle" is equal to zero.

In Fig. 2.43 a *controlling* chatter is shown. In this case the upward jump is again followed by a jump downward, but owing to the steep slope of F, in its jump downward it does not pass zero and the threshold $-\theta$. Therefore the function u is positive for the time τ_d but negative for a longer time[1] $\mu + \tau_d$. Consequently, u_{av} of a cycle is not equal to zero. A quantitative study of the chatter motion will be given in Sec. 3.3. This discussion is intended only to introduce the phenomenon.

Figure 2.44 shows a phase trajectory for the system $(b_1 s + 1)/s^2$ with $F = e + k_1 e'$ and $k_1 > 0$. Since $u' = 0$ between two switchings, the trajectory is still composed of portions of parabolas

$$\frac{e'^2}{2} = u(e + \text{const})$$

Observe that chatter starts as soon as F passes the switching line, first

[1] We can also say that F does not change sign every switching but only every other switching (see Sec. 3.3.2 for general treatment).

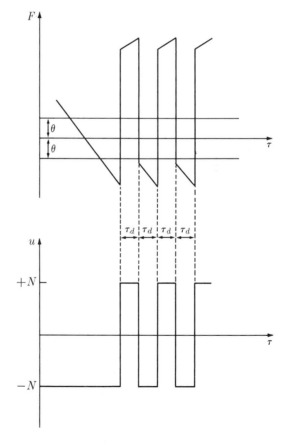

Fig. 2.42 Behavior of switching function in noncontrolling chatter.

as noncontrolling chatter and then as controlling chatter. The motion ends in a small limit cycle around the point $Q = (-b_1 k_1 u_s, 0) = (-b_1 k_1, 0)$. At this point e is finite and $e' = 0$. The limit cycle is indicated, and the average motion during controlling chatter (according to Sec. 3.3) is shown.

The same phase trajectory is plotted in Fig. 2.45 with other coordinates. The system $e'' = b_1 u' + u$ may be represented by a system of two first-order equations. With $e_1 = e$ we have

$$
\begin{aligned}
e_1' &= b_1 u + e_2 \\
e_2' &= u
\end{aligned}
\tag{2.66}
$$

and $\quad F = e + k_1 e' = e_1 + k_1(b_1 u + e_2)$

The coordinates e_1 and e_2 are continuous, but there are two lines $F = 0$

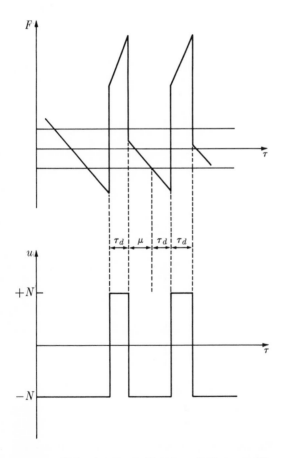

Fig. 2.43   Behavior of switching function in controlling chatter.

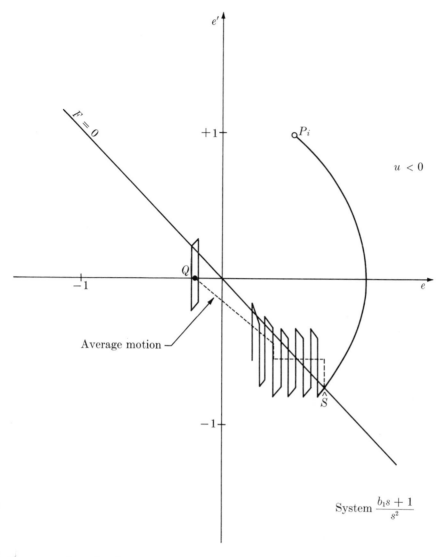

Fig. 2.44 Second-order system with one zero; transfer function $(b_1 s + 1)/s^2$; $b_1 > 0$.

(see Fig. 2.45) in the $e_1 e_2$ plane. Between these two lines the relay cannot stay in either position longer than the delay time allows; hence this strip between the two lines $F = 0$ is the region of noncontrolling chatter.

Although the trajectory is composed of portions of parabolas, $e'^2/2 = u(e + \text{const})$ leads to

$$\frac{(b_1 u + e_2)^2}{2} = u(e_1 + \text{const}) \tag{2.67}$$

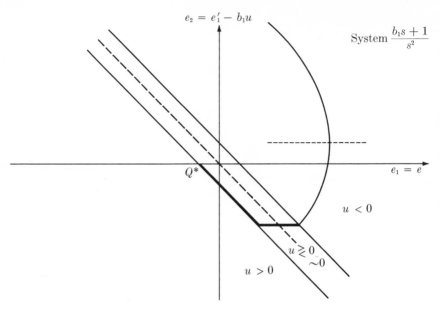

Final state: limit cycle around $e_2 = 0$ $e_1 = -k_1 b_1$ Chatter: heavy line

Fig. 2.45   System of Fig. 2.44 shown in another coordinate system; system $(b_1 s + 1)/s^2$.

which means that the vertices of the parabolas lie on the lines $-b_1 u = e_2$. The final state around Q^* is indicated, and the final limit cycle can be drawn easily.   At this point Q^* the average control variable u_{av} reaches the value zero; hence $e_2'(Q^*) = 0$ and $e_1'(Q^*) = e_2(Q^*) = 0$.

In Fig. 2.46 a trajectory is shown for the same plant, but with

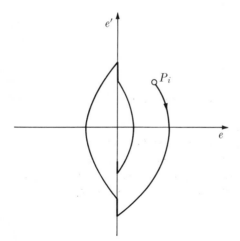

Fig. 2.46   Same system as in Figs. 2.44 and 2.45, but $k_1 = 0$.

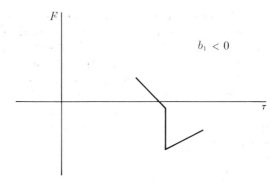

Fig. 2.47 Switching function behavior for a system $(b_1 s + 1)/s^2$ with negative b_1.

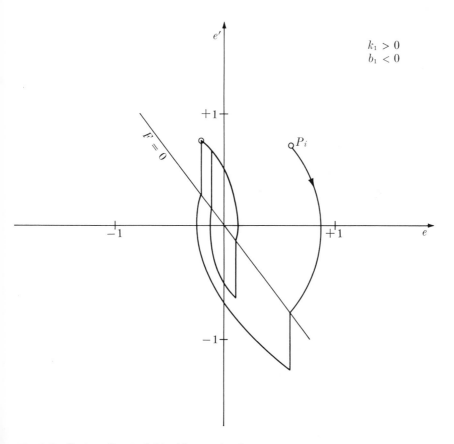

Fig. 2.48 System $(b_1 s + 1)/s^2$ with negative b_1.

$k_1 \equiv 0$.   In this case $F = e$.   Therefore F is continuous, with a discontinuous slope at switching points because the derivative e' is still discontinuous, so no chatter occurs.   All discontinuities lie on the e' axis, and the final state is a limit cycle around the origin.

The behavior of such a system with a zero is quite different if b_1 is negative.   Figure 2.47 depicts the switching function F at switching and shows clearly that no chatter can start because the discontinuity pushes the curve away from the zero line.   A corresponding trajectory is shown in Fig. 2.48, with the steady state given by a limit cycle around the origin.

Thus far no negative k_1 has been chosen.   Figure 2.49 shows a divergent motion for positive b_1 and negative k_1.   If b_1 were negative, the trajectory would enter a noncontrolling chatter motion at S_1, after

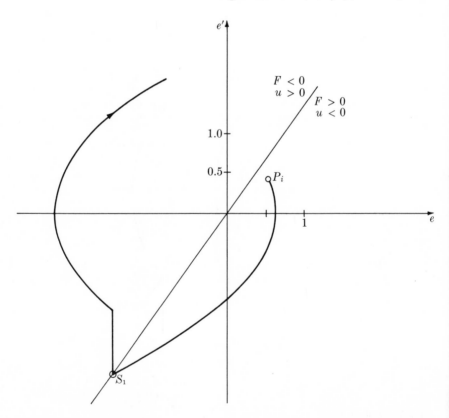

Divergent motion: $k_1 < 0$, $b_1 > 0$ $b_1 = 0.8$

Fig. 2.49   System $(b_1 s + 1)/s^2$ with positive b_1 and negative k_1 in the switching function.

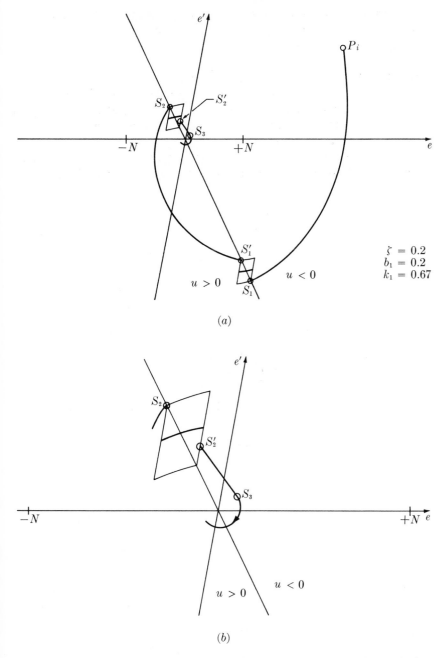

$$\zeta = 0.2$$
$$b_1 = 0.2$$
$$k_1 = 0.67$$

(a)

(b)

Fig. 2.50 System $(b_1s + 1)/(s^2 + 2\zeta s + 1)$. (a) Regular motion on P_iS_1 and $S_1'S_2$; noncontrolling chatter on S_1S_1' and S_2S_2'; controlling chatter on $S_2'S_3$ (only average motion is traced); final noncontrolling chatter after S_3 (only average motion is traced). (b) Inner part of a enlarged; heavy lines after S_2 mark average motion.

which regular motion would occur until the switching line was again approached. A divergent motion would occur which contained non-controlling chatter regions.

As a second example consider the system $(b_1 s + 1)/(s^2 + 2\zeta s + 1)$. Figures 2.50a and b show a trajectory with $F = e + k_1 e'$ and $k_1 > 0$. Since $b_1 > 0$, noncontrolling chatter occurs after S_1. At S_1' regular motion starts again and continues until S_2. From S_2 to S_2' there is again noncontrolling chatter, which passes over into controlling chatter and continues until S_3. After S_3 the motion proceeds in noncontrolling chatter. Since the uncontrolled system is damped, the origin will be reached in infinite time in a spiral motion. The location of the points

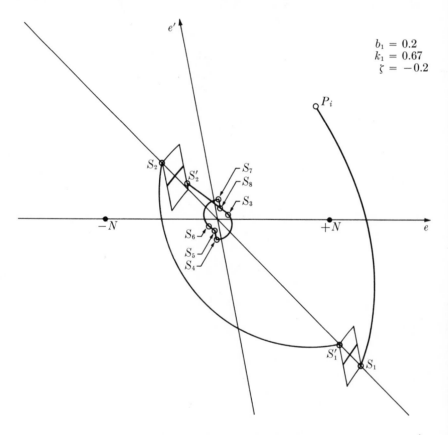

$b_1 = 0.2$
$k_1 = 0.67$
$\zeta = -0.2$

Fig. 2.51 System $(b_1 s + 1)/(s^2 + 2\zeta s + 1)$. Regular motion on $P_i S_1$ and $S_1' S_2$; noncontrolling chatter on $S_1 S_1'$ and $S_2 S_2'$; controlling chatter (average motion) on $S_2' S_3$; final noncontrolling chatter (average motion) on $S_3 S_4$; controlling chatter starts again at S_5. $S_3 S_4 S_5 S_6 S_7 S_8$ = limit cycle (average motion, composed of noncontrolling chatter $S_3 S_4$ and $S_6 S_7$ and of controlling chatter $S_5 S_6$ and $S_8 S_3$).

S_2' and S_3 can be determined by analytic expressions, as will be shown in Sec. 3.3.

In designing a trajectory it is advisable at this point to assume a small time delay in order to obtain the essential features of the motion. Figures 2.50a and b are traced for an infinitesimal time delay. During controlling chatter the average trajectory is described by

$$e_{av}'(-0.817) + e_{av}(-0.861) = u_s(0.133) = -0.133$$

Note that the presence of the zero makes approach to the origin slower than in a system without a zero; in a system without a zero

$$e_{av}'(0.67) + e_{av} = 0$$

An analysis shows that $k_{1,av} > k_1$ for positive b_1, positive k_1, and $|\zeta| < 1$. Figure 2.51 shows the trajectory for a system with negative ζ. In this case the final motion is a periodic motion of alternating controlling and noncontrolling chatter. Only the average motion in this final state is shown.

These two examples illustrate clearly the strong influence of zeroes on the motion of the phase point. Naturally, discontinuities in the control function F could have been avoided merely by using $F = e$; then $F = e'$ would have been discontinuous. There would have been no noncontrolling chatter, as seen in Fig. 2.46 for the system $(b_1s + 1)/s^2$, and the final state would have been a limit cycle determined by the imperfections of the relay. However, the choice $k_1 = 0$ leads to a very slow approach to the origin of the phase plane because the trajectory winds often around the origin when the distance of the initial point is about the size of N or larger.

2.2 REACTION TO VARIABLE INPUT

The preceding sections deal with the response of second-order systems to a single disturbance and to step inputs. The response to step inputs provides a possibility of obtaining some information about the response to variable inputs. A review of the responses to step inputs with linear switching functions indicates that it is preferable to design a system (that is, choose k_1 and N) that works mostly in the chatter region. Such a design will produce a good follow-up system.

Assume a second-order system described by

$$c'' + \alpha c' + \beta c = N \operatorname{sgn} (e + k_1 e') \tag{2.68}$$

Then for a time-variable input $r(\tau)$ we obtain the following differential equation for the error e:

$$e'' + \alpha e' + \beta e = -N \text{ sgn } (e + k_1 e') + r'' + \alpha r' + \beta r \qquad (2.69)$$

If we denote $r'' + \alpha r' + \beta r = f^*(\tau)$, we have the control problem

$$e'' + \alpha e' + \beta e = -N \text{ sgn } (e + k_1 e') + f^*(\tau) \qquad (2.70)$$

If $f^*(\tau)$ is a constant, this problem would pose no difficulty. However, if the maximum and minimum values of the variable function $f^*(\tau)$ are known and if it is assumed that this function does not contain frequencies of the order that occur in the chatter, N and k_1 can simply be chosen such that the system starts to chatter and remains in chatter.

It may help clarify the value of this design suggestion to replace $f^*(\tau)$ by a piecewise constant curve (see Fig. 2.52). In Sec. 3.3 we shall compute the average motion analytically for such a case and for more general ones to show that the average motion stays close to the line $e + k_1 e' = 0$, and the deviation from this line increases with the time delay τ_d and becomes zero for vanishing τ_d.

There is a very different way of designing a control to make a second-order system follow a given input $r(\tau)$. This idea is based on the fact that the follow-up would be perfect if $r(\tau)$ were a solution of the homogeneous differential equation describing the plant dynamics; that is, in the case considered here, a solution of

$$c'' + 2\zeta c' + c = 0 \qquad (2.71)$$

where $0 \leq \zeta \leq 1$. Primes indicate differentiation with respect to the dimensionless time τ, and the variable is $\tau = \omega_\nu t$, where ω_ν is the natural frequency of the undamped linear system.

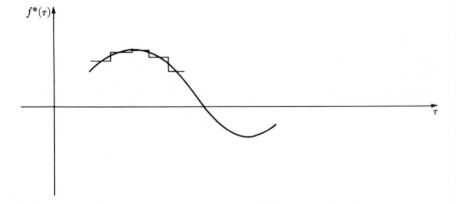

Fig. 2.52 Study of response to variable input; replacement of $f^*(\tau) = r'' + \alpha r' + \beta r$ by a piecewise constant curve.

Since in general $r(\tau)$ is not a solution of Eq. (2.71), we shall adjust the system dynamics in such a way that $r(\tau)$ becomes a solution at least in small intervals. The system with the variable input is now described by

$$c'' + 2\zeta\beta c' + \gamma c = r(\tau) \tag{2.72}$$

The values β and γ are constants but can change discontinuously at certain instances of time in order to let $c(\tau)$ approach $r(\tau)$. This idea was first investigated analytically by Flügge-Lotz and Wunch (Ref. 2.1); the investigation was continued with the assistance of Taylor (Ref. 2.2),[1] who then actually built such systems.

Equation (2.73) shows the form of the system that allows a good follow-up:

$$c'' + 2\zeta(1 + \beta_m)c' + (1 + \gamma_n)c = r(\tau) \tag{2.73}$$

Let us now consider the manner in which β_m and γ_n should change discontinuously. If the follow-up were perfect, that is, if $c(\tau) \equiv r(\tau)$, Eq. (2.73) would yield

$$c'' + 2\zeta(1 + \beta_m)c' + \gamma_n c = 0 \tag{2.74}$$

The characteristic equation of this system is

$$\lambda^2 + 2\zeta(1 + \beta_m)\lambda + \gamma_n = 0$$

and the roots are

$$\lambda_{1,2} = -\zeta(1 + \beta_m) \pm \sqrt{\zeta^2(1 + \beta_m)^2 - \gamma_n} \tag{2.75}$$

Thus the sign and magnitude of γ_n determine the type of the system. For negative γ_n there are two real roots of opposite sign. For positive γ_n there are two cases: first, $|\gamma_n| \leq \zeta^2(1 + \beta_m)^2$ yields two real negative roots; second, $|\gamma_n| \geq \zeta^2(1 + \beta_m)^2$ yields two complex roots. In the latter case trajectories are of a spiral type.

A systematic but discontinuous change of β_m and γ_n allows approximation of the curve $r(\tau)$ in the fashion shown in Fig. 2.53 in the phase plane. Actually, a more refined approximation is used; the portions nearly parallel to $r'(r)$ and the portion nearly normal to $r'(r)$ will have an additional break in slope at an intermediate point of the interval under consideration.

The following choice of β_m and γ_n have proved to provide good follow-up. First four constants are chosen.

$$_1\beta \qquad _2\beta \qquad _1\gamma \qquad _2\gamma \tag{2.76}$$

[1] Reference 2.2 contains an appendix by H. E. Lindberg on the influence of time delays in the relays on the performance of the system.

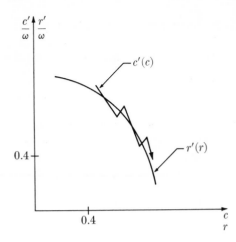

Fig. 2.53   Followup of an input; see Eq. (2.74).

Then the following laws determine β_m and γ_n:

$$\beta_m = -_1\beta \text{ sgn } c'e - _2\beta \text{ sgn } c'e' \qquad m = 0, 1, 2, 3 \qquad (2.77)$$

and $\gamma_n = -_1\gamma \text{ sgn } ce - _2\gamma \text{ sgn } ce' \qquad n = 0, 1, 2, 3 \qquad (2.78)$

The subscript convention is

$$
\begin{aligned}
\beta_3 &= _1\beta + _2\beta & \gamma_3 &= _1\gamma + _2\gamma \\
\beta_2 &= _1\beta - _2\beta & \gamma_2 &= _1\gamma - _2\gamma \\
\beta_1 &= -_1\beta + _2\beta = -\beta_2 & \gamma_1 &= -_1\gamma + _2\gamma = -\gamma_2 \\
\beta_0 &= -_1\beta - _2\beta = -\beta_3 & \gamma_0 &= -_1\gamma - _2\gamma = -\gamma_3
\end{aligned}
\qquad (2.79)
$$

Figure 2.54 illustrates the stepwise change of β_m and γ_n.

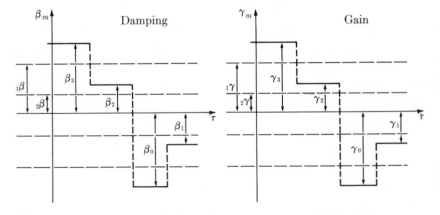

Fig. 2.54   Illustration of the stepwise nature of parameters β_m and γ_n.

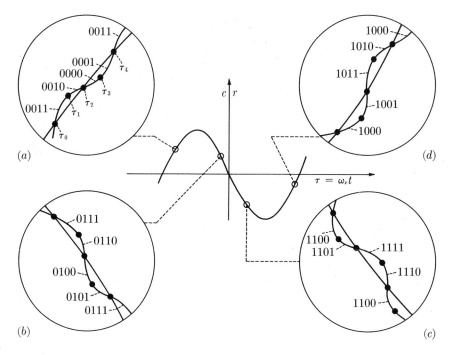

Fig. 2.55 Sketch showing portions of superposed input and output of a nonlinear system magnified approximately 100 times.

In Fig. 2.55 the follow-up of a sinusoidal input ($\omega \neq \omega_\nu$) is shown in an $r(\tau)$ diagram. In the center of this figure input $r(\tau)$ and output $c(\tau)$ are shown. The follow-up is so good that only enlargements can show the details. In these enlargements it can be observed that $e = 0$ and $e' = 0$ determine the change of β_m and γ_n according to the laws given by Eqs. (2.77) and (2.78). The possible combinations of β_m and γ_n can be described by a simple logic with only the numbers 0 and 1.

As an illustration, let us adopt the binary-system convention that $c > 0$ is denoted by 0 and $c < 0$ is denoted by 1, with similar notation for c', e, and e'. Then, for example, for $c > 0$, $c' < 0$, $e > 0$, and $e' > 0$ we have the description

$$cc'ee' \to 0100$$

and the coefficients

$$\beta_3 = {}_1\beta + {}_2\beta$$
$$\gamma_0 = -{}_1\gamma - {}_2\gamma$$

In Fig. 2.55 the coefficients used in the four intervals of a "cycle" are shown. Let us consider circular cutout (a) first. The error changes sign at τ_0 and the binary number 0011 characterizes the situation for $\tau > \tau_0$, so the combination $\beta_3\gamma_3$ governs the follow-up. At τ_1 the derivative e' changes sign, the binary number 0010 characterizes the situation for $\tau > \tau_1$, and the combination $\beta_2\gamma_2$ should be used. At τ_2 the error changes sign, for $\tau > \tau_2$ the binary number is 0000, and the combination used is $\beta_0\gamma_0$. At τ_3 the derivative e' changes sign, for $\tau > \tau_3$ the binary number is 0001, and the combination used is $\beta_1\gamma_1$. For $\tau > \tau_4$ the situation is the same as for $\tau_0 < \tau < \tau_1$, and so on.

The occurrence of products of c and e, c and e', c' and e, and c' and e' assures that the follow-up is the same for $r(\tau)$ and $-r(\tau)$ and that in a curve $r(\tau)$ symmetric to $\tau = 0$ the follow-up is the same for $\tau_1 = -\tau_2$ (for details see Ref. 2.1).

In Table 1 the coding scheme is shown; observe that there are 16 coding numbers, but Table 2 shows that there are only eight allowed combinations of β_m and γ_n, because 0000 and 1111 are identical. The block diagram of Fig. 2.56 shows the complete physical interpretation of Eq. (2.73).

Table 1 Coding scheme for switching logic
0, function > 0; 1, function < 0

Binary coded decimal				Decimal
c	c'	e	e'	0
0	0	0	0	0
0	0	0	1	1
0	0	1	0	2
0	0	1	1	3
0	1	0	0	4
0	1	0	1	5
0	1	1	0	6
0	1	1	1	7
1	0	0	0	8
1	0	0	1	9
1	0	1	0	10
1	0	1	1	11
1	1	0	0	12
1	1	0	1	13
1	1	1	0	14
1	1	1	1	15

**Table 2 Matrix of allowed β_m, γ_n combinations as determined by encoded switching logic obtained from Eqs. (2.77) and (2.78)*

	β_0	β_1	β_2	β_3
γ_0	0000 1111			0100 1011
γ_1		0001 1110	0101 1010	
γ_2		0110 1001	0010 1101	
γ_3	0111 1000			0011 1100

* Examples:
1. $\beta_3\gamma_0$ is chosen when 0100 occurs ($c > 0$, $c' < 0$, $e > 0$, $e' > 0$), or when 1011 occurs ($c < 0$, $c' > 0$, $e < 0$, $e' < 0$).
2. $\beta_2\gamma_1$ is chosen when 0101 occurs ($c > 0$, $c' < 0$, $e > 0$, $e' < 0$), or when 1010 occurs ($c < 0$, $c' > 0$, $e < 0$, $e' > 0$).
3. $\beta_1\gamma_3$ is not possible.

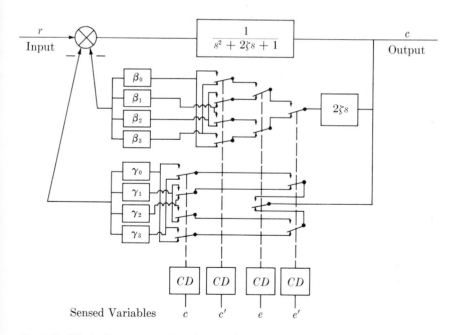

Fig. 2.56 Block diagram showing the complete physical interpretation of Eq. (2.73). CD = zero-coincidence detectors.

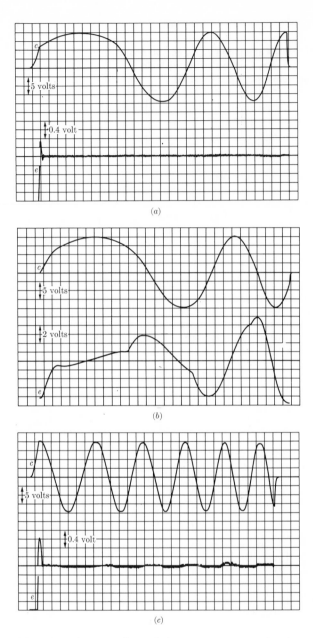

Fig. 2.57 Linear and nonlinear system responses for 20-volt peak-to-peak sinusoidal inputs with frequency Ω varied. $\zeta = 0.6$; 2.5 small divisions on the time scale equal one normalized time unit; tick marks at the bottom of figures indicate when frequency was varied. (*a*) Nonlinear and (*b*) linear system, $\Omega = \omega/\omega_\nu = 0.1$ to 0.4 in 0.1 steps. (*c*) Nonlinear and (*d*) linear system, $\Omega = \omega/\omega_\nu = 0.5$ to 0.8 in 0.1 steps. (*e*) Nonlinear and (*f*) linear system, $\Omega = \omega/\omega_\nu = 1$ to 2 in 0.2 steps.

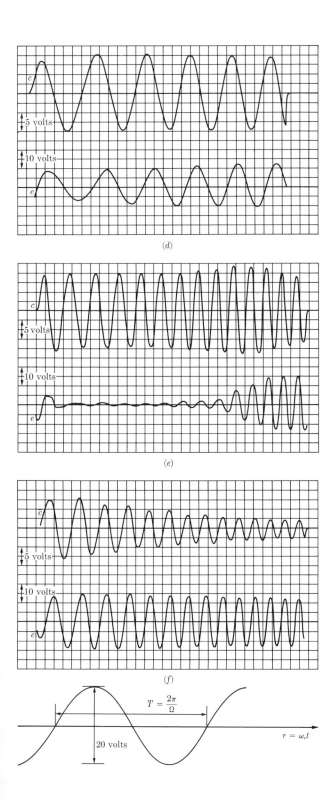

c

5 volts

10 volts

e

(d)

c

5 volts

10 volts

e

(e)

$\bar{c}$

5 volts

10 volts

e

(f)

$$T = \frac{2\pi}{\Omega}$$

20 volts

$\tau = \omega_v t$

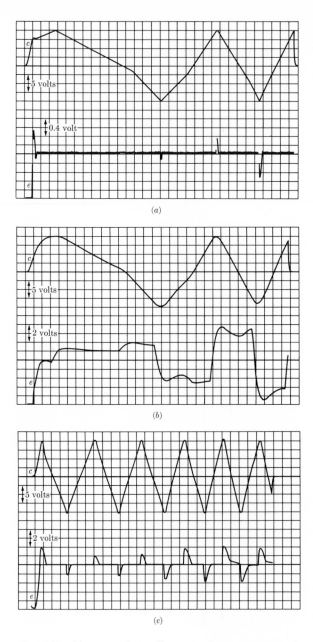

(a)

(b)

(c)

Fig. 2.58 Linear and nonlinear system responses to 20-volt peak-to-peak triangular-wave inputs with period T varied. $\zeta = 0.6$; 2.5 small divisions on the time scale equal one normalized time unit; tick marks at the bottom of figures indicate when periods were varied. (a) Nonlinear and (b) linear system, $\Omega = 2\pi/T = 0.1$ to 0.4 in 0.1 steps. (c) Nonlinear and (d) linear system, $\Omega = 2\pi/T = 0.5$ to 0.8 in 0.1 steps. (e) Nonlinear and (f) linear system, $\Omega = 2\pi/T = 1$ to 2 in 0.2 steps.

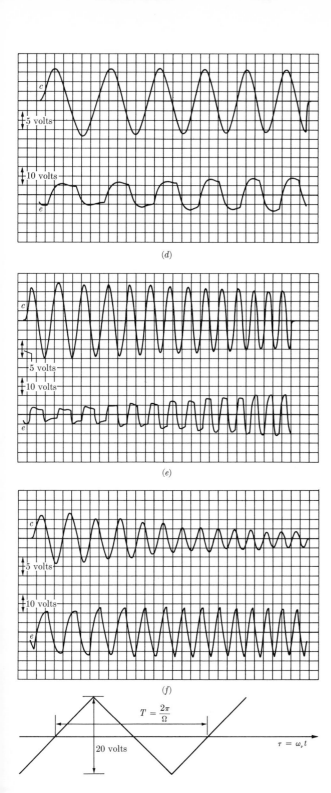

c

5 volts

10 volts

e

(d)

c

5 volts

10 volts

e

(e)

c

5 volts

10 volts

e

(f)

$$T = \frac{2\pi}{\Omega}$$

20 volts

$\tau = \omega_v t$

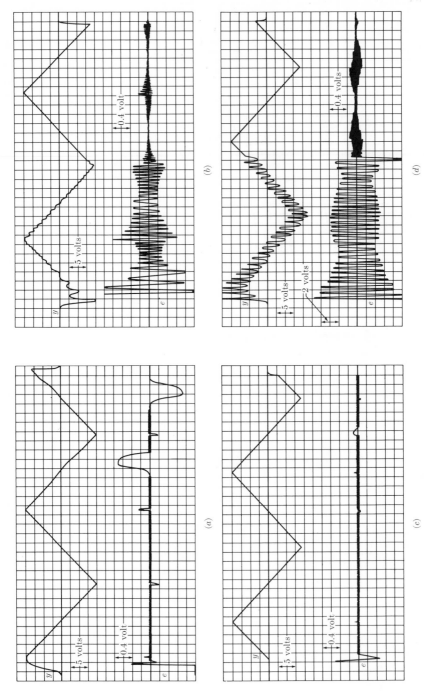

Fig. 2.59 Responses of nonlinear system with four different parameter sets to a 20-volt peak-to-peak triangular-wave input with fixed period $T = 10\pi$. $\zeta = 0.6$; 2.5 small divisions on the time scale equal one normalized time unit; tick marks at the bottom of figures indicate demarcation between systems. For systems' numbering, see Table 3.

It is obvious that good follow-up is possible only if $c(\tau)$ contains much higher frequencies than $r(\tau)$. Figure 2.57 shows this clearly. Note that in this follow-up there is no phase shift between output and input. Figure 2.58 shows the follow-up of a sawtooth curve. Reference 2.2 shows more examples. Figure 2.59 shows the change of performance in the follow-up if simpler feedbacks are used instead of the complete system, as given by Eqs. (2.77) and (2.78). Table 3 summarizes the cases shown in Fig. 2.59.

A word should still be said about the choice of $_1\beta$, $_2\beta$, $_1\gamma$, and $_2\gamma$. These values determine β_m and γ_n, which in turn determine the eight types of trajectories used to approximate $r'(r)$. With some advance information about $r(\tau)$, and hence about $r'(r)$, the slopes of the approximating curves $c'(c)$ [see Eq. (2.74)] can be compared with those of $r'(r)$ in characteristic points of the phase plane as a guide for the choice of β_m and γ_n. Details can be found in Ref. 2.2.

Experiments for systems with $0 \leq \zeta \leq 1$ have shown that the value

Table 3   Parameters for Fig. 2.59

Figs. 2.59a and b	Figs. 2.59c and d
Complete system	
System 1:	System 5:
$\beta_3 = -\beta_0 = 2 \qquad \gamma_3 = -\gamma_0 = 2$	$\beta_3 = -\beta_0 = 10 \qquad \gamma_3 = -\gamma_0 = 10$
$\beta_2 = -\beta_1 = 0.5 \quad \gamma_2 = -\gamma_1 = 0.5$	$\beta_2 = -\beta_1 = 1 \qquad \gamma_2 = -\gamma_1 = 1$
Case 1 *No derivative feedback*	
System 2:	System 6:
$\beta_3 = -\beta_0 = 0 \qquad \gamma_3 = -\gamma_0 = 2$	$\beta_3 = -\beta_0 = 0 \qquad \gamma_3 = -\gamma_0 = 10$
$\beta_2 = -\beta_1 = 0 \qquad \gamma_2 = -\gamma_1 = 0.5$	$\beta_2 = -\beta_1 = 0 \qquad \gamma_2 = -\gamma_1 = 1$
Case 2 *No e' sensing*	
System 3:	System 7:
$\beta_3 = -\beta_0 = 2 \qquad \gamma_3 = -\gamma_0 = 2$	$\beta_3 = -\beta_0 = 10 \qquad \gamma_3 = -\gamma_0 = 10$
$\beta_2 = -\beta_1 = 2 \qquad \gamma_2 = -\gamma_1 = 2$	$\beta_2 = -\beta_1 = 10 \qquad \gamma_2 = -\gamma_1 = 10$
Case 3 *No e sensing in derivative feedback loop and no e' sensing in proportional feedback loop*	
System 4:	System 8:
$\beta_3 = -\beta_0 = 2 \qquad \gamma_3 = -\gamma_0 = 2$	$\beta_3 = -\beta_0 = 10 \qquad \gamma_3 = -\gamma_0 = 10$
$\beta_2 = -\beta_1 = -2 \quad \gamma_2 = -\gamma_1 = 2$	$\beta_2 = -\beta_1 = -10 \quad \gamma_2 = -\gamma_1 = 10$

of ζ does not affect the design of a good follow-up system.   Good response is possible even if ζ varies during operation (see Ref. 2.2).

The basic idea of improving follow-up by influencing the coefficients in the differential equations that describe the dynamic system can be extended to other equations, including those for higher-order systems.

Both the use of linear switching functions restricted to work in the chatter region and the change of the system's dynamic by feedback introduce very high frequencies.   Hence these methods of follow-up can be used only if such high frequencies can be tolerated.   If so, these designs provide good follow-up at lower expense than linear feedback systems.

REFERENCES

2.1   Flügge-Lotz, I., and W. S. Wunch: On a Nonlinear Transfer System, *J. Appl. Phys.*, vol. 26, no. 4, pp. 484–488, 1955.
2.2   Flügge-Lotz, I., C. F. Taylor, and H. E. Lindberg: Investigation of a Nonlinear Control System, *NACA Tech. Rept.* 1391, 1958.

APPENDIX 2.1 CONSTRUCTION OF LOGARITHMIC SPIRALS BY AN APPROXIMATE METHOD[1]

A logarithmic spiral of the type shown in Fig. 2.60 may be represented by the relation

$$r = r_0 e^{-m\theta}$$

where

$$m = \cot \alpha = \frac{\zeta}{\nu} \text{ and } \theta = \nu\tau$$

The method of construction suggested here has been found to give good results for values of ζ as high as 0.5.   For values greater than this the method should be employed with discretion.

Assume that the points P_0 and P_1 (Fig. 2.60) are given as exact points on the spiral for $\theta = 0$ and $\theta = \pi/2$.   Using the radii r_0 and r_1 of the two points P_0 and P_1, compute the value d_0 from the relation

$$d_0 = \frac{r_0 - r_1}{\sqrt{2}}$$

Now construct a line Oa at 45° to the positive x axis and mark off the distance d_0 along this line, measuring from the origin, thus fixing the point N_0.   Then (referring to Fig. 2.60) it may be seen that $\overline{P_0 N_0} = \overline{P_1 N_0}$,

[1] This method is due to L. S. Jacobsen of Stanford University, and appreciation is expressed to him for allowing the use of this unpublished material.

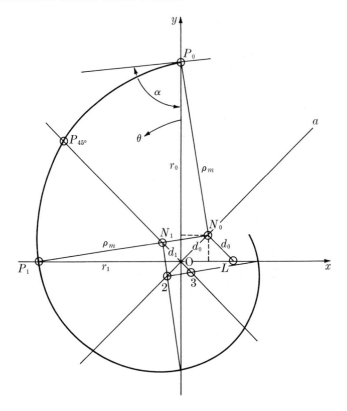

Fig. 2.60 Design of a spiral.

since the triangles P_1LN_0 and P_0ON_0 are congruent. Now it can be shown that a circle, with N_0 as center and radius equal to

$$\overline{P_0N_0} = \overline{P_1N_0} = \rho_m$$

will pass through a third exact point $P_{45°}$, of the spiral:

$$\rho_m{}^2 = \left(r_0 - \frac{d_0}{\sqrt{2}}\right)^2 + \left(\frac{d_0}{\sqrt{2}}\right)^2 = \left(\frac{r_0 + r_1}{2}\right)^2 + \left(\frac{r_0 - r_1}{2}\right)^2$$

$$(\overline{P_{45°}O})^2 = \rho_m{}^2 - d_0{}^2 = r_0r_1$$

Since $r_1 = r_0e^{-\cot\alpha(\pi/2)}$

it is found that

$$(\overline{P_{45°}O})^2 = r_0{}^2e^{-\cot\alpha(\pi/2)} = r_{45°}{}^2$$

It is now clear that the circle given by a radius of ρ_m and center N_0 will pass through the exact points of the spiral P_0, P_1, and $P_{45°}$. The deviations of this circular arc from the corresponding portion of the spiral will be so small as to be undetectable in a finished drawing, as long as the restriction imposed on ζ mentioned earlier is not disregarded.

To continue the construction of the spiral past this stage, it would appear necessary to repeat the procedure for the region between $\theta = \pi/2$ and $\theta = \pi$. The result of such a construction would be to have the center of the circular arc at the point N_1, a distance d_1 from the origin measured along a 45° line in the second quadrant. Then

$$d_1 \sqrt{2} = r_1 - r_2 = r_1(1 - e^{-\cot \alpha(\pi/2)})$$

but since we had previously obtained

$$d_0 \sqrt{2} = r_0 - r_1 = r_0(1 - e^{-\cot \alpha(\pi/2)})$$

we see that $\dfrac{d_0}{d_1} = \dfrac{r_0}{r_1}$

and therefore N_1 lies on the line $\overline{P_1 N_0}$, since the triangles $P_0 O N_0$ and $P_1 O N_1$ are similar (also $\sphericalangle N_1 O P_1 = \sphericalangle N_0 O P_0 = 45°$). This analysis shows that constructions succeeding the original one may be made without computation of the d_n values. More simply, if lines at 45° to the axes are drawn in each of the other quadrants, the center for the desired circular arc is readily found as the point where the last radius of the preceding arc intersects the 45° line of its quadrant.

3
General investigation of discontinuously controlled systems

3.1 DESCRIPTION OF THE CONTROLLED SYSTEM BY ONE OR MORE DIFFERENTIAL EQUATIONS

Figure 3.1 shows the block diagram of a controlled system. The plant is described by its transfer function (employed for further computations only if linear controls were used) $P(s)/Q(s)$, where Q is a polynomial of nth order and P is a polynomial of $(n-1)$st or lesser order. The relation between c and u is given by

$$c^{(n)} + a_1 c^{(n-1)} + \cdots + a_n c = b_1 u^{(n-1)} + \cdots + b_{n-1} u' + u$$

$$(3.1)$$

(a normalization has made $a_0 \equiv 1$ and $b_n \equiv 1$). The control variable u depends on F, with $u = -\operatorname{sgn} F$; but F depends on $e(t)$, and therefore u depends on t. If F is a continuous function of time, $u(t)$ can be plotted easily. It contains discontinuities, and its derivatives will contain singularities of higher order. The situation is more complicated if F is discontinuous; this case will be considered later.

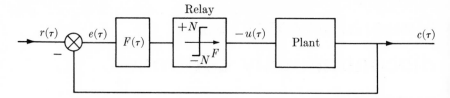

Fig. 3.1 Block diagram of controlled system; transfer function of plant $P(s)/Q(s)$.

A choice of the phase variables $c, c', c'', \ldots, c^{(n-1)}$ for tracing the phase trajectory would result in curves in the n space with discontinuities, as was shown for the simple second-order example (Sec. 2.1.2 and Fig. 1.42). This difficulty can be overcome, but for systems higher than third order it seems preferable to work with continuous variables. Hence the system (3.1) will be represented in a $\mathbf{y}$ space with continuous variables y_i, with $i = 1, 2, \ldots, n$, which are the components of the vector $\mathbf{y}$. Thus

$$\mathbf{y}' = A\mathbf{y} + \mathbf{D}u \tag{3.2}$$

with $c \equiv y_1$. The matrix A is defined by

$$A \equiv \begin{bmatrix} 0 & 1 & 0 & \cdots & 0 & 0 & 0 \\ 0 & 0 & 1 & \cdots & 0 & 0 & 0 \\ \cdot & \cdot & \cdot & \cdot & \cdot & \cdot & \cdot & \cdot & \cdot & \cdot & \cdot \\ 0 & 0 & 0 & \cdots & 0 & 1 & 0 \\ 0 & 0 & 0 & \cdots & 0 & 0 & 1 \\ -a_n & -a_{n-1} & -a_{n-2} & \cdots & -a_3 & -a_2 & -a_1 \end{bmatrix} \tag{3.3}$$

and the vector D is defined by

$$\mathbf{D} \equiv \begin{bmatrix} d_1 \\ d_2 \\ \cdots \\ d_n \end{bmatrix} \tag{3.4}$$

whose components are yet to be determined.

Equation (3.2) yields

$$y_1' = y_2 + d_1 u$$
$$\cdots \cdots \cdots \cdots$$
$$y_i' = y_{i+1} + d_i u$$
$$\cdots \cdots \cdots \cdots \tag{3.5}$$
$$y_{n-1}' = y_n + d_{n-1} u$$
$$y_n' = -a_n y_1 - a_{n-1} y_2 - \cdots - a_n y_n + d_n u$$

The relation of the continuous y_i to the derivatives of y_1 (that is, to the $c^{(i)}$) is given by the equations

$$y_2 = y_1' - d_1 u \tag{3.6}$$

$$y_3 = y_2' - d_2 u = (y_1 - d_1 u)' - d_2 u = c'' - d_1 u' - d_2 u \tag{3.7}$$

$$y_{i+1} = c^{(i)} - d_1 u^{(i-1)} - \cdots - d_i u = c^{(i)} - \sum_{j=1}^{i} d_j u^{(i-j)} \tag{3.8}$$

$$y_n = c^{(n-1)} - \sum_{i=1}^{n-1} d_i u^{(n-i-1)} \tag{3.9}$$

Differentiation of Eq. (3.9) gives

$$y_n' = c^{(n)} - \sum_{i=1}^{n-1} d_i u^{(n-i)} \tag{3.10}$$

Equation (3.10) and the last equation of system (3.5) yield

$$c^{(n)} - \sum_{i=1}^{n-1} d_i u^{(n-i)} = -a_n y_1 - a_{n-1} y_2 - \cdots - a_1 y_n + d_n u \tag{3.11}$$

or $\quad c^{(n)} + \sum_{i=1}^{n} a_i y_{n-i+1} = \sum_{i=1}^{n} d_i u^{(n-i)} \tag{3.12}$

Equation (3.8) yields

$$y_{n-i+1} = c^{(n-i)} - \sum_{j=1}^{n-i} d_j u^{(n-i-j)}$$

which is substituted into Eq. (3.12) to give

$$c^{(n)} + \sum_{i=1}^{n} a_i c^{(n-i)} = \sum_{i=1}^{n} d_i u^{(n-i)} + \sum_{i=1}^{n} \sum_{j=1}^{n-i} a_i \, d_j u^{(n-i-j)} \tag{3.13}$$

In the last term of Eq. (3.13) a notation change provides a better form. The substitutions $i + j = i^*$ and $j^* = i$ are introduced, and the asterisks are dropped; this leads to

$$c^{(n)} + \sum_{i=1}^{n} a_i c^{(n-i)} = \sum_{i=1}^{n} d_i u^{(n-i)} + \sum_{j=1}^{n} \sum_{i=j+1}^{n} a_j \, d_{i-j} u^{(n-i)} \tag{3.14}$$

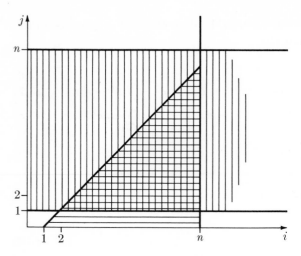

Fig. 3.2   Region of summation of last term in Eq. (3.14).

Figure 3.2 shows the region of summation of the last term of Eq. (3.14); the same region is covered if $i = 1, \ldots, n$ and $j = 1, \ldots, i - 1$. Therefore Eq. (3.14) can be written [see Eq. (3.1)] as

$$\sum_{i=0}^{n} a_i c^{(n-i)} = \sum_{i=1}^{n} \left(d_i + \sum_{j=1}^{i-1} a_j d_{i-j} \right) u^{(n-i)} \tag{3.15}$$

Comparison of Eq. (3.15) with Eq. (3.1), the original equation, shows that

$$b_i = d_i + \sum_{j=1}^{i-1} a_{i-j} d_j \qquad i = 1, \ldots, n \tag{3.16}$$

Thus the components d_i of the vector $\mathbf{D}$ [see Eq. (3.4)] depend on the coefficients b_k and a_k of Eq. (3.1).[1]

It should be noted that $d_0 = 0$ and $b_1 = d_1$. In addition, if $b_i = 0$ for $i = 1, \ldots, n - 1$, then the plant transfer function has no zeros and $d_i = 0$ for $i = 1, \ldots, n - 1$ and $d_n = b_n = 1$. Hence the $c_i = c^{(i-1)}$ are equal to the y_i, and no transformation is needed.

In general, the system equations (3.2) are not employed in computations because these first-order differential equations are coupled directly by the y_i, not just through the control function u. To decouple them it

[1] There are other ways of arriving at these relations. By repeated integration over an interval $t_0 - \epsilon$ to $t_0 + \epsilon$, where t_0 denotes the switching instant, we can determine the discontinuity in each derivative of c. Then we introduce new coordinates by adding to $c^{(i)}$ a term proportional to u, which cancels the discontinuity.

is necessary to introduce new coordinates

$$\mathbf{y} = G\mathbf{x} \tag{3.17}$$

and choose the constant matrix G appropriately. To proceed formally, we obtain from Eq. (3.2)

$$\mathbf{x}' = G^{-1}AG\mathbf{x} + G^{-1}\mathbf{D}u \tag{3.18}$$

Now it is desired that $G^{-1}AG$ be a matrix in which only the diagonal terms differ from zero; that is,

$$G^{-1}AG = \Lambda = \begin{bmatrix} \lambda_1 & 0 & \cdot & \cdot & \cdot & 0 & \cdot & \cdot & \cdot \\ 0 & \lambda_2 & \cdot & \cdot & \cdot & 0 & \cdot & \cdot & \cdot \\ 0 & 0 & \cdot & \cdot & \cdot & \cdot & \cdot & \cdot & \cdot \\ \cdot & \cdot & \cdot & \cdot & \cdot & \cdot & \cdot & \cdot & \cdot \\ \cdot & \cdot & \cdot & \cdot & \cdot & \cdot & \cdot & \cdot & \cdot \\ 0 & 0 & 0 & \cdot & \cdot & \cdot & \cdot & 0 & \lambda_n \end{bmatrix} \tag{3.19}$$

It is well known (see, for instance, Ref. 3.1, chap. 3) that the λ_i are the roots of the equation

$$\lambda^n + a_1\lambda^{n-1} + \cdots + a_n = 0$$

or the poles of the transfer function. We shall assume that the roots are all different, that is, that no double or multiple roots occur.[1]

This decoupling of Eq. (3.2) has one disadvantage. Complex roots result in first-order differential equations with complex coefficients. Therefore it is better to decouple only partially. If there are complex roots, there are always two conjugate complex roots. If we assume that the system has $2k_1$ complex roots, k_1 pairs of conjugate roots $\zeta_i\omega_i \pm \nu_i\omega_i \sqrt{-1}$ and k_2 real roots λ_m, then system (3.2) can be transformed to a system of k_1 pairs of coupled differential equations and k_2 uncoupled ones. The procedure will be explained for a third-order system (Refs. 3.2 and 3.3).

Let us begin with a system without zeros (see Fig. 3.3) given by

$$c''' + a_1c'' + a_2c' + a_3c = u \tag{3.20}$$

The roots of the characteristic equation

$$\lambda^3 + a_1\lambda^2 + a_2\lambda + a_3 = 0 \tag{3.21}$$

---

[1] Otherwise a special treatment is necessary, as indicated in any book on differential equations. However, the case of equal roots does not occur very often.

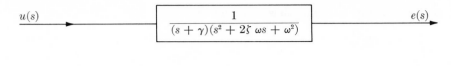

$$u(s) \longrightarrow \boxed{\dfrac{1}{(s + \gamma)(s^2 + 2\zeta\,\omega s + \omega^2)}} \longrightarrow e(s)$$

$$(a)$$

$$(b)$$

Fig. 3.3   Typical third-order system.

are $\lambda_{1,2} = -\zeta\omega \pm i\nu\omega$, with $\nu = \sqrt{1 - \zeta^2}$ and $|\zeta| < 1$; the third root is $-\gamma$.   Then the following relations exist between the a_i and the roots (see Ref. 3.4, sec. 2.1):

$$
\begin{aligned}
a_1 &= \gamma + 2\zeta\omega \\
a_2 &= \omega^2 + 2\zeta\omega\gamma \\
a_3 &= \omega^2\gamma
\end{aligned}
\qquad (3.22)
$$

The desired partially uncoupled system is

$$
\frac{d}{dt}
\begin{bmatrix} x_1 \\ x_2 \\ x_3 \end{bmatrix}
=
\begin{bmatrix}
-\zeta\omega & \nu\omega & 0 \\
-\nu\omega & -\zeta\omega & 0 \\
0 & 0 & -\gamma
\end{bmatrix}
\mathbf{x}
+
\begin{bmatrix} \zeta\omega \\ \nu\omega \\ 1 \end{bmatrix}
u
\qquad (3.23)
$$

It is now necessary to find a transformation

$$\mathbf{y} = G\mathbf{x} \qquad (3.24)$$

that will transform the system

$$\frac{d\mathbf{c}}{dt} = \begin{bmatrix} 0 & 1 & 0 \\ 0 & 0 & 1 \\ -\gamma\omega^2 & -(\omega^2 + 2\zeta\omega\gamma) & -(\gamma + 2\zeta\omega) \end{bmatrix} \mathbf{c} + \begin{bmatrix} 0 \\ 0 \\ 1 \end{bmatrix} u \qquad (3.25)$$

into system (3.23). Since $\mathbf{c}' = A\mathbf{c} + \mathbf{D}u,$[1] then

$$\mathbf{x}' = G^{-1}AG\mathbf{x} + G^{-1}\mathbf{D}u \qquad (3.26)$$

which should be identical with Eq. (3.23).

Systems (3.20) and (3.23) can be visualized in the block diagrams of Fig. 3.3. Between switchings the system behaves as a linear system, so the notation of linear systems is used here. From Fig. 3.3a,

$$(s + \gamma)(s^2 + 2\zeta\omega s + \omega^2)c(s) = u(s) \qquad (3.27)$$

and from Fig. 3.3b,

$$x_1(s) = \frac{u(s) + (\zeta/\omega)su(s)}{s^2 + 2\zeta\omega s + \omega^2}$$

$$x_2(s) = \frac{(\nu/\omega)su(s)}{s^2 + 2\zeta\omega s + \omega^2} \qquad (3.28)$$

$$x_3(s) = \frac{u(s)}{s + \gamma}$$

where $\nu = \sqrt{1 - \zeta^2}$.

From partial-fraction expansion of Eq. (3.27) it follows that

$$c(s) = \frac{u(s)}{\gamma^2 - 2\zeta\omega\gamma + \omega^2} \left(\frac{1}{s + \gamma} + \frac{\gamma - 2\zeta\omega - s}{s^2 + 2\zeta\omega s + \omega^2} \right) \qquad (3.29)$$

The variable $x_1(s)$ determined in Eqs. (3.28) can now also be expressed by using Eqs. (3.24) and (3.27):[2]

$$x_1(s) = \frac{[1 + s(\zeta/\omega)]u(s)}{s^2 + 2\zeta\omega s + \omega^2} = \frac{[g_{11}^{-1} + g_{12}^{-1}s + g_{13}^{-1}s^2]u(s)}{(s + \gamma)(s^2 + 2\zeta\omega s + \omega^2)}$$

Comparison of the two fractions yields the values for g_{11}^{-1}, g_{12}^{-1}, and g_{13}^{-1}. Similarly, $x_2(s)$ and $x_3(s)$ are expressed in two ways as functions of $u(s)$.

[1] Similar to Eq. (3.2) with (3.3) and (3.4), except in this case $c = y$ because there are no zeros.

[2] g_{ik}^{-1} are the elements of the matrix G^{-1}, and $\mathbf{c}$ has three components, $c_1 = c$, $c_2 = c'$, and $c_3 = c''$.

Finally all g_{ik}^{-1} are determined, and we can write $\mathbf{x} = G^{-1}\mathbf{c}$ as

$$
\mathbf{x} = \begin{bmatrix} \gamma & 1 + \dfrac{\zeta\gamma}{\omega} & \dfrac{\zeta}{\omega} \\ 0 & \dfrac{\gamma\nu}{\omega} & \dfrac{\nu}{\omega} \\ \omega^2 & 2\zeta\omega & 1 \end{bmatrix} \mathbf{c} \tag{3.30}
$$

We see immediately that $G^{-1}\,\mathbf{D}u$ delivers the last member of Eq. (3.23). The differential equation of a system with zeros,

$$
c''' + a_1 c'' + a_2 c' + a_3 c = b_1 u'' + b_2 u' + u \tag{3.31}
$$

can be transformed easily.   The same transformation $\mathbf{y} = G\mathbf{x}$ is used, and it is necessary only to consider that $\mathbf{c} \neq \mathbf{y}$, or that Eq. (3.25) is replaced by

$$
\frac{d\mathbf{y}}{dt} = \begin{bmatrix} 0 & 1 & 0 \\ 0 & 0 & 1 \\ -\gamma\omega^2 & -(\omega^2 + 2\zeta\omega\gamma) & -(\gamma + 2\zeta\omega) \end{bmatrix} \mathbf{y}
$$
$$
+ \begin{bmatrix} b_1 \\ b_2 - a_2 b_1 \\ 1 - a_2 b_1 - a_1 b_2 + a_1^2 b_1 \end{bmatrix} u \tag{3.32}
$$

which is transformed into

$$
\frac{d\mathbf{x}}{dt} = \begin{bmatrix} -\zeta\omega & \nu\omega & 0 \\ -\nu\omega & -\zeta\omega & 0 \\ 0 & 0 & -\gamma \end{bmatrix} \mathbf{x}
$$
$$
+ \begin{bmatrix} b_1\zeta\omega(-3 + 4\zeta^2) + b_2(1 - 2\zeta^2) + \dfrac{\zeta}{\omega} \\ b_1\omega\nu(4\zeta^2 - 1) - 2\zeta\nu b_2 + \dfrac{\nu}{\omega} \\ b_1\gamma(\gamma + 4\zeta\omega) - b_2\gamma + 1 \end{bmatrix} u \tag{3.33}
$$

with a_1 and a_2 replaced by the expressions given in Eqs. (3.22).

The solution of systems (3.23) or (3.33) is very simple where u is a constant.   The projection of the trajectory of the state point (coordinates x_1, x_2, and x_3) into the $x_1 x_2$ plane is composed of portions of spirals; the $x_3(\tau)$ curve is given by portions of exponential functions.   It is therefore quite easy to design the trajectory in the $x_1 x_2 x_3$ space.

In systems of higher order the determination of poles and zeros is more laborious but is easily understood.   The transformation of the nth-order differential equation to a system of n first-order equations is time consuming and is generally done only numerically because partial fraction and the inversion of the matrix G are involved.   The outcome is a system of the form in Eq. (3.34).

$$\frac{d\mathbf{x}}{dt} =
\left[\begin{array}{cc|cc|cc|c|cc|cccc}
-\zeta_1\omega_1 & \nu_1\omega_1 & 0 & 0 & 0 & 0 & \cdots & 0 & 0 & 0 & 0 & 0 & 0 & 0 \\
-\nu_1\omega_1 & -\zeta_1\omega_1 & 0 & 0 & 0 & 0 & \cdots & 0 & 0 & 0 & 0 & 0 & 0 & 0 \\
\hline
0 & 0 & -\zeta_2\omega_2 & \nu_2\omega_2 & 0 & 0 & \cdots & 0 & 0 & 0 & 0 & 0 & 0 & 0 \\
0 & 0 & -\nu_2\omega_2 & -\zeta_2\omega_2 & 0 & 0 & \cdots & 0 & 0 & 0 & 0 & 0 & 0 & 0 \\
\hline
0 & 0 & 0 & 0 & -\zeta_3\omega_3 & \nu_3\omega_3 & \cdots & 0 & 0 & 0 & 0 & 0 & 0 & 0 \\
0 & 0 & 0 & 0 & -\nu_3\omega_3 & -\zeta_3\omega_3 & \cdots & 0 & 0 & 0 & 0 & 0 & 0 & 0 \\
\hline
\vdots & & & & & & \ddots & & & & & & & \vdots \\
\hline
0 & 0 & 0 & 0 & 0 & 0 & \cdots & -\zeta_m\omega_m & \nu_m\omega_m & 0 & 0 & 0 & 0 & 0 \\
0 & 0 & 0 & 0 & 0 & 0 & \cdots & -\nu_m\omega_m & -\zeta_m\omega_m & 0 & 0 & 0 & 0 & 0 \\
\hline
0 & 0 & 0 & 0 & 0 & 0 & \cdots & 0 & 0 & \gamma_1 & 0 & 0 & 0 & 0 \\
0 & 0 & 0 & 0 & 0 & 0 & \cdots & 0 & 0 & 0 & \gamma_2 & 0 & 0 & 0 \\
0 & 0 & 0 & 0 & 0 & 0 & \cdots & 0 & 0 & 0 & 0 & \ddots & 0 & 0 \\
0 & 0 & 0 & 0 & 0 & 0 & \cdots & 0 & 0 & 0 & 0 & 0 & \gamma_{n-1} & 0 \\
0 & 0 & 0 & 0 & 0 & 0 & \cdots & 0 & 0 & 0 & 0 & 0 & 0 & \gamma_n
\end{array}\right]\mathbf{x} + G^{-1}\mathbf{D}u \qquad (3.34)$$

From this form it is immediately apparent that projections of a trajectory into certain planes are extremely simple if u is piecewise constant. Nevertheless, the trajectory is difficult to visualize because we are accustomed to the restriction of three dimensions.

Because $u = -\operatorname{sgn} F$, such a construction requires the switching function $F = \mathbf{k}^T \mathbf{e}$ in the new state variables. Since $y_1 \equiv c = -e$ (if initial disturbances are considered), the variable y_{i+1} is given by Eq. (3.8) for $1 \leq i + 1 \leq n - 1$, and y_n is given by Eq. (3.9), that is, in terms of linear relations which contain derivatives of $u(t)$. The switching-function equation thus becomes $F = \boldsymbol{\alpha}^T \mathbf{y} + \boldsymbol{\beta}$; the switching surface splits into two surfaces, and neither surface goes through the origin of the $\mathbf{y}$ space (see, for example, Fig. 2.45).

We shall always keep the general form $F = \mathbf{k}^T \mathbf{e}$, where $\mathbf{k}$ is a vector with K components. However, in most practical problems there is no direct access to all derivatives, and if such derivatives must be obtained by differentiation, it is generally not practical to use more than two. In other words, even if the number of zeros suggests a choice of $K > 2$, it cannot practically be used.

3.2 LINEAR SWITCHING FUNCTIONS AND THEIR INFLUENCE ON DISCONTINUITIES IN PHASE-PLANE VARIABLES

In the preceding section the output c and its derivatives were related to the continuous vector components y_i by $y_1 \equiv c$ and Eqs. (3.6) to (3.10). It is obvious that the behavior of the control function $u = -\operatorname{sgn} F$ influences the behavior of the output derivative $c^{(i)}$. For example, the continuous function y_{i+1} satisfies

$$y_{i+1} = c^{(i)} + \sum_{j=1}^{i} d_j u^{(i-j)} \tag{3.8}$$

That is, $c^{(i)}$ must include all irregularities contained in the derivatives $u^{(i-j)}$. In principle it is still possible to trace a trajectory in the phase space (c and its time derivatives are the coordinates of this space), but we have already seen that it is preferable to work with the equations for y_i, which are continuous coordinates and are less strongly coupled.

The behavior of the output c and its derivatives can be checked in another, simpler way. It does not give us all the details, but it does provide a very quick insight into the behavior. Assume that the system under consideration has n poles and $B \leq n - 1$ zeros:

$$c^{(n)} + a_1 c^{(n-1)} + \cdots + a_n c = b_{n-B}^{(B)} + b_{n-B+1}^{(B-1)} + \cdots + b_{n-1} u' + u \tag{3.35}$$

Thus the first $n - B - 1$ derivatives of c will have no singularities. This can easily be verified by integrating Eq. (3.35) repeatedly from $t_s - \epsilon$ to $t_s + \epsilon$, where t_s is the instant at which $u(t)$ jumps [see Eq. (2.64)]. If the switching function F is linear and has K zeros, we have

$$F = e + k_1 e' + k_2 e'' + \cdots + k_K e^{(K)}$$

F is continuous with discontinuous first derivative, if $e^{(K+1)}$ is the first discontinuous derivative of e. Therefore

$$n - B - 1 = K \qquad \text{or} \qquad K + B = n - 1 \tag{3.36}$$

A discontinuous F' assures the possibility of endpoints (points of indecision).

A discontinuous F appears if

$$K + B = n \tag{3.37}$$

As we shall see later, this choice may have some advantage over $K + B \leq n - 1$, but it imposes certain conditions on the added zero in the switching function F.

Equation (3.36) should serve as a reminder of the treatment of linear systems with linear controls. The sum of zeros in the control function and in the plant must be smaller than the sum of the plant poles (see Refs. 3.5 and 3.6).

3.3 CHATTER

In Chap. 2 the control of the plant $1/s^2$ was examined in detail, and the phenomenon of chatter was introduced. At this point we need a general criterion for the *occurrence* of chatter. The relation $u(t) = -\text{sgn } F$ will be assumed. F may be a linear or a nonlinear function of time or of the phase or the state variables. We shall examine $F(t)$ in both the continuous case and as a discontinuous function of time. However, the discussion will be restricted to simple discontinuities [a jump in $F(t)$ at certain instants t_{s_i}]. In addition, this investigation will be restricted to *linear plants* with relay inputs governed by such switching functions (Ref. 3.7).

Our main purpose will be to determine the *average motion* in the chatter region. Therefore it is necessary at this point to give an exact definition of average motion during chatter. The differential equation

$$y^{(n)} + a_1 y^{(n-1)} + \cdots + a_n y = b_1 u^{(n-1)} + \cdots + b_{n-1} u' + u \tag{3.38}$$

can be written as

$$\sum_{i=0}^{n} a_i y^{(n-i)} = \sum_{i=1}^{n} b_i u^{(n-i)} \tag{3.39}$$

where

$$a_0 \equiv 1, \qquad b_n \equiv 1, \qquad \text{and } a_n \neq 0 \qquad (3.40)$$

When the relay is chattering, Eq. (3.39) can be written as

$$\sum_{i=0}^{n} a_i y_{\text{av}}^{(n-i)} + \sum_{i=0}^{n} a_i y_{\text{ch}}^{(n-i)} = \sum_{i=1}^{n} b_i u_{\text{av}}^{(n-i)} + \sum_{i=1}^{n} b_i u_{\text{ch}}^{(n-i)} \qquad (3.41)$$

where the subscript ch signifies the high-frequency chatter motion. The prior assumption that the chatter frequency is much higher than the frequency spectrum of the plant dynamics means that the overlap of the average and chatter spectra is so small as to be negligible. Therefore we can extract from Eq. (3.41)

$$\sum_{i=0}^{n} a_i y_{\text{av}}^{(n-i)} = \sum_{i=1}^{n} b_i u_{\text{av}}^{(n-i)} \qquad (3.42)$$

as the equation of the average motion of a chattering system.

3.3.1 Continuous switching function F

Figure 3.4 shows the behavior of F near $F = 0$ if chatter occurs. Switching delays arising from both threshold and time are assumed. The threshold $|\Delta F| = \theta$ is symmetrical, and the delay is assumed to be constant. At point A in Fig. 3.4a $F = 0$, but owing to the threshold and time delay, the change in u from $u_0 = -N$ to $u_1 = +N$ does take place at point B. The new slope F_1' is of opposite sign to the sign of F_0'. We can easily follow the behavior of the slope of F through a number of cycles. Analytically, we have the following behavior:

$$\begin{aligned} F_0' &< 0 \\ F_1' &> 0 \end{aligned} \qquad -u_1 = +u_0 = -N \qquad (3.43)$$

where $F_1' = F_0' + \Delta_1 F' \qquad (3.44)$

Both equations together yield

$$0 > F_0' > -\Delta_1 F' \qquad (3.45)$$

Figure 3.4b is described by

$$\begin{aligned} F_0' &> 0 \\ F_1' &< 0 \end{aligned} \qquad -u_1 = u_0 = +N \qquad (3.46)$$

and from Eq. (3.44),

$$0 < F_0' < -\Delta_1 F' \qquad (3.47)$$

Both results [Eqs. (3.45) and (3.47)] can be combined as

$$0 < u_0 F_0' < -u_0 \Delta_1 F' \qquad (3.48)$$

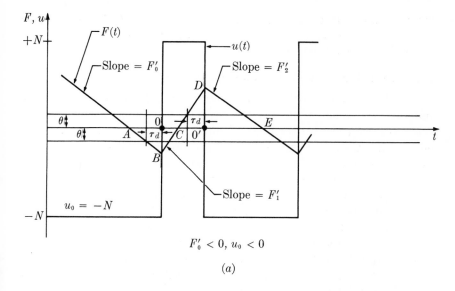

$$F_0' < 0, u_0 < 0$$

$$(a)$$

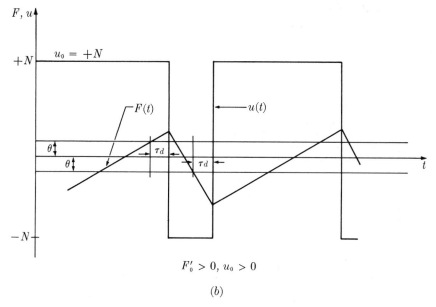

$$F_0' > 0, u_0 > 0$$

$$(b)$$

Fig. 3.4   Chatter of a continuous switching function; $\theta \equiv$ threshold, $\tau_d \equiv$ time delay.

which is valid regardless of the sign of F_0'. Equation (3.48) and the statement that $u_1 = -u_0$ (that is, that F passes through zero) are the necessary and sufficient conditions for chatter.

3.3.2 Discontinuous switching function, $\Delta_1 F \neq 0$

When switching occurs in a system with a discontinuous switching function, two kinds of chatter are possible, *controlling* chatter and *noncontrolling* chatter. As their names imply, the former exerts some control effect, while the latter has no effect on the system. (These are discussed in Refs. 3.8 to 3.10, where they are called respectively "controlled" and "uncontrolled" chatter.) In noncontrolling chatter the contactor stays in the up and down positions for the same lengths of time (these lengths are the time lags, which are assumed to be the same for both positions), having a net effect of zero. This situation is depicted in Fig. 3.5. In controlling chatter the contactor does not switch at equal intervals and consequently exerts a (nonzero) average control effort.

For the region in which controlling chatter is possible refer to Fig. 3.6. In addition to a symmetrical time delay, it is also assumed that the threshold imperfection is symmetrical. For controlling chatter to occur $\Delta_1 F$ should not cause F to change its sign every time there is a switching; rather, it should cause F to change sign every *other* switching. The

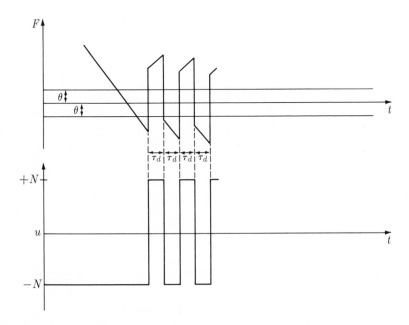

Fig. 3.5 Discontinuous switching function, noncontrolling chatter.

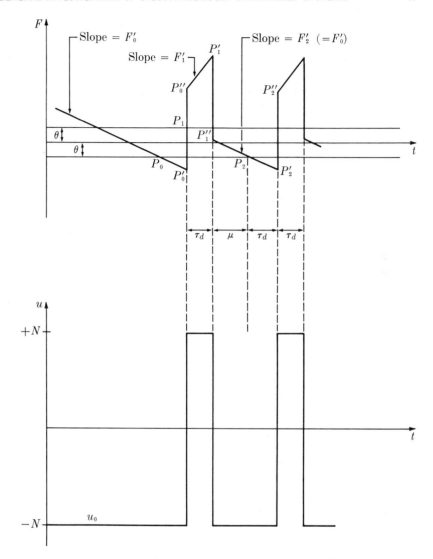

Fig. 3.6 Discontinuous switching function, controlling chatter; $F_0' < 0$, $u_0 = -N$.

contactor is given the command to switch when the threshold has been reached or surpassed, but the switching does not occur until after a delay of τ_d. In Fig. 3.6 the command to switch is first given at P_0, when F crosses the lower threshold; the switching is executed at P_0', and F jumps (through P_1) to P_0''. F is given another switching command at P_1, which takes place at P_1'. But note that in switching to P_1' F has not crossed the lower threshold; it must wait μ sec until the command to switch is given.

From closer examination of Fig. 3.6 we can easily determine the conditions for controlling chatter. Not only must the signs of F_0' and F_1' differ, but $|F_1'|$ must be greater than $|F_0'|$. Furthermore, F_0' must be negative (in this figure). Combining all these conditions yields

$$0 > F_0' > -F_1' \tag{3.49}$$

and multiplying through by u_0, a negative number in this case, yields

$$0 < u_0 F_0' < -u_0 F_1' \tag{3.50}$$

or $\quad 0 < u_0 F_0' < -u_0(F_0' + \Delta_1 F') \tag{3.51}$

since, by the definition of $\Delta_1 F'$, $F_1' = F_0' + \Delta_1 F'$ [see Eq. (3.44)]. We can manipulate Eq. (3.51) to get

$$0 < u_0 F_0' < -u_0 \frac{\Delta_1 F'}{2} \tag{3.52}$$

as a necessary condition for controlling chatter after F_0 reaches $u_0 \theta / N$. Note that this holds as well for a case which starts with $F_0' > 0$.

From $\Delta_1 u = u_1 - u_0 = -2u_0$ [see Eq. (3.46)], we can write Eq. (3.52) as

$$0 < u_0 F_0' < u_0{}^2 \frac{\Delta_1 F'}{\Delta_1 u} \tag{3.53}$$

3.3.3   Motion in the chatter region

The equation governing the motion of a system that is not in chatter is easily found; since the input is either N or $-N$ in any interval between switchings, it is possible to solve for all the error-state variables in an interval, form the switching function F, and switch when F crosses zero. This procedure can often be carried out graphically in state space and is fairly simple for linear plants. However, it applies only when the input is constant. In chatter there is a rapid succession of inputs, particularly if θ and τ_d are small, so that it is preferable to study the average motion [Eq. (3.41)]. This study, however, introduces a new variable u_{av}, the average control input to the plant. Consequently, it is necessary to obtain another equation in order to compute this motion. When the switching function is continuous, the supplementary equation is given by determining F_{av} as a function of the state variables. When F is discontinuous it is easier to determine u_{av}, as will be seen later.

3.3.3a   *Continuous switching function.*   Figure 3.4a shows one cycle in the time history of a chattering switching function. It is assumed that the first-order approximation

$$F_2' = F_0' \tag{3.54}$$

is a good approximation.

The average value of F over this cycle is equal to the total area divided by the time length of the cycle. If we let

$$b_0 \equiv |AC| \tag{3.55}$$
$$h_0 \equiv |OB| \tag{3.56}$$
$$b_1 \equiv |CE| \tag{3.57}$$
$$h_1 \equiv |O'D| \tag{3.58}$$

we get $F_{av} = \dfrac{1}{2} \dfrac{-b_0 h_0 + b_1 h_1}{b_0 + b_1}$ \hfill (3.59)

However, the triangles ABC and CDE are similar because of Eq. (3.54). Hence

$$\frac{b_0}{b_1} = \frac{h_0}{h_1} \equiv \alpha^{-1} \tag{3.60}$$

and $F_{av} = \dfrac{1}{2} \dfrac{b_0 h_0 (\alpha^2 - 1)}{b_0 (\alpha + 1)}$ \hfill (3.61)

$$F_{av} = \tfrac{1}{2} h_0 (\alpha - 1) \tag{3.62}$$
$$F_{av} = \tfrac{1}{2} (h_1 - h_0) \tag{3.63}$$

Inspection of Fig. 3.4a shows that

$$h_0 = |OB| = \theta - F_0' \tau_d \tag{3.64}$$
$$h_1 = |O'D| = \theta + F_1' \tau_d \tag{3.65}$$

and Eq. (3.63) becomes, via Eq. (3.44),

$$F_{av} = \left(F_0' + \frac{\Delta_1 F'}{2} \right) \tau_d \tag{3.66}$$

for a continuous switching function in chatter.

Equation (3.66) can be used to obtain the differential equation of the average motion for a linear plant with a continuous switching function. Consider the system

$$\mathbf{y}' = A\mathbf{y} + \mathbf{D}u \tag{3.67}$$
$$u = -N \operatorname{sgn} F \tag{3.68}$$
$$F = \mathbf{k}^T \mathbf{y} \tag{3.69}$$

Then $F' = \mathbf{k}^T A \mathbf{y} + \mathbf{k}^T \mathbf{D} u$ \hfill (3.70)

$$F_{av} = \left[(\mathbf{k}^T A \mathbf{y} + \mathbf{k}^T \mathbf{D} u)_0 + \frac{\Delta_1 F'}{2} \right] \tau_d \tag{3.71}$$

But from Eq. (3.70) and $\Delta_1 u = -2u_0$,

$$\Delta_1 F' = \mathbf{k}^T \mathbf{D}(u_1 - u_0) = -2\mathbf{k}^T \mathbf{D}u_0 \qquad (3.72)$$

and Eq. (3.71) becomes

$$F_{av} = (\mathbf{k}^T A \mathbf{y}_0)\tau_d \qquad (3.73)$$

Since F is continuous, at the same time we have from Eq. (3.69)

$$F_{av} = (\mathbf{k}^T \mathbf{y}_0)_{av} \qquad (3.74)$$

Combining Eqs. (3.73) and (3.74), we have

$$\mathbf{k}^T(A\tau_d - I)\mathbf{y}_{av} = 0 \qquad (3.75)$$

as the equation governing continuous chatter for a linear plant controlled by a linear switching function. The subscript zero has been dropped from Eq. (3.75) because it holds for any instant of time during chatter. This means that the relay-controlled system, which is a nonlinear system, behaves as a linear system in the chatter region.

If $\tau_d \to 0$, then

$$\mathbf{k}^T I \mathbf{y}_{av} = 0$$

which gives $F = 0$ for the average motion. This motion is sometimes called *sliding* (see, for example, Ref. 3.11).

In general a finite time delay enforces switching on surfaces which are not parallel to the plane $F = 0$. Let us take as an example a second-order system $1/(s^2 + 2\zeta s + 1)$ and a switching function $F = e + k_1 e'$. The system can be described by $e_1 = e$ and the differential equations

$$\begin{aligned} \dot{e}_1 &= e_2 \\ \dot{e}_2 &= -2\zeta e_2 - e_1 + u \end{aligned} \qquad (3.76a)$$

with $u = -\operatorname{sgn}(e_1 + k_1 e_2)$ (3.76b)

This yields the average motion in chatter

$$(1, k_1) \left\{ \begin{bmatrix} 0 & 1 \\ -1 & -2\zeta \end{bmatrix} \tau_d - \begin{bmatrix} 1 & 0 \\ 0 & 1 \end{bmatrix} \right\} \begin{bmatrix} e_{1,av} \\ e_{2,av} \end{bmatrix} = 0 \qquad (3.77)$$

or

$$(1 + k_1\tau_d)e_{1,av} + [k_1 - (1 + 2\zeta k_1)\tau_d]e_{2,av} = 0$$

It is immediately evident that the choice of a very small k_1 can make a system unstable if

$$k_1 - (1 + 2\zeta k_1)\tau_d \leq 0 \qquad (3.78)$$

Equation (3.75) allows a simple computation of the equation of the average motion for linear systems of any order.

Equation (3.77) yields, for $e_{2,\text{av}} = e'_{1,\text{av}}$, a first-order differential equation for the average motion. Since at the beginning of chatter $e_{\text{av},s+} = e_{s-}$, the only free constant can be determined easily. For systems of higher order K initial conditions must be determined if $F = 0$ has K zeros. However, this is not difficult. The average motion in the chatter region starts at the last point of the regular motion which lies on the surface $F = 0$ (this can be a line, a plane, or a hyperplane). The last regular point has n coordinates for an nth-order system. Only K coordinates, those related to the function e and its first $n - B - 1$ derivatives, can be used for determining the K free constants of the average motion on the surface $F = 0$ (remember that $B + K \leq n - 1$). There is no continuous transition for higher derivations at the start of the average motion.

3.3.3b *Discontinuous switching function.* For a continuous switching function it was fairly easy to include the effect of a time lag on the average motion; the difficulty of analyzing the average motion when the switching function is discontinuous precludes consideration of the effects of small but finite imperfections, although it is assumed that an infinitesimal time delay and a very small threshold exist. For studying the average motion in chatter region we shall make ample use of Eq. (3.12) and the following relations. Thus we are well informed about the discontinuities and singularities in the derivatives of the output of the system.

Consider again the system

$$\mathbf{y}' = \mathbf{A}\mathbf{y} + \mathbf{D}u \qquad\qquad (3.67)$$

with $u = -N \operatorname{sgn} F$

$$= -N \operatorname{sgn} (y + \hat{k}_1 y' + \hat{k}_2 y'' + \cdots + \hat{k}_{n-1} y^{(n-1)})$$

$$y_1 \equiv y \qquad\qquad (3.79)$$

but $y'_1 = y_2 + d_1 u$ and so on. $\qquad\qquad (3.80)$

(In our former notation, $y_1{}^{(i)} = c^{(i)}$.) Note that $\hat{k}_i \neq k_i$; in Eq. (3.69) F was written as a function of y_i instead of $y^{(i)}$.

The contactor switches when $F = F_s = 0$; then at the switching command

$$\sum_{i=0}^{n-1} \hat{k}_i y_s{}^{(i)} = 0 \qquad\qquad (3.81)$$

The subscript s denotes the value of the variable immediately before the trajectory reaches the switching surface.

Equation (3.8) shows the discontinuities in the $y^{(i)}$ at switching. When F is discontinuous the controller immediately begins to chatter (if the $\hat{k}_i$ are correctly chosen), and it is more convenient to study the average motion. However, in going from the actual motion to the average motion, every variable that is discontinuous at switching undergoes a transition (see Ref. 3.10, p. 27).   Then

$$y_{av} = y_s + y_d = y_s \qquad\qquad\qquad (3.82)$$
$$y_{av}{}^{(i)} = y_s{}^{(i)} + y_d{}^{(i)} \qquad i = 1, \ldots, n \qquad (3.83)$$
and $$u_{av} = u_s + u_d \qquad\qquad\qquad (3.84)$$
$$u_{av}{}^{(i)} = u_s{}^{(i)} + u_d{}^{(i)} = u_d{}^{(i)} \qquad i = 1, \ldots, n \qquad (3.85)$$

The subscript d on a variable, as defined by Eqs. (3.82) and (3.83), denotes the difference between the average value of the variable and its value immediately before switching; Fig. 3.7 illustrates the use of this subscript. Equation (3.82) simplifies because y is continuous and Eq. (3.85) simplifies because u_s is a constant.   Then Eq. (3.81) becomes

$$\sum_{i=0}^{n-1} \hat{k}_i(y_{av}{}^{(i)} - y_d{}^{(i)}) = 0 \qquad y_d = 0 \qquad (3.86)$$

Since the left-hand side of Eq. (3.8) is continuous, we can use $y_1 \equiv y$ to obtain

$$y_d{}^{(i)} = \sum_{j=1}^{i} d_j u_d{}^{(i-j)} \qquad\qquad (3.87)$$

If we employ Eqs. (3.84) and (3.85), Eq. (3.87) becomes

$$y_d{}^{(i)} = \sum_{j=1}^{i} d_j u_{av}{}^{(i-j)} - d_i u_s \qquad\qquad (3.88)$$

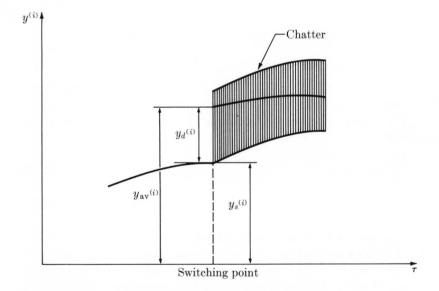

Fig. 3.7   Behavior of a discontinuous variable at switching.

and Eq. (3.86) becomes

$$\sum_{i=0}^{n-1} \hat{k}_i y_{av}^{(i)} - \sum_{i=0}^{n-1} \sum_{j=1}^{i} \hat{k}_i d_j u_{av}^{(i-j)} = - \sum_{i=0}^{n-1} \hat{k}_i d_i u_s \tag{3.89}$$

where $d_0 \equiv 0$ $\qquad\qquad\qquad\qquad\qquad\qquad\qquad\qquad\qquad$ (3.90)

We can combine Eq. (3.89) with Eq. (3.42) to get the equation of (average) motion of the system in the chatter region. First we take the Laplace transform of these two equations and obtain the characteristic equation, which is

$$\begin{vmatrix} \sum_{i=0}^{n-1} \hat{k}_i s^i & - \sum_{i=0}^{n-1} \sum_{j=1}^{i} \hat{k}_i d_j s^{i-j} \\ \sum_{i=0}^{n} a_i s^{n-i} & - \sum_{i=1}^{n} b_i s^{n-i} \end{vmatrix} = 0 \tag{3.91}$$

Although it appears that Eq. (3.91) is of order $2n - 2$, it will be shown that the characteristic equation is at most of order $n - 1$. Expansion of Eq. (3.91) gives

$$\left(\sum_{i=0}^{n-1} \hat{k}_i s^i \right) \left(\sum_{i=1}^{n} b_i s^{n-i} \right) - \left(\sum_{i=0}^{n} a_i s^{n-i} \right) \left(\sum_{i=0}^{n-1} \sum_{j=1}^{i} \hat{k}_i d_j s^{i-j} \right) = 0 \tag{3.92}$$

or $\quad \sum_{i=0}^{n-1} \sum_{j=1}^{n} \hat{k}_i b_j s^{n+i-j} - \sum_{i=0}^{n-1} \sum_{j=1}^{i} \sum_{r=0}^{n} \hat{k}_i d_j a_r s^{n+i-j-r} = 0 \tag{3.93}$

If we make use of Eqs. (3.40) and (3.79), we can write Eq. (3.93) as

$$1 + \sum_{i=1}^{n-1} \hat{k}_i s^i + \sum_{i=1}^{n-1} b_i s^{n-i} + \sum_{i=1}^{n-1} \sum_{j=1}^{n-1} \hat{k}_i b_j s^{n+i-j} - \sum_{i=1}^{n-1} \sum_{j=1}^{i} \hat{k}_i d_j s^{n+i-j}$$
$$- \sum_{i=1}^{n-1} \sum_{j=1}^{i} \sum_{r=1}^{n} \hat{k}_i d_j a_r s^{n+i-j-r} = 0 \tag{3.94}$$

The last three terms of Eq. (3.94) are the only ones that contain powers of s of nth order or greater. We shall show that all these powers cancel out. The fourth and fifth terms can be combined to give

$$\sum_{i=1}^{n-1} \sum_{j=i+1}^{n-1} \hat{k}_i b_j s^{n+i-j} + \sum_{i=1}^{n-1} \sum_{j=1}^{i} \hat{k}_i (b_j - d_j) s^{n+i-j} \tag{3.95}$$

The powers of s in the first term of (3.95) are all less than nth order, so we shall disregard this term for the present. We can substitute Eq. (3.16) into the second term in (3.95); then the higher powers of s in the last three terms of Eq. (3.94) become

$$\sum_{i=1}^{n-1} \sum_{j=1}^{i} \sum_{r=1}^{j-1} \hat{k}_i a_{j-r} d_r s^{n+i-j} - \sum_{i=1}^{n-1} \sum_{j=1}^{i} \sum_{r=1}^{n} \hat{k}_i d_j a_r s^{n+i-j-r} \tag{3.96}$$

Therefore with the help of (3.96) we must show that the following equation holds for all powers of s greater than $n - 1$:

$$\sum_{i=1_j}^{n-1} \hat{k}_i s^{n+i} \sum_{j=1}^{i} \sum_{r=1}^{j-1} a_{j-r} d_r s^{-j} = \sum_{i=1}^{n-1} \hat{k}_i s^{n+i} \sum_{j=1}^{i} \sum_{r=1}^{n} a_r d_j s^{-j-r} \qquad (3.97)$$

We can rearrange the right-hand side of Eq. (3.97) by substituting $t = j$ and $p = r + j = r + t$ into it to get

$$\sum_{i=1}^{n-1} \hat{k}_i s^{n+i} \sum_{j=1}^{i} \sum_{r=1}^{j-1} a_{j-r} d_r s^{-j} = \sum_{i=1}^{n-1} \hat{k}_i s^{n+i} \sum_{t=1}^{i} \sum_{p=t+1}^{t+n} a_{p-t} d_t s^{-p} \qquad (3.98)$$

Now we make the substitutions $r = t$ and $j = p$ and get

$$\sum_{i=1}^{n-1} \hat{k}_i s^{n+i} \sum_{j=1}^{i} \sum_{r=1}^{j-1} a_{j-r} d_r s^{-j} = \sum_{i=1}^{n-1} \hat{k}_i s^{n+i} \sum_{r=1}^{i} \sum_{j=r+1}^{r+n} a_{j-r} d_r s^{-j} \qquad (3.99)$$

The areas over which we are summing (for arbitrary i) can be shown in the (j,r) plane. Figure 3.8a shows the area for the left-hand side of Eq. (3.99) and Fig. 3.8b that for the right-hand side. In each case the double-cross-hatched areas are the areas of summation. The area that is not common to both (not canceled out) is a contribution from the right-hand side of Eq. (3.99); it is

$$(r = 1, \ldots ,i; j = i + 1, \ldots ,n + r)$$

In this area the power of s is less than n, since j is greater than i, so Eq. (3.99) does hold for all powers of s greater than $n - 1$.

Recapitulating, then, we find that the characteristic equation of a linear plant with a linear (discontinuous) switching function undergoing controlling chatter is

$$1 + \sum_{i=1}^{n-1} \hat{k}_i s^i + \sum_{i=1}^{n-1} b_i s^{n-i} + \sum_{i=1}^{n-1} \sum_{j=i+1}^{n-1} \hat{k}_i b_j s^{n+i-j}$$
$$- \sum_{i=1}^{n-1} \hat{k}_i s^{n+i} \sum_{r=1}^{i} \sum_{j=r+1}^{r+n} a_{j-r} d_r s^{-j} = 0 \qquad (3.100)$$

The switching function can be made continuous if its order is less than the difference between the orders of the denominator and numerator of the plant. Let K be the order of the switching function and B be the order of the plant numerator; then for a continuous switching function

$$B + K < n \qquad (3.101)$$

For a Kth-order switching function $\hat{k}_{K+1}, \ldots , \hat{k}_{n-1}$ are all zero, and the $\hat{k}_i$ exist for $0 \leq i \leq K$ with $k_0 \equiv 1$. For a Bth-order numerator $b_1, \ldots , b_{n-B-1}$ are all zero, and the limits of summation of the b_i are

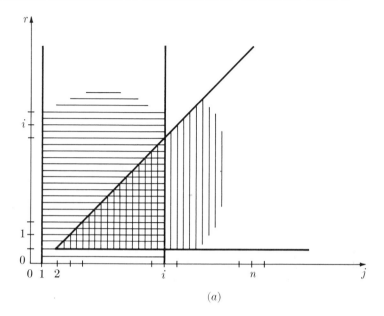

(a)

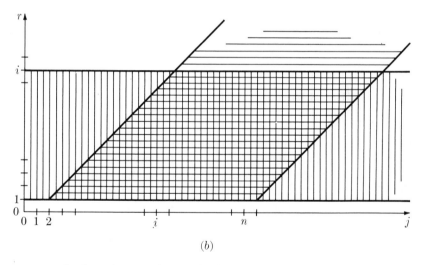

(b)

Fig. 3.8   Regions of summation for Eq. (3.99).

$n - B, \ldots, n - 1$. From Eq. (3.16) it is seen that $d_1, \ldots, d_{n-B-1}$ are also zero, and the same limits of summation apply to the d_i as to the b_i. If we now let

$$B + K = n - 1 \tag{3.102}$$

then Eq. (3.89) becomes

$$\sum_{i=0}^{K} \hat{k}_i y_{\mathrm{av}}^{(i)} = 0 \tag{3.103}$$

since the indices of summation are such that where the $\hat{k}_i$ are nonzero the d_i and d_j are zero; Eq. (3.103), then, is the differential equation of a chattering system with a continuous switching function. This is equivalent to the result that we obtained by letting τ_d approach zero in Eq. (3.75).

It has been found (Ref. 3.12, pp. 45–46) that if there is a small but finite time delay at switching, the addition of a slight amount of first-order (jump) discontinuity to the switching function improves the performance of the system by diminishing the peak-to-peak steady-state error. In this case

$$B + K = n \tag{3.104}$$

and Eq. (3.100) becomes

$$1 + \sum_{i=1}^{K} \hat{k}_i s^i + \sum_{i=K}^{n-1} b_i s^{n-i} + \sum_{i=1}^{K-1} \sum_{j=K}^{n-1} \hat{k}_i b_j s^{n+i-j} + \sum_{j=K+1}^{n-1} \hat{k}_K b_j s^{n+K-j}$$

$$- \sum_{j=1}^{n} b_K \hat{k}_K a_j s^{n-j} = 0 \tag{3.105}$$

since, from Eq. (3.16),

$$d_K = b_K \tag{3.106}$$

Equation (3.105) is the characteristic equation of the average motion when the switching function has a jump discontinuity.

Thus far we have not commented on the choice of the k_i, although Eq. (3.91) gives some advice. Only if all roots have negative real parts can we expect an average motion leading toward zero. The motion may never actually reach zero, because generally the chatter changes from controlling to noncontrolling chatter very close to the origin of the error space. Nevertheless, we must insist on negative real parts of the roots; otherwise the motion would not diminish the error.

Solution of the characteristic equation (3.91) provides us with the eigenfunctions, and we can then write y_{av} and u_{av} for $a_n \neq 0$ as

$$y_{\mathrm{av}} = \sum_{i=1}^{n-1} M_p e^{\lambda_p t} + L_1 \tag{3.107}$$

$$u_{\mathrm{av}} = \sum_{i=1}^{n-1} N_p e^{\lambda_p t} + L_2 \tag{3.108}$$

where M_p, N_p, L_1, and L_2 are constants to be determined. Equation (3.42) immediately yields

$$a_n L_1 = b_n L_2 = L_2 \tag{3.109}$$

Hence $L_2 \equiv 0$ if $a_n \equiv 0$. The second basic equation, Eq. (3.89), yields, for $t \to \infty$,

$$L_1 - \left(\sum_1^{n-1} \hat{k}_i d_i \right) L_2 = - \left(\sum_0^{n-1} \hat{k}_i d_i \right) u_s \tag{3.110}$$

Combining these last two equations delivers

$$L_1 = \frac{-u_s \sum_1^{n-1} k_i d_i}{1 - a_n \sum_1^{n-1} k_i d_i} \tag{3.111}$$

because $d_0 \equiv 0$.

After introducing expressions (3.107) and (3.108) into Eqs. (3.42) and (3.89), we have $n - 1$ equations which contain the unknowns M_p and N_p. Now,

$$M_p(a_0 \lambda_p^n + a_1 \lambda_p^{n-1} + \cdots + a_{n-1} \lambda_p)$$
$$= N_p(b_1 \lambda_p^{n-1} + b_2 \lambda_p^{n-2} + \cdots + b_{n-1} \lambda_p) \tag{3.112}$$

where λ_p are the roots of the characteristic equation of the system, with $n - 1$ values. Hence $n - 1$ boundary conditions are needed to determine the free constants—either $n - 1$ values of M_p or $n - 1$ values of N_p; these values must be determined according to the available initial conditions (start of chatter). One initial condition is continuous transition from y_{s-} to $y_{av,s+}$. The other $n - 2$ initial conditions can be obtained by determining the initial values of $u_{av,s+}$ and its derivatives.

This is possible, but tedious. In general, the knowledge of λ_p and L_1 and L_2 will suffice for design purposes. Note that a motion usually ends with noncontrolling chatter. Hence L_1 does not give the size of $y_{av}(\infty)$ even for the last portion of controlling chatter. In this portion u_{av} reaches zero and the change from controlling to noncontrolling chatter occurs, so the y_{av} value at this instant will determine the average steady-state value.

3.4 LIMIT CYCLES

As pointed out in the preceding section, particularly for linear switching functions, the steady state of real systems around the origin of the state space is given by a small-amplitude periodic motion, the limit cycle. This fact alone justifies the study of periodic motions. However, earlier studies of second-order systems with relays showed that periodic motions of finite and even large amplitudes may occur. These motions are important because they sometimes limit the region of stable operation. This limitation is apparent in second-order systems. In higher-order systems the small limit cycle resulting from imperfections can be handled in the same manner. However, the region of stability in an nth-order system is expected to be bounded by a surface of $(n - 1)$st order or less; hence a single periodic motion which may lie on such a surface would not give sufficient information for construction of the surface. The stability region must be found by other means, such as *Lyapunov's second method* (see, for example, Ref. 3.12 or 3.13).

Periodic motions in nonlinear systems have interested many researchers; we shall examine here only those methods particularly suited to relay systems. Hamel (Ref. 3.14) and Tsypkin (Ref. 3.15) have developed diagrams which allow a relatively fast determination of periodic motions. However, in both cases the procedure is limited to the assumption that the switching is determined by a continuous function F which depends only on the error e and its first derivative e'. Since this is often the case, we shall go into detail.

Their procedures have been developed for continuous projections of trajectories only [more specifically, where $e(\tau)$ and $e'(\tau)$ are continuous]. In this case, for linear switching functions only two corner points are expected to occur in the (e,e') plane. However, when discontinuities occur because of zeros in the transfer function of the plant, the determination of the periodic motion becomes more complicated,[1] and it is not actually known whether more than two switchings will occur in one cycle. Aizerman has made a strong point of this fact in his recent book (Ref. 3.16). In addition, there are periodic motions that can consist of portions of regular and of chatter motion; their occurrence was first noticed years ago by S. Brown, who studied with Flügge-Lotz the reaction of relay systems to step inputs.

The simplest way to investigate periodic motions consisting of two antisymmetric halves is to assume that the control input $u(\tau)$ is a periodic function with an unknown period ω and to solve for the plant output for this input $u(\tau)$ (see Fig. 3.9):

$$u(\tau) = \frac{4N}{\pi} \left(\sin \omega\tau + \frac{1}{3} \sin 3\omega\tau + \cdots + \frac{1}{n} \sin n\omega\tau + \cdots \right)$$

$$= \frac{4N}{\pi} \sum_{1}^{\infty} \frac{\sin n\omega\tau}{n} \qquad n = 1, 3, 5, \ldots \qquad (3.113)$$

The Laplace transform of the linear plant is $\mathcal{L}(s)$. Its response to

[1] See, for instance, the discussion following Fig. 3.21 and Ref. 3.10.

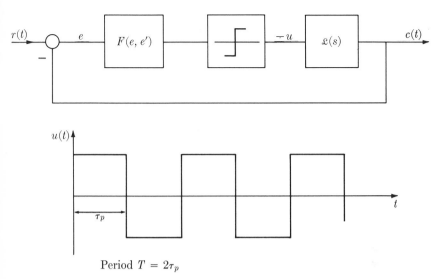

Period $T = 2\tau_p$

Fig. 3.9 Periodic solutions.

periodic inputs (sinusoidal motion) is given by (see Fig. 3.10a)

$$\mathcal{L}(j\bar{\omega}) = A(\bar{\omega}) \exp [j\Phi(\bar{\omega})] = U(\bar{\omega}) + jV(\bar{\omega})$$
$$\bar{\omega} = \omega, 3\omega, 5\omega, 7\omega, \ldots \quad (3.114)$$

Therefore the output

$$c(\tau) = \frac{4N}{\pi} \sum_1^\infty \frac{1}{n} A(n\omega) \sin [n\omega\tau + \Phi(n\omega)] \quad (3.115)$$

and its derivative is

$$\frac{dc}{d\tau} = c'(\tau) = \frac{4N}{\pi} \omega \sum_1^\infty A(n\omega) \cos [n\omega\tau + \Phi(n\omega)] \quad (3.116)$$

Higher derivatives can be obtained if the differentiated Fourier series are still convergent. Suppose we are interested in plotting $c(\tau)$ against $c'(\tau)$. This can be done in a very efficient way by making use of the *Nyquist diagram*.

Since $r(\tau) = 0$, $c(\tau) = -e(\tau)$. We are considering periodic solutions with two corner points [see Eq. (3.113)], so we have

$$e(0) = -e\left(\frac{\pi}{\omega}\right) = -e(\tau_p)$$

$$e'(0) = -e'\left(\frac{\pi}{\omega}\right) = -e'(\tau_p)$$

$$(3.117)$$

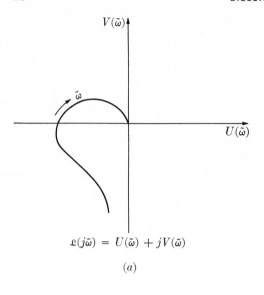

$$\mathcal{L}(j\tilde{\omega}) = U(\tilde{\omega}) + jV(\tilde{\omega})$$

(a)

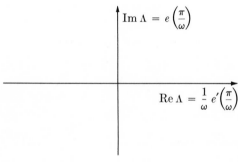

(b)

Fig. 3.10 Laplace transform $\mathcal{L}(j\tilde{\omega}) = U(\tilde{\omega}) + jV(\tilde{\omega})$.

Let us form a complex function (see Fig. 3.10b)

$$\Lambda(\omega) = \operatorname{Re} \Lambda(\omega) + j \operatorname{Im} \Lambda(\omega) \tag{3.118}$$

where $\operatorname{Re} \Lambda(\omega) = \dfrac{1}{\omega} \dfrac{de}{d\tau}\bigg|_{\pi/\omega}$

$$\operatorname{Im} \Lambda(\omega) = e\left(\frac{\pi}{\omega}\right)$$

With the notation of Eq. (3.114) we obtain

$$\operatorname{Re} \Lambda(\omega) = \frac{4N}{\pi} [U(\omega) + U(3\omega) + U(5\omega) + \cdots]$$

$$\operatorname{Im} \Lambda(\omega) = \frac{4N}{\pi} \left[V(\omega) + \frac{1}{3} V(3\omega) + \frac{1}{5} V(5\omega) + \cdots \right] \tag{3.119}$$

The Λ curve can best be drawn in the plane of the $\mathcal{L}$ curve, with the help of the $\mathcal{L}$ curve (see Fig. 3.11).[1]

The Λ curve can now be used to find the periodic solution for a given switching criterion; for example,

$$e + k_1 e' = 0$$

which must be written as

$$e + k_1 \omega \frac{e'}{\omega} = 0 \tag{3.120}$$

The intersection of this straight line and the Λ curve allows us to

[1] By permission, from Ref. 3.17.

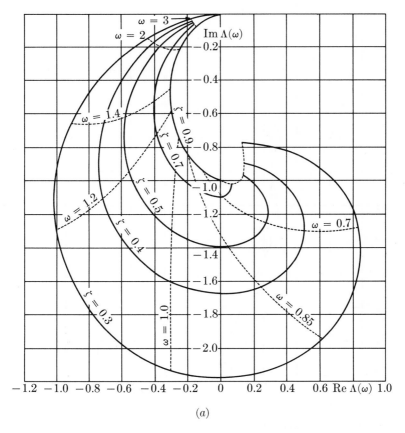

(a)

Fig. 3.11 (a) Tsypkin loci for $\mathcal{L}(s) = 1/(s^2 + 2\zeta s + 1)$, $\zeta < 1$.

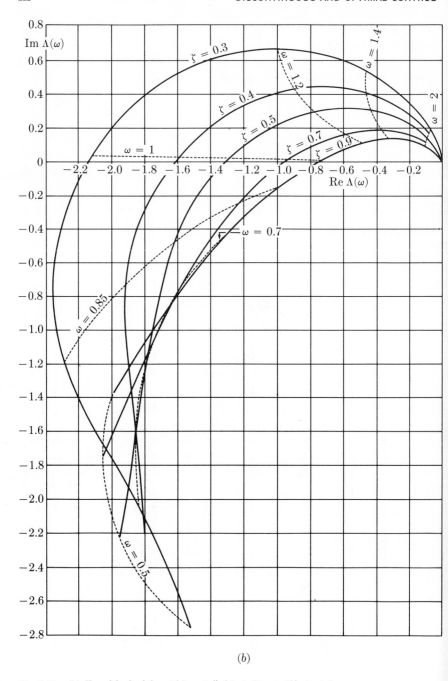

(b)

Fig. 3.11   (b) Tsypkin loci for $\mathcal{L}(s) = 1/[s(s^2 + 2\zeta s + 1)]$, $\zeta < 1$.

compute the length of period for a given k_1. However, the numerical problem of the Tsypkin locus should not be overlooked. For small τ_p the value ω is rather large, since

$$2\tau_p = \frac{2\pi}{\omega}$$

In general, there is no difficulty in finding a reasonably accurate solution. However, for limit cycles of stability regions ω may be rather small, and it may be necessary to use a computing machine.

For this example we have assumed a switching criterion given only by e and e'. For a higher-order plant and, say, a switching criterion $e + k_1e' + k_2e'' = 0$, it would be necessary to generalize Tsypkin's procedure by adding an e'' axis and developing a projection such as $e'(e'')$. Then the intersection of the corner-point locus with the plane

$$e + k_1e' + k_2e'' = 0$$

would give the corner-point coordinates for a periodic solution. Since Tsypkin's representation involves the derivation of Fourier series, it loses in accuracy rather quickly, and the series for e'' must be checked for convergence.

For final steady-state limit cycles arising from relay imperfections the Tsypkin locus gives fine possibilities (see Fig. 3.12). Instead of reading $U(n\omega)$ and $V(n\omega)$ from the $\mathcal{L}(j\bar{\omega})$ curve, we can develop an expansion for a curve, as given in Fig. 3.10a for high ω, and the corresponding Tsypkin locus (see examples in Ref. 3.17).

Hamel has also developed a method for determining periodic solutions of control systems with relays. The computation of the Hamel locus is based on the fact that the Laplace transform of linear systems

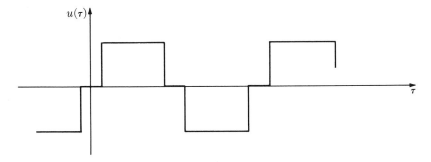

Fig. 3.12   Behavior of $u(\tau)$ for periodic solutions if the relay has a dead zone.

can be written as

$$L(s) = \frac{P(s)}{Q(s)} = \sum_1^n \frac{A_i}{s - p_i} \tag{3.121}$$

where $A_i = \dfrac{P(p_i)}{Q'(p_i)} \qquad Q'(p_i) = \left(\dfrac{dQ}{ds}\right)_{p_i}$ (3.122)

This allows us to replace the description of the dynamic system by n first-order differential equations of the type

$$c_i' - p_i c_i = A_i(\mp N) \tag{3.123}$$

where N is the output of the relay (see Fig. 3.13).

If we assume that a period of $T = 2\tau_p$ is possible, then

$$c_i' - p_i\left(c_i \mp \frac{A_i N}{p_i}\right) = 0 \tag{3.124}$$

yields $c_i = \pm \dfrac{A_i N}{p_i} + \mathfrak{M}_i e^{p_i \tau}$ (3.125)

With the assumption that the periodic motion consists of two halves

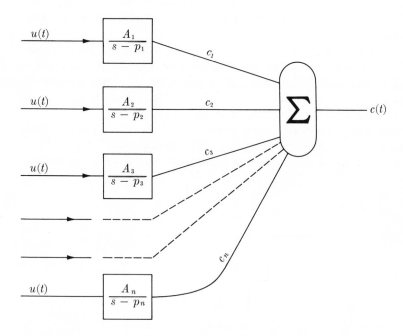

Fig. 3.13 Plant with Laplace transform $\mathfrak{L}(s) = \dfrac{P(s)}{Q(s)} = \sum_i^n \dfrac{A_i}{s - p_i}$.

(contains two switching points), we have the condition

$$c_i(0) = -c_i(\tau_p) \tag{3.126}$$

and a similar condition on the first derivative of c',

$$c_i'(0) = -c_i'(\tau_p) \tag{3.127}$$

Condition (3.126) allows the determination of the free integration constant $\mathfrak{M}_i$ and guarantees that

$$c(0) = -c(\tau_p) \tag{3.128}$$

because

$$c = \sum_1^n c_i$$

We obtain first

$$\mathfrak{M}_i = \mp \frac{2NA_i}{p_i} \frac{1}{1 + e^{p_i\tau_p}} \tag{3.129}$$

which yields

$$c_i(\tau_p) = \pm \frac{NA_i}{p_i} \frac{1 - e^{p_i\tau_p}}{1 + e^{p_i\tau_p}} = \pm \frac{NA_i}{p_i} \tanh p_i \frac{\tau_p}{2} \tag{3.130}$$

By summation we finally arrive at

$$c(\tau_p) = \sum c_i(\tau_p) = \pm \sum \frac{NA_i}{p_i} \tanh p_i \frac{\tau_p}{2} \tag{3.131}$$

and from Eq. (3.124) we have

$$c'(\tau_p) = \sum \pm A_iN \pm A_iN \tanh p_i \frac{\tau_p}{2} \tag{3.132}$$

The signs $\pm$ are optional in both equations. They merely provide the freedom to attribute the time $\tau = 0$ to the desired switching point.

The derivation given by Gille et al. (Ref. 3.17, p. 453) is much more complicated because the periodic input $u(\tau)$ is built up with step-input functions. In this case the constant term in $c'(\tau_p)$ must be determined by the final-value theorem

$$\lim_{s \to \infty} NsL(s) = \hat{K}$$

However, we find immediately that

$$NsL(s) = N \frac{sP(s)}{Q(s)} = Ns \sum \frac{A_i}{s - p_i}$$

$$= N \sum \frac{A_is}{s - p_i} = N \sum \frac{A_i}{1 - p_i/s}$$

and that therefore

$$\hat{K} = \lim_{s \to \infty} NsL(s) = N\Sigma A_i$$

which agrees with Eq. (3.132).

To plot the Hamel locus we must first solve for the characteristic roots of the transfer function. $\tanh p_i(\tau_p/2)$ is a direct representation only for real p_i and needs some further work if p_i is complex. There is, however, the advantage that no differentiation of Fourier series is involved. Figure 3.14 shows the Hamel locus for a system with the transfer function $1/[(1 + s)(1 + as)]$, and Fig. 3.15 shows the Hamel locus for a system with the transfer function $1/(s^2 + 2\zeta s + 1)$, with

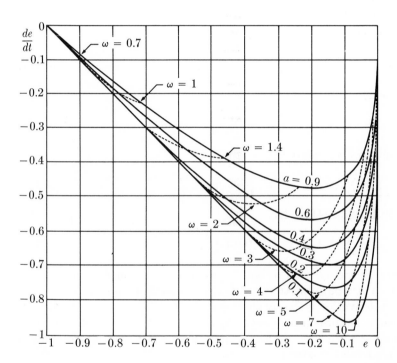

Fig. 3.14 Hamel loci for $\mathcal{L}(s) = 1/[(1 + s)(1 + \alpha s)]$ and $N = 1$. Equations are:

$$e = -\frac{1}{1 - \alpha}\tanh\frac{\pi}{2\omega} + \frac{\alpha}{1 - \alpha}\tanh\frac{\pi}{2\alpha\omega}$$

$$\frac{de}{dt} = \frac{1}{1 - \alpha}\left(\tanh\frac{\pi}{2\omega} - \tanh\frac{\pi}{2\alpha\omega}\right)$$

For the $\alpha = 0$ locus, $e = -(\pi/2\omega) + \tanh(\pi/2\omega)$. *(From Gille et al., Ref. 3.17.)*

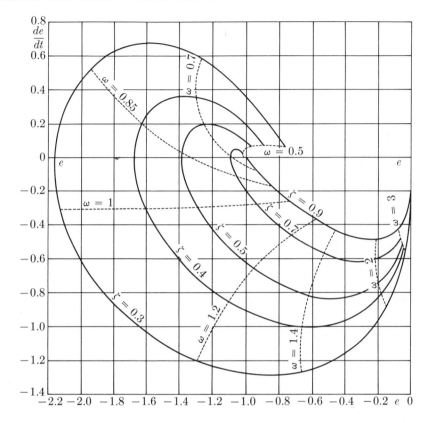

Fig. 3.15   Hamel loci for $\mathcal{L}(s) = 1/(s^2 + 2\zeta s + 1)$, $\zeta < 1$ and $N = 1$.   Equations are

$$e = \frac{1}{(1 - \zeta^2)^{1/2}} A \sin (\theta - \phi)$$

$$\frac{de}{dt} = \frac{1}{(1 - \zeta^2)^{1/2}} A \sin \theta$$

where $$\tan \phi = \frac{(1 - \zeta^2)^{1/2}}{\zeta}$$

$$Ae^{j\theta} = \tanh \left(\frac{\pi}{2\omega}\right) [\zeta + j(1 - \zeta^2)^{1/2}]$$

(*From Gille et al., Ref. 3.17.*)

$0 < \zeta < 1$.   It is interesting to compare Figs. 3.11a and 3.15, which depict the same system, one in Tsypkin's and one in Hamel's method of presentation.   Hamel's formulas clearly relate to our Eqs. (2.54).

Periodic motions which are at the same time limit cycles were described in Figs. 2.36 and 2.41.   It should now be evident that periodic motions of nonlinear control systems are quite complex. Although motions that contain portions of chatter or *sliding* motion are particularly interesting, they have been very little investigated.

3.5 PLANTS WITH ONE OR TWO CONTROL INPUTS

Section 3.4 indicated some methods of investigating the behavior of systems higher than second order with relays. Let us now examine the behavior of some specific systems.

3.5.1 Third-order plants with one control input (with and without zeros)

Let us assume a third-order system

$$c''' + a_1 c'' + a_2 c' + a_3 c = b_1 u'' + b_2 u' + u \qquad (3.133)$$

where $u = N \operatorname{sgn} F$.[1] If there is an input $r(\tau) = 0$ for $\tau > 0$, we can write $c = -e$. The characteristic roots of the system under consideration are $-\gamma$ and $-\zeta \pm i\nu$, with $\nu = \sqrt{1 - \zeta^2}$ and $|\zeta| \leq 1$; that is, there are one real and two conjugate complex roots.

This system can be written as

$$e''' + (\gamma + 2\zeta)e'' + (1 + 2\gamma\zeta)e' + \gamma e = b_1 u'' + b_2 u' + u \quad (3.134)$$

The general solution for a portion with constant u, that is, a phase-trajectory portion m where u'' and u' are zero, is given by

$$e_m = a_{1m} e^{\lambda_1 \tau_m} + A_{2m} e^{\lambda_2 \tau_m} + A_{3m} e^{-\gamma \tau_m} - \frac{N}{\gamma} \operatorname{sgn} F \qquad (3.135)$$

where $\lambda_1 = -\zeta + i\nu$
$\qquad \lambda_2 = -\zeta - i\nu$

In principle we could now go through the general transformation indicated by Eq. (3.24), but for the third-order case this general procedure does not yet pay off, as it is immediately apparent that certain new coordinates will allow us to profit from some of our experience with second-order systems. The error function e can also be expressed as

$$e_m(\tau) = c_{1m} e^{-\zeta \tau_m} \cos\left(\nu \tau_m + \epsilon_m\right) + c_{2m} e^{-\gamma \tau_m} - \frac{N}{\gamma} \operatorname{sgn} F \qquad (3.136)$$

---

[1] These examples are taken from two NASA Technical Notes (Refs. 3.18 and 3.10), both by Flügge-Lotz and Ishikawa. The notation in these works is not always identical to that used here (for example, b_1).

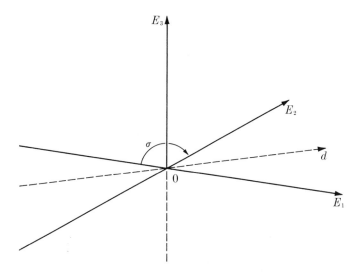

Fig. 3.16   Illustration of phase space for third-order plant.

The following new coordinates are useful:

$$E_1 = \gamma e' + e''$$
$$E_2 = \gamma e + e' \qquad\qquad (3.137)$$
$$E_3 = e'' + 2\zeta e' + e$$

We see immediately that E_1 and E_2 do not contain the exponential function $e^{-\gamma\tau_m}$ and that E_3 does not contain any damped cosine or sine terms.

The following arrangement is suggested. The positive E_2 axis forms the angle σ ($\cos \sigma = -\zeta$) with the E_1 axis, and the E_3 axis is normal to the $E_1 E_2$ plane. Hence projections of the phase-point trajectory into the $E_1 E_2$ plane will consist of portions of logarithmic spirals. Of course, the locus of the switching points in the new coordinate frame must be found. If the switching function is given by

$$F = e + k_1 e' + k_2 e'' = l_1 E_1 + l_2 E_2 + l_3 E_3 \qquad\qquad (3.138)$$

then $F = 0$ determines a plane in the $E_1 E_2 E_3$ space. Figure 3.16 gives a perspective of the coordinate frame, and Fig. 3.17a shows a projection of a phase trajectory in the $E_1 E_2$ plane.[1] To clarify the attitude of the switching plane an axis d is shown in the $E_1 E_2$ plane normal to $F = 0$ for $E_3 = 0$, that is, normal to the intersection of the switching plane with

[1] Note the arrows which indicate increasing time. Their direction is determined by the fact that $E_1 = E_2'$.

the E_1E_2 plane.   Figure 3.17b shows a projection of a phase trajectory
in the E_3d plane.   The switching plane appears as a line in this plane
because it is normal to the E_3d plane.   This E_3d plane is important in
drawing such trajectories.   (The procedure would be different if one
computes them with an analog or a digital computer).   Finally, Fig.
3.17c and d shows E_3 as a function of τ for $\gamma \neq 0$ and $\gamma = 0$.   The there
examples shown in Figs. 3.18 to 3.20 give characteristic features.
Certainly the choice of k_1 and k_2 in Fig. 3.20 is not a good one.   All
three examples are plants without zeros.

It may be worthwhile at this point to review the general criteria
for the appearance of endpoints and the beginning of chatter (see Sec.
3.3.1).   It is also interesting to look critically at the projections of the

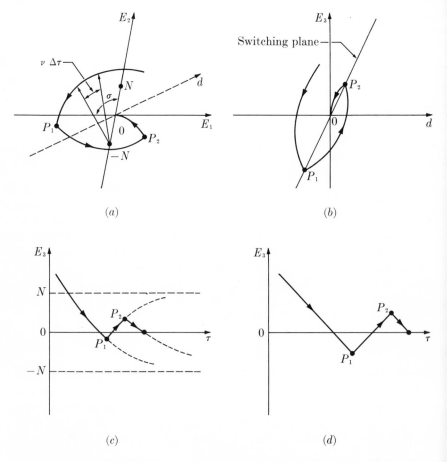

(a)   (b)

(c)   (d)

Fig. 3.17 Projection of trajectory.   (a) Projection into E_1E_2 plane; (b) projection
into E_3d plane; (c) diagram of E_3 against τ, $\gamma \neq 0$; (d) diagram of E_3 against τ,
$\gamma = 0$.

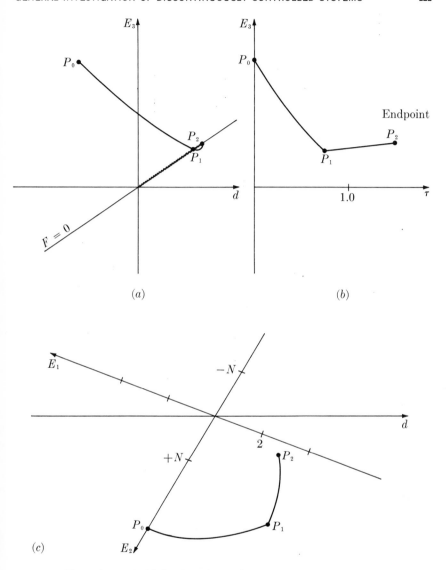

Fig. 3.18 Example 1 of third-order plant without zero (chatter sketched in E_3d plane); $\gamma \neq 0$. Note that parts a and c are the vertical and horizontal projections of the same trajectory.

phase-point trajectory into the E_1E_2 plane. It is clear that the projection in Fig. 3.20 could be produced by a badly chosen direction of switching line in a second-order system, resulting in a periodic function. Figures 3.18 and 3.19 display projections into the E_1E_2 plane which clearly lead us to expect, without checking the criteria, that the phase point will

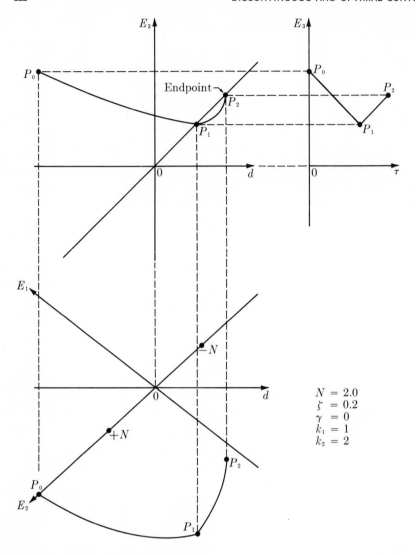

Fig. 3.19   Third-order plant without zero; $\gamma = 0$.

chatter toward the origin. It is thus apparent that the roots of the switching-plane equation alone

$$e + k_1e' + k_2e'' = 0 \rightarrow 1 + k_1s + k_2s^2 = 0 \tag{3.139}$$

do not give an assurance for zeroing a disturbance. In Fig. 3.20 the roots would have negative real parts.

Figure 3.21 shows projections of a phase trajectory of a system with zeros.[1]   The system is given by

$$e''' + 2\zeta e'' + e' = -b_1 u' - u$$

with $u = -N \operatorname{sgn} F = -N \operatorname{sgn} (e + k_1 e' + k_2 e'')$
where $N = 25$
$\zeta = 0.2$
$b_1 = 0.1$
$k_1 = 1.0$
$k_2 = 0.5$

It is apparent that this is a third-order system with poles at $-0.2 \pm i\, 0.98$ and 0.   One derivative of the control function appears in the system equation.   The zero of the transfer function $(-0.1s + 1)/(s^3 + 2\zeta s^2 + s)$ of the plant, together with the two zeros of the transfer function of F, provides an example of a case in which the number of zeros is equal to the number of poles (see Sec. 3.3.3b).

Figure (3.21)[2] shows clearly the appearance of noncontrolling chatter

[1] This example is described in all details as example 1 in sec. 1.2 of Ref. 3.10.
[2] It is assumed that before the start of the phase-point trajectory the control was set at zero.

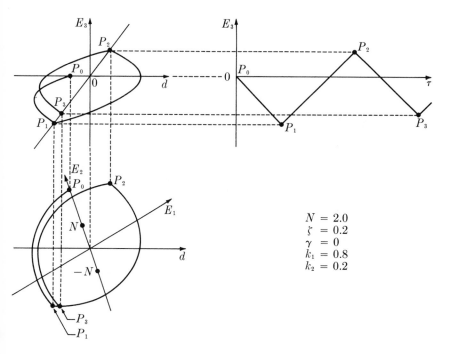

$$N = 2.0$$
$$\zeta = 0.2$$
$$\gamma = 0$$
$$k_1 = 0.8$$
$$k_2 = 0.2$$

Fig. 3.20   Third-order plant; example with improper selection of switching plane; $\gamma = 0$.

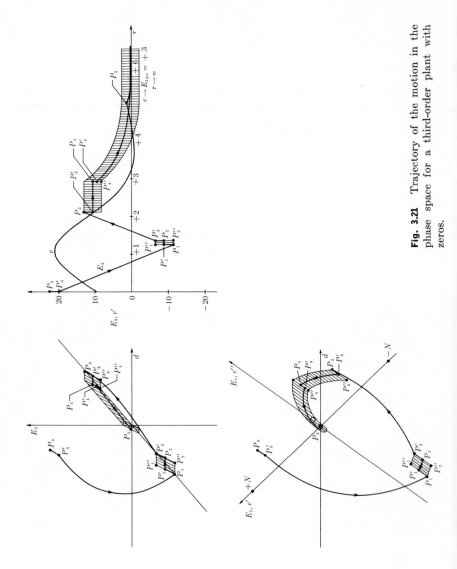

Fig. 3.21 Trajectory of the motion in the phase space for a third-order plant with zeros.

at each switching, followed by controlling chatter as soon as the region of possible endpoints is entered.   More examples, with detailed descriptions, appear in Ref. 3.10, and every reader familiar with an analog computer should be able to trace such $E_i(\tau)$ graphs easily.   The projections of a trajectory in the planes are somewhat more difficult; without a very good xy plotter, the chatter will not come out clearly.

The final steady-state operation of these systems is of great interest. It has been found that this final state will generally be a limit cycle corresponding to the average value $u_{av} = 0$, or noncontrolling chatter.

Let us now have a brief look at the possible shapes of small periodic motions in these third-order systems.   Figure 3.22 shows a projection

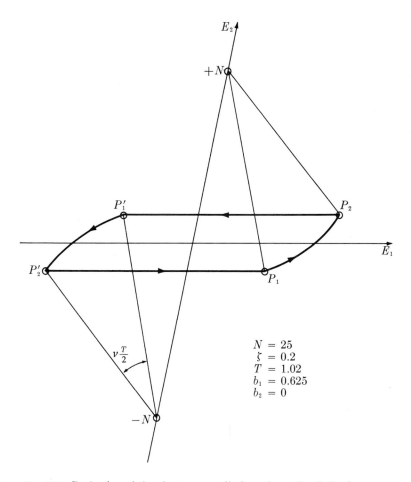

Fig. 3.22   Projection of the chatter-error limit cycle on the E_1E_2 plane.

of such a limit cycle into the E_1E_2 plane. In this case, because $b_2 = 0$, jumps take place only in the E_1 coordinates at the corner points, although in the general case jumps can also occur in the E_2 coordinate. More interesting is the projection of limit cycles in the E_3d plane. Figure 3.23 shows the limit locations of periodic motions that correspond to non-controlling chatter, and Fig. 3.24 shows an intermediate cycle. If these jumps at the corner points are parallel to the switching plane, controlling chatter will result. We see immediately from Fig. 3.25 that the period of controlling chatter is longer than $2\tau_d$. This generally results in a larger peak-to-peak error, and it may be good to allow some noncontrolling chatter to occur in order to lessen this error. Shortening the interval

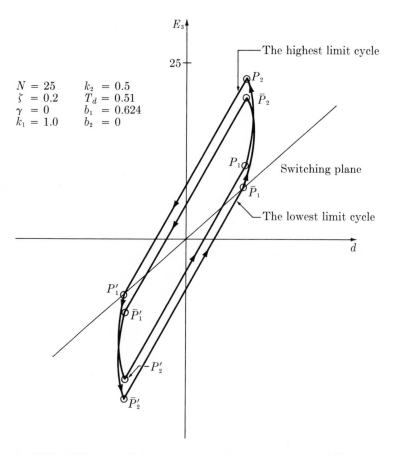

Fig. 3.23 Projection of the chatter-error limit cycle on the E_3d plane; system $\gamma = 0$.

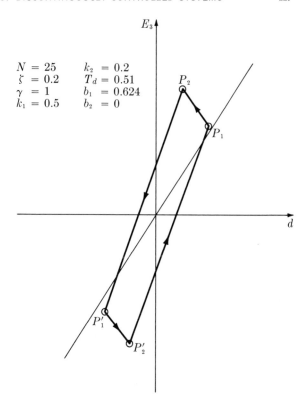

$N = 25$ $k_2 = 0.2$
$\zeta = 0.2$ $T_d = 0.51$
$\gamma = 1$ $b_1 = 0.624$
$k_1 = 0.5$ $b_2 = 0$

Fig. 3.24 Projection of the chatter-error limit cycle on the $E_3 d$ plane; system $\gamma \neq 0$.

μ between P_1 and P_0 in Fig. 3.25 by a calculable amount (see Fig. 3.26) will cause such noncontrolling chatter.

In Ref. 3.10 two formulas are developed to suggest the k_i that might be applied to provide some noncontrolling chatter, and hence a discontinuous F, before the system develops serious undesirable features. Figure 3.27 shows how the addition of a small value of k_2 can help to decrease the peak-to-peak error of the steady-state limit cycle of a given system. This small amount of k_2 will cause only very brief intervals of noncontrolling chatter at the switching plane before the neighborhood of the origin is reached.

3.5.2 Fourth-order plants with one control input (with zeros)[1]

The next example, control of a missile, is an interesting indication of the form in which the control engineer usually receives the description

---

[1] This example is treated in more detail in Ref. 3.19, pp. 125ff.

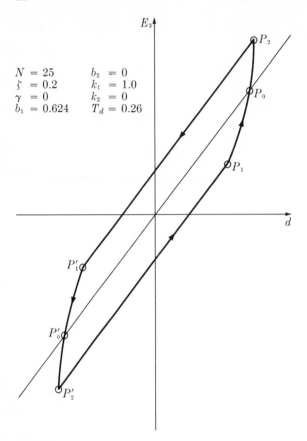

$N = 25$ $b_2 = 0$
$\zeta = 0.2$ $k_1 = 1.0$
$\gamma = 0$ $k_2 = 0$
$b_1 = 0.624$ $T_d = 0.26$

Fig. 3.25   Projection of the controlled limit cycle on the
$E_3 d$ plane.

of the plant to be controlled.   He is given neither an nth-order ordinary
differential equation nor a system of n first-order differential equations.
Instead, for the missile given in Fig. 3.28a, with the notation in Tables 4
and 5, he might be given the following equations[1] for a symmetrical
motion without control:

Equilibrium of forces in the X direction:

$$(C'_{D_0} - C_{L_0})\alpha + (C_W \cos \gamma_0)\theta + \left(2C^*_{D_0} + \frac{d}{d\tau}\right)\frac{v}{V_0} = 0 \qquad (3.140a)$$

[1] These equations correspond to those in B. M. Jones, Dynamics of the Airplane,
in W. F. Durand (ed.), *Aerodynamic Theory*, vol. V, div. N, p. 171, California Institute of Technology, 1943.   Jones uses different notation (explained on p. 133 of
his article).   For instance, $(w/V)_{Jones} = \alpha$, and $(u/V)_{Jones} = v/V_0$ of our notation.   Also, Jones relates forces to $\rho V_0^2 S$ instead of to the customary $\frac{1}{2}\rho V_0^2 S$; thus
$(k_L)_{Jones} = \frac{1}{2}C_L$.

Equilibrium of forces in the Z direction:

$$\left(C'_{L_0} + C_{D_0} + \frac{d}{d\tau}\right)\alpha + \left(C_W \sin \gamma_0 - \frac{d}{d\tau}\right)\theta + 2C^*_{L_0}\frac{v}{V_0} = 0 \quad (3.140b)$$

Equilibrium of moments about the Y axis:

$$\left(\mu C_{M_0} + C_{M\dot{\alpha}}\frac{d}{d\tau}\right)\alpha + \left(C_{M_q}\frac{d}{d\tau} - \frac{k_y^2}{c^2}\frac{d^2}{d\tau^2}\right)\theta = 0 \quad (3.140c)$$

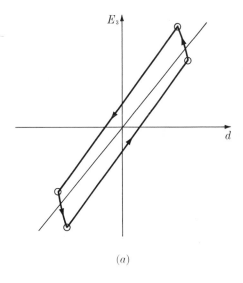

(a)

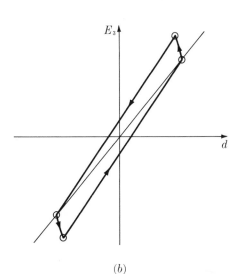

Fig. 3.26 Chatter-error limit cycles with compensation. (a) General case; (b) critical case.

(b)

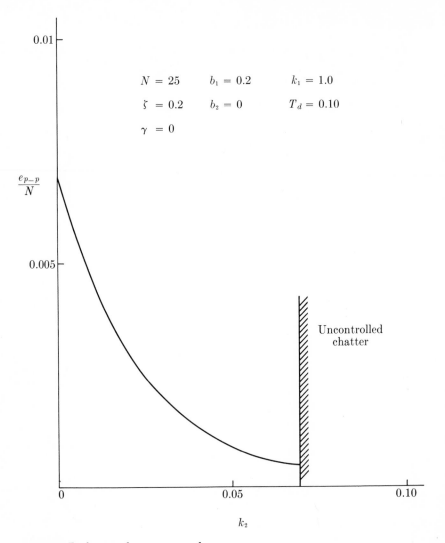

Fig. 3.27 Peak-to-peak error versus k_2.

For ease the coefficients in these equations may be abbreviated as

$$a_{10}\alpha + b_{10}\theta + \left(c_{10} + c_{11}\frac{d}{d\tau}\right)\frac{v}{V_0} = 0 \qquad (3.140a^*)$$

$$\left(a_{20} + a_{21}\frac{d}{d\tau}\right)\alpha + \left(b_{20} + b_{21}\frac{d}{d\tau}\right)\theta + c_{20}\frac{v}{V_0} = 0 \qquad (3.140b^*)$$

$$\left(a_{30} + a_{31}\frac{d}{d\tau}\right)\alpha + \left(b_{31}\frac{d}{d\tau} + b_{32}\frac{d^2}{d\tau^2}\right)\theta = 0 \qquad (3.140c^*)$$

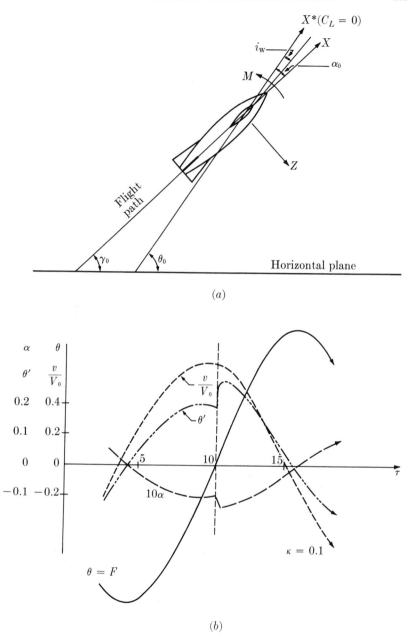

(a)

(b)

Fig. 3.28 (a) Flying missile; desired path is indicated by subscripts "zero" on α, γ, and θ; deviations from the desired values are called α, γ and θ. (b) Behavior of θ, θ', α, and v/V_0 in the neighborhood of a switching point.

Table 4   Notation for Sec. 3.5.2

c = chord	$N_2 = \dfrac{\partial L}{\partial \eta} \dfrac{1}{q_0 S}$ = rate of change of lift with η
b = span	
S = wing area	
W = weight	
m = mass	$N_3 = \dfrac{\partial M}{\partial \eta_h} \dfrac{1}{q_0 S c}$ = rate of change of moment with η_h
ρ = density	
V_0 = velocity of undisturbed missile	
t = time	$C_L = \dfrac{\text{lift}}{q_0 S}$
$T_m = \dfrac{2m}{\rho S V_c}$ = special time unit	
	$C_D = \dfrac{\text{drag}}{q_0 S}$
$\tau = \dfrac{t}{T_m}$ = nondimensional time variable	
	$C_M = \dfrac{\text{pitching moment}}{q_0 S c}$
$\bar{\mu} = \dfrac{2m}{\rho S c}$	
	$C_W = \dfrac{W}{q_0 S}$
$I_y = m k_y^2$ = moment of inertia about y axis	$C_{D_0}^* = C_{D_0} - \left(\dfrac{\partial T}{\partial q_0}\right)_{\alpha_0} \dfrac{\cos(\alpha_0 - i_w)}{S}$
$q_0 = \dfrac{\rho V_0^2}{2}$ = dynamic pressure	$C_{L_0}^* = C_{L_0} + \left(\dfrac{\partial T}{\partial q_0}\right)_{\alpha_0} \dfrac{\sin(\alpha_0 - i_w)}{S}$
T = thrust	
X, Y, Z = rectangular coordinates (wind axes)	$C_{D_0}' = \left(\dfrac{dC_D}{d\alpha}\right)_{\alpha_0}$
α = angle of attack	
θ = angle of pitch	$C_{L_0}' = \left(\dfrac{dC_L}{d\alpha}\right)_{\alpha_0}$
$\gamma = \theta - \alpha$ = flight-path angle	
$\epsilon = k_1 \alpha$ = downwash angle at tail-plane	$C_{M_0}' = \left(\dfrac{dC_M}{d\alpha}\right)_{\alpha_0}$
v = increment of velocity in x direction	$q = \dfrac{d\theta}{dt} = \dot{\theta}$
$\bar{s}$ = coordinate along path of undisturbed flying missile	$\dot{\alpha} = \dfrac{d\alpha}{dt}$
n = normal deviation from undisturbed path of missile	
i_w = wing-incidence angle (relative to thrust line)	$C_{Mq} = \left(\dfrac{dC_M}{dq}\right)_{\alpha_0}$
η = angle of aileron	$C_{M\dot{\alpha}} = \dfrac{d\epsilon}{d\alpha} C_{Mq} = k_1 C_{Mq}$
η_h = angle of elevator	

Note: The subscript 0 refers to undisturbed straight flight of the missile.

Table 5   Numerical values for disturbance of the gliding flight

$C_{L_0} = 0.213$	$\bar{\mu} = 550$
$C_{D_0} = 0.022$	$T_m = 3.25$ sec
$C'_{L_0} = 3.55$	$\dfrac{d\epsilon}{d\alpha} = k_1 = 1.6$
$C'_{M_0} = -0.365$	
$C'_{D_0} = 0.197$	$\dfrac{k_y{}^2}{c^2} = 1.66$
$a_{10} = C'_{D_0} - C_{L_0} = -0.016$	$b_{10} = C_W \cos \gamma_0 = 0.213$
$a_{20} = C'_{L_0} + C_{D_0} = 3.57$	$b_{20} = C_W \sin \gamma_0 = -0.022$
$a_{21} = 1$	$b_{21} = -1$
$a_{30} = \bar{\mu} C'_{M_0} = -201$	$b_{31} = C_{Mq} = -10$
$a_{31} = C_{M\dot{\alpha}} = -16$	$b_{32} = -\dfrac{k_y{}^2}{c^2} = -1.66$
$c_{10} = 2C^*_{D_0} = 0.044$	
$c_{11} = 1$	$|N_{2\eta_0}| = 0.05$
$c_{20} = 2C^*_{L_0} = 0.426$	$\lambda_{1,2} = -0.02937 \pm 0.2777i$
$C_{Mq} = -10.0$	$\lambda_{3,4} = -9.609 \pm 7.062i$

	$k = 1$	$k = 3$
A_k	$0.01383e^{4.842i}$	$1.282e^{0.229i}$
C_k	$0.7658e^{1.625i}$	$0.01624e^{0.612i}$
λ_k	$0.2792e^{1.676i}$	$11.93e^{2.508i}$

The values of a_{mn}, b_{mn}, and c_{mn} for this missile are given in Table 5. The uncontrolled system is denoted by L_1.

This system of differential equations with constant coefficients has well-known solutions in the form of sums of exponential functions:

$$\theta = \sum_{k=1}^{4} M_k e^{\lambda_k r}$$

$$\frac{v}{V_0} = \sum_{k=1}^{4} C_k M_k e^{\lambda_k r} \tag{3.141}$$

$$\alpha = \sum_{k=1}^{4} A_k M_k e^{\lambda_k r}$$

The λ_k are the roots of the characteristic determinant of the system

$$D = \begin{vmatrix} a_{10} & b_{10} & c_{10} + c_{11}\lambda \\ a_{20} + a_{21}\lambda & b_{20} + b_{21}\lambda & c_{20} \\ a_{30} + a_{31}\lambda & b_{31}\lambda + b_{32}\lambda^2 & 0 \end{vmatrix} \tag{3.142}$$

or $r_4\lambda^4 + r_3\lambda^3 + r_2\lambda^2 + r_1\lambda + r_0 = 0$ (3.143) where r_k are constants dependent upon a_{mn}, b_{mn}, c_{mn}. Since $D = 0$ is a fourth-order equation, there are only four roots for λ.[1] If the uncontrolled missile is dynamically stable, all roots λ must have a negative real part. In this case the ratios r_3/r_4, r_2/r_4, r_1/r_4, and r_0/r_4 are positive, and

$$r_3 r_2 r_1 - r_4 r_1{}^2 - r_0 r_3{}^2 > 0$$

The constants M_k are determined by the initial conditions $v(0)/V_0$, $\alpha(0)$, $\theta(0)$, and $\theta'(0)$. The C_k and A_k are determined by the coefficients of the system given in Table 5.

The longitudinal motion of the missile may be controlled either by the ailerons or by the horizontal tailplane. The control-surface deflection will be determined by the missile deviations. The remaining question is which of the deviations to be used for correcting the disturbed motion is best detected by instruments. A record of θ and $\theta' = d\theta/d\tau$ is easily obtained by gyroscopic measurements. Records of α and v/V_0 are more difficult to obtain and are less accurate. Therefore we shall study a control system depending on θ and θ'. In particular, the angle of the control surface will depend on the sign of a linear function F of θ and θ', $F = \theta + \kappa\theta'$. In other words, we shall choose a position control.

In the case of aileron control we may assume that only a force in the Z direction is applied and that the equilibrium of momentum is not affected. Introducing p_{mn} for the coefficients of α, θ, v/V_0 into the equations of motion (for example $p_{31} = a_{30} + a_{31}\,d/d\tau$), we have for aileron control the following system L_2 instead of Eqs. (3.140a^*) to (3.140c^*).

$$p_{11}\alpha + p_{12}\theta + p_{13}\frac{v}{V_0} = 0$$

$$p_{21}\alpha + p_{22}\theta + p_{23}\frac{v}{V_0} = -N_z\eta \tag{3.144a}$$

$$p_{31}\alpha + p_{32}\theta = 0$$

where $\eta = \pm\eta_0\,\mathrm{sgn}\,(\theta + \kappa\theta') = \pm\eta_0\,\mathrm{sgn}\,F$ \hfill (3.144b)

The two signs before $\eta_0\,\mathrm{sgn}\,F$ again indicate that there are two essentially different control systems. It will be practical to give preference to that system in which the force applied by the control element is added to the existing restoring forces.

In the case of horizontal tailplane control it may be assumed that only the equilibrium of momentum is influenced and that the effect on the balance of forces is negligible [Eq. (3.144a)].

[1] A system with three degrees of freedom may lead to a characteristic determinant of sixth order at most.

Corresponding to Eqs. (3.144), we obtain a system L_3:

$$p_{11}\alpha + p_{12}\theta + p_{13}\frac{v}{V_0} = 0$$

$$p_{21}\alpha + p_{22}\theta + p_{23}\frac{v}{V_0} = 0 \qquad\qquad (3.145a)$$

$$p_{31}\alpha + p_{32}\theta = N_3\eta_h$$

where $\eta_h = \pm\eta_{h0}\,\mathrm{sgn}\,(\theta + \kappa\theta') = \pm\eta_{h0}\,\mathrm{sgn}\,F \qquad (3.145b)$

Systems L_2 and L_3 both remain linear between two consecutive switching points of the control system. The solutions are sums of exponential functions in every interval m between two switching points, but there are additional constant terms:

$$\theta_m = \sum_{k=1}^{4} M_{k_m}e^{\lambda_k\tau} + B$$

$$\frac{v_m}{V_0} = \sum_{k=1}^{4} C_{k_m}M_{k_m}e^{\lambda_k\tau} + C \qquad\qquad (3.146)$$

$$\alpha_m = \sum_{k=1}^{4} A_{k_m}M_{k_m}e^{\lambda_k\tau} + A$$

These constant A, B, and C are given by Table 6.

We can now decide which sign to take before η_0 or η_{h0}. The control function $F = \theta + k\theta'$ will vary as θ for small k; θ is determined by a fourth-order differential equation which may replace system L_2 or L_3:

$$r_4\theta^{IV} + r_3\theta''' + r_2\theta'' + r_1\theta' + r_0(\theta - B) = 0$$

For a stable missile without control $r_0/r_4 > 0$. If we assume this basic stability to exist, then a negative value of B for positive θ would increase the term r_0/r_4 by a factor $(\theta - B)/\theta$ and thus reinforce the restoring force.

Table 6

L_2: control by aileron, Eqs. (3.144)	L_3: control by horizontal tailplane, Eqs. (3.145)
$A = 0$	$A = \dfrac{1}{a_{3c}}N_3(\pm\eta_{h0}\,\mathrm{sgn}\,F)$
$B = \dfrac{c_{10}}{b_{1c}c_{20} - c_{10}b_{20}}N_2(\pm\eta_0\,\mathrm{sgn}\,F)$	$B = \dfrac{c_{10}a_{20}}{a_{30}(b_{10}c_{20} - c_{10}b_{20})}N_3(\pm\eta_{h0}\,\mathrm{sgn}\,F)$
$C = \dfrac{-b_{10}}{b_{10}c_{20} - c_{10}b_{20}}N_2(\pm\eta_v\,\mathrm{sgn}\,F)$	$C = \dfrac{a_{10}b_{20} - b_{10}a_{20}}{a_{30}(b_{10}c_{20} - c_{10}b_{20})}N_3(\pm\eta_{h0}\,\mathrm{sgn}\,F)$

Hence we find that if

$$\frac{c_{10}}{b_{10}c_{20} - c_{10}b_{20}} > 0$$

the lower sign before η_0 should be chosen for system L_2. But because $a_{20}/a_{30} < 0$, the upper sign before η_{h0} should be chosen for system L_3.

Thus far only practical design considerations have suggested the choice of a switching function $F = \theta + k\theta'$. This choice requires further discussion. In a space $(\theta, \theta', v/V_0, \alpha)$ the switching plane would be normal to the (θ, θ') plane; however, this is a geometric condition in four-dimensional space, and we can no longer visualize the phase-point trajectory. Hence the behavior of F must be investigated analytically.

The functions θ, θ', v/V_0, and α will be continuous because they are continuous in any interval, and their values at the end of any interval are equal to the initial values for the following interval. In system L_2 the function $-N_2\eta$ is discontinuous, and similarly, in system L_3 the function $N_3\eta_h$ is discontinuous. We can easily determine the continuity qualities of the solutions in general with respect to the continuity of θ, θ', v/V_0, and α. In both systems the control function will have a discontinuous slope at the switching points of the phase space (Table 7).

Figure 3.28b shows the behavior of $\theta(\tau)$, $\theta'(\tau)$, $v(\tau)/V_0$, and $\alpha(\tau)$ in the neighborhood of a switching point. The portion shown is taken from the general figure describing the motion of the missile described by the physical data in Table 5 after a disturbance from straight forward flight.[1] The aileron control is utilized in system L_2. The discontinuous slopes of α and θ' are very conspicuous.

The motion is composed of two superposed oscillations of very differ-

[1] The linearization of the flight equations sets certain limits for the maximum values of θ, θ', v/V_0, and α. For better visualization in this example initial disturbances are chosen too large in this respect.

Table 7

Continuity quality	Function in system L_2					Function in system L_3			
Smooth	$\dfrac{v}{V_0}$	———	θ	———		$\left(\dfrac{v}{V_0}\right)'$	α	θ	———
Broken line	$\left(\dfrac{v}{V_0}\right)'$	α	θ'	$F = \theta + \kappa\theta'$	———	———	α'	θ'	$F = \theta + \kappa\theta'$
Step	———	α'	θ''	$F' = \theta' + \kappa\theta''$		———	———	θ''	$F' = \theta' + \kappa\theta''$

ent frequencies (for the missile in question $\nu_1 = 0.2777$ and $\nu_3 = 7.062$). It is obvious that the discontinuity of the slopes of θ' and α at the switching points is nicely smoothed by high-frequency oscillation. Hence neglect of this oscillation would seriously affect the validity of any computational results.

There are two pairs of complex roots, and it is certainly possible to write the system equations in such a way that the fourth-order system (with no controls) is replaced by four first-order differential equations for the variables x_i, with $i = 1, 2, 3, 4$. The equations are grouped in pairs because we want equations with real coefficients and we have two conjugate complex pairs of roots. Thus, if oblique coordinate axes are used, in the x_1x_2 and x_3x_4 planes the projections of the phase-point trajectory are composed of portions of logarithmic spirals. Since there is a control, however, the pairs of first-order ordinary differential equations are coupled through the control function.

In both the x_1x_2 plane and the x_3x_4 plane the intersection of the chosen $F = 0$ plane with the coordinate plane can be traced. This provides an easy indication of the system behavior in some cases, and many detailed examples, drawn and checked by digital computing, can be found in Ref. 3.19. It is currently considered preferable to determine the modes and establish the transfer functions, and then to select the variables for control and determine the possible chatter region in terms of their dependence on the available coefficients k_i, with possible values of k checked against plots given by analog or digital computers. Nevertheless, the graphically obtained results of the well-chosen examples of Ref. 3.19 are still worth studying.

3.5.3   Third-order plants with one control input (with zeros)

Frederickson (Ref. 3.20) has studied the control of a simplified and a complete roll-yaw system, and his work contains many examples concerning operation of the same missile under different flight conditions. The equations of motion and other information about the missile were obtained from the Boeing Airplane Company. Table 8 contains the aerodynamic nomenclature used in this section (see also Fig. 3.29a).

The control system for the missile is designed so that the missile will operate over a large range of flight conditions, that is, a large range of altitude and Mach number. This means that the equations of motion of the missile are constantly changing. In analyzing such a system a number of different operating points are considered, and at each operating point the aerodynamic coefficients are assumed to remain constant. Such an assumption is normally quite good, since for a given maneuver of the missile the velocity and altitude do not change appreciably. Frederickson examined 11 different flight conditions.

Table 8

---

a_x = linear acceleration along X axis
a_y = linear acceleration along Y axis
a_z = linear acceleration along Z axis
ϕ = angular displacement about X axis
θ = angular displacement about Y axis
ψ = angular displacement about Z axis
p = angular velocity about X axis
q = angular velocity about Y axis
r = angular velocity about Z axis
F_x = force along X axis
F_y = force along Y axis
F_z = force along Z axis
L = moment about X axis
M = moment about Y axis
N = moment about Z axis
A = moment of inertia about X axis
B = moment of inertia about Y axis
C = moment of inertia about Z axis
$\left. \begin{array}{l} D = I_{yz} \\ E = I_{zz} \\ F = I_{xy} \end{array} \right\}$ = products of inertia
δ_a = aileron angle; positive δ_a gives positive roll
δ_E = elevator angle; positive δ_E gives negative pitch
δ_R = rudder angle; positive δ_R gives negative yaw
U = missile velocity parallel to relative wind
$\left. \begin{array}{l} \mathbf{x} \\ \mathbf{y} \\ \mathbf{z} \end{array} \right\}$ = space coordinates as shown in Fig. 3.29a
V_a = output level of aileron-angle contactor

The equation of motion for the missile indicate that the roll-yaw system is coupled to the pitch system. For this discussion we shall disregard the coupling to the pitch system and assume that during a roll-yaw maneuver the pitch system does not change. However, as in the case of changing flight conditions, a number of different operating points must be considered. If we examine three different pitching conditions—one corresponding to maximum positive pitch acceleration a_z, one for $a_z = 0$, and one for minimum pitch acceleration—we are considering 33 different operating points, since there are three different pitching conditions for each of the 11 flight conditions.

The transfer function (roll rate versus aileron angle) is given by

$$\frac{p}{\delta_a}(s) = \frac{a_2 s^2 + a_1 s + a_0}{s^3 + b_2 s^2 + b_1 s + b_0} \tag{3.147}$$

Table 9 shows the coefficients for the different flight conditions.

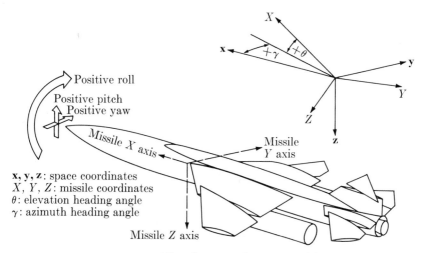

$\mathbf{x}, \mathbf{y}, \mathbf{z}$: space coordinates
X, Y, Z: missile coordinates
θ: elevation heading angle
γ: azimuth heading angle

All surfaces are shown rotated in positive direction

(a)

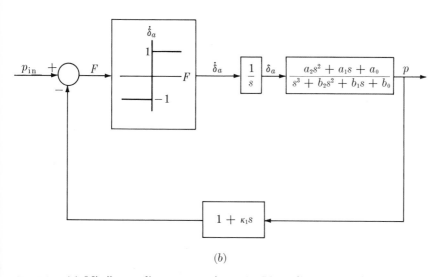

(b)

Fig. 3.29 (a) Missile coordinate convention. (b) Block diagram of missile roll-rate contactor controller.

Table 9   Coefficients of the p/δ_a transfer function for the different flight conditions and pitching conditions

Flight condi- tions	All three values of a_z				$a_z = 1.75g$		$a_z = 0$		$a_z = -1.75g$	
	a_2	a_1	a_0	b_2	b_1	b_0	b_1	b_0	b_1	b_0
11.5	180.0	233.0	2725.0	4.57	6.83	13.70	19.83	37.50	32.83	61.30
21.2	101.0	84.0	749.0	2.94	−1.20	−2.10	9.30	11.42	19.80	24.90
22.0	178.3	175.5	2030.0	3.18	1.96	2.90	13.86	18.61	25.76	34.30
31.2	65.3	36.3	311.0	1.98	−5.00	4.19	5.64	4.94	16.20	14.07
32.6	156.8	121.5	1135.0	2.16	1.95	2.48	8.55	9.35	15.15	16.22
41.2	40.5	14.2	120.0	1.26	−7.17	−3.74	3.33	2.03	13.83	7.80
42.6	97.5	48.2	438.0	1.38	−1.45	−1.06	5.03	3.29	11.51	7.64
51.2	25.3	5.7	46.8	0.79	−8.61	−2.90	1.99	0.76	12.59	4.42
52.6	60.5	18.6	168.0	0.85	−3.62	−1.45	2.98	1.27	9.58	3.98
61.5	18.6	2.8	28.8	0.52	−11.36	−2.28	1.64	0.43	14.64	3.14
62.6	37.5	7.1	64.3	0.53	−4.82	−1.19	1.82	0.49	8.46	2.18

The ailerons are driven by a hydraulic system utilizing an on-off valve.   Hence

$$\dot{\delta}_a = V_a \operatorname{sgn} F_a \tag{3.148}$$

where F_a is the aileron switching function and V_a is the capacity of the hydraulic valve.   Equations (3.147) and (3.148) describe the motion of the system.

The first step in the design of the system is to determine F_a, the switching function.   We know from preceding discussions that F_a should be chosen such that it is continuous at switching and $\Delta_1 \dot{F}_a = -a \, \Delta_1 \dot{\delta}_a$, where a is a positive constant.   This last condition ensures that endpoint chatter motion can occur.   In addition, it is desirable to make F_a a function only of p and its derivatives, so that during endpoint chatter motion, where $F_a = 0$, the equation for p is independent of the flight condition. We see from Eqs. (3.147) and (3.148) that both p and $\dot{p}$ are continuous and $\ddot{p}$ is discontinuous, with $\Delta_1 \ddot{p} = a_2 \, \Delta_1 \dot{\delta}_a$ and a_2 a positive constant depending on the flight condition.   Thus F_a is chosen to be of the form

$$F_a = p_{\text{in}} - p - \kappa_1 \dot{p} \tag{3.149}$$

This switching function is easily obtained in practice, since both p and $\dot{p}$ can be measured quite easily.   With the form of F_a now specified, the motion is described by

$$\dddot{p} + b_2 \ddot{p} + b_1 \dot{p} + b_0 p = a_2 \ddot{\delta}_a + a_1 \dot{\delta}_a + a_0 \delta_a \tag{3.150}$$

$$\delta_a = V_a \operatorname{sgn} (p_{\text{in}} - p - \kappa_1 \dot{p}) \tag{3.151}$$

A block diagram of this system is shown in Fig. 3.29b.

Next those values of V_a and κ_1 which give good system performance should be determined. If p_{in}/V_a becomes larger, κ_1 must be made larger for a well-damped response. The response time increases with κ_1, however, so p_{in}/V_a should not become too large. Let us investigate two values of V_a, $V_a = 0.5$ rad/sec and $V_a = 1$ rad/sec. The value of κ_1 for each of these V_a and the response time are best determined by analog simulation.

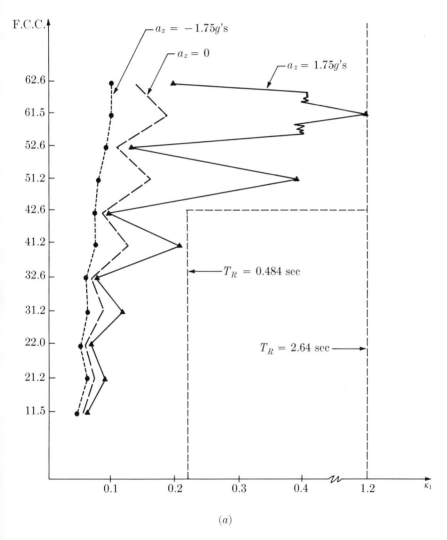

(a)

Fig. 3.30 κ_1 versus flight conditions for fastest response times without overshoot. (a) $V_a = 0.5$ rad/sec and $a_z = -1.75$, 0, and 1.75 g.

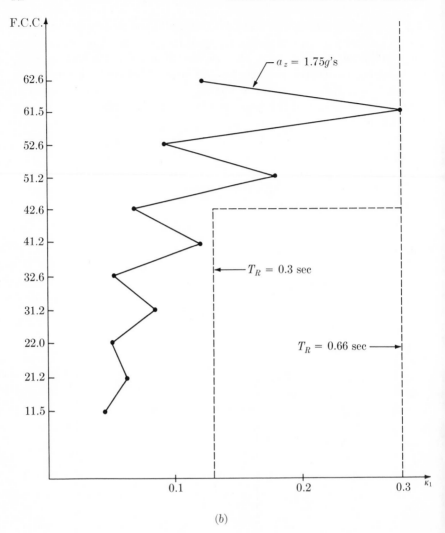

Fig. 3.30 κ_1 versus flight conditions for fastest response time without overshoot. (b) $V_a = 1.0$ rad/sec and $a_z = 1.75$ g.

Since a certain damping is required, it follows that κ_1 should be picked to give this damping for the largest input. Thus in the simulation of the contactor system the value of κ_1 is plotted at each operating point for $p_{\text{in}} = 1.5$ rad/sec, which is the largest input. In addition, the value of κ_1 which gives the fastest response without overshoot is tabulated, since it represents the minimum permissible κ_1 without overshoot. Figure 3.30a shows the values of κ_1 at all the operating points for $V_a = 0.5$

rad/sec. Note that for the unstable p/δ_a transfer function corresponding to $a_z = 1.75g$ large values of κ_1 are necessary.

If a single value of κ_1 is to control the system with $V_a = 0.5$ rad/sec for all flight conditions, it should be equal to or greater than 1.2. For $\kappa_1 = 1.2$ the 10 to 90 percent rise time T_R has been found experimentally to be 2.64 sec for all flight conditions. From Fig. 3.30a it is apparent that much faster response would be obtained at the lower-numbered flight conditions with a smaller value of κ_1. For instance, with $\kappa_1 = 0.22$ for flight conditions 11.5 to 42.6 the rise time is $T_R = 0.484$ sec. We clearly see that a second value of κ_1 for the lower-numbered flight conditions will result in improved performance.

Figure 3.30b shows the values of κ_1 for $V_a = 1$ rad/sec, but only the values for $a_z = 1.75g$ are considered, since they give the minimum value κ_1 can have. For $V_a = 1$ rad/sec κ_1 must be equal to or greater than 0.28 if a single value is used for all flight conditions. As for $V_a = 0.5$ rad/sec, the response time for the lower-numbered flight conditions can be shortened by using a second value of $\kappa_1 = 0.13$ for flight conditions 11.5 to 42.6.

Figures 3.31 to 3.33 show oscillograph traces of the response of the system for $V_a = 1$ rad/sec. The response of the system for $\kappa_1 = 0.28$ in four different flight conditions is shown in Figs. 3.31 and 3.32, and the response of the system for $\kappa_1 = 0.13$ in flight conditions 11.5 and 41.2 is shown in Fig. 3.33. From Figs. 3.31 and 3.32, where $\kappa_1 = 0.28$, it is seen that the output response p is essentially identical for the different flight conditions and has a rise time of $T_R = 0.66$ sec. For the two flight conditions with $\kappa_1 = 0.13$ (Fig. 3.33) the output response p is also identical and has a rise time $T_R = 0.3$ sec.

The insensitivity of the contactor system to changes in the p/δ_a transfer function is easily explained by the fact that the switching function F in Figs. 3.31 to 3.33 goes to zero very rapidly, and endpoint chatter motion begins. Hence the output response for all operating points is given by

$$F_a = p_{\text{in}} - p - \kappa_1 \dot{p} = 0 \qquad (3.152)$$

If the motion of the system is given by Eq. (3.152), the time solution is

$$p = p_{\text{in}}(1 - e^{-t/\kappa_1}) \qquad (3.153)$$

The 10 to 90 percent rise time T_R is then equal to 2.2 times the time constant τ^*, or

$$T_R = 2.2\tau^* = 2.2\kappa_1 \qquad (3.154)$$

For $V_a = 1$ rad/sec and $\kappa_1 = 0.28$ the calculated rise time $T_R = 0.62$ sec checks very closely with the measured rise time $T_R = 0.66$ sec. The

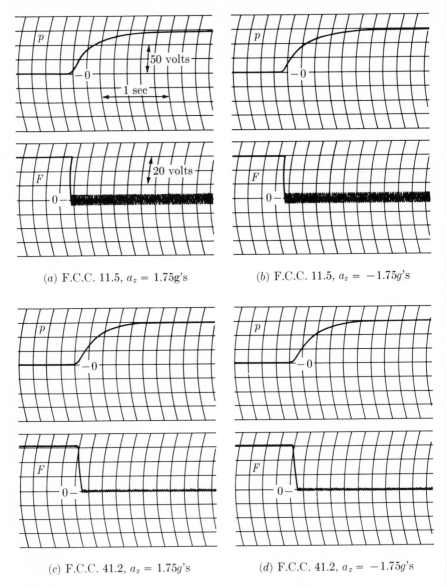

(a) F.C.C. 11.5, $a_z = 1.75$g's

(b) F.C.C. 11.5, $a_z = -1.75$g's

(c) F.C.C. 41.2, $a_z = 1.75g$'s

(d) F.C.C. 41.2, $a_z = -1.75g$'s

Fig. 3.31 Oscillograph traces of the roll-rate response of the contactor system with $V_a = 1$ rad/sec and $\kappa_1 = 0.28$.

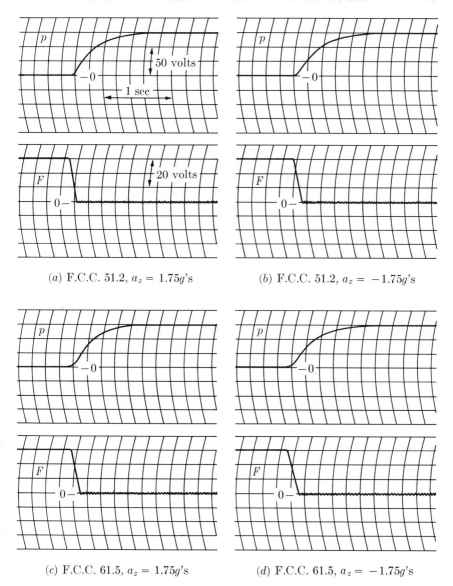

(a) F.C.C. 51.2, $a_z = 1.75g$'s

(b) F.C.C. 51.2, $a_z = -1.75g$'s

(c) F.C.C. 61.5, $a_z = 1.75g$'s

(d) F.C.C. 61.5, $a_z = -1.75g$'s

Fig. 3.32 Oscillograph traces of the roll-rate response of the contactor system with $V_a = 1$ rad/sec and $\kappa_1 = 0.28$.

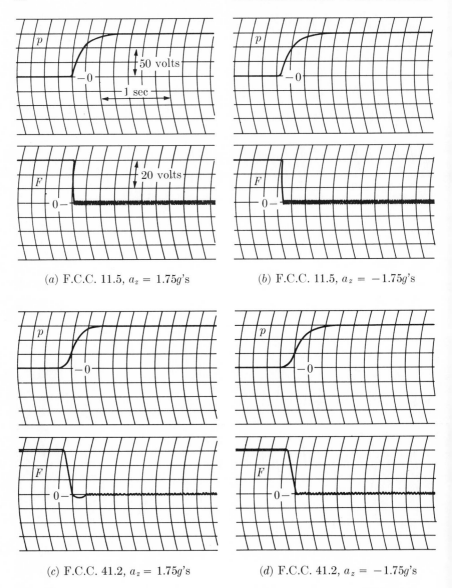

(a) F.C.C. 11.5, $a_z = 1.75g$'s

(b) F.C.C. 11.5, $a_z = -1.75g$'s

(c) F.C.C. 41.2, $a_z = 1.75g$'s

(d) F.C.C. 41.2, $a_z = -1.75g$'s

Fig. 3.33 Oscillograph traces of the roll-rate response of the contactor system with $V_a = 1$ rad/sec and $\kappa_1 = 0.13$.

measured and calculated rise times for the other values of κ_1 also check very closely.

It is now interesting to compare the response times for $V_a = 1$ rad/sec and $V_a = 0.5$ rad/sec. In both cases the rise time is given by $T_R = 2.2\kappa_1$; however, for $V_a = 0.5$ rad/sec κ_1 is restricted to be equal to or greater than 1.2 for flight condition 61.5, while κ_1 must only be equal to or greater than 0.28 for $V_a = 1$ rad/sec. Hence the rise time of the system with $V_a = 1$ rad/sec can be one-fourth that of the system with $V_a = 0.5$ rad/sec. The choice of V_a then depends upon the rise time that is desired and the hydraulic power available. Clearly, to obtain a fast rise time the hydraulic power must be increased.

Frederickson (Ref. 3.20) has compared the action of the relay control to that of a good linear control with saturation limits corresponding to the relay output.[1] The figures of Ref. 3.20 are particularly instructive in showing the most outstanding feature of the contactor system, the fact that output response in a contactor system is insensitive to changes in the system being controlled. It is also apparent that the contactor gives response times equal to or less than the linear system.

3.5.4 Fourth-order plant with two control inputs

As our next example let us examine the small-angle-attitude motion of a satellite in a circular orbit about a spherical earth, investigated by Flügge-Lotz and Maltz (Ref. 3.7). If the configuration of the satellite (inertia moments I_1, I_2, and I_3) is correctly chosen (see Ref. 3.21), the attitude motion will be neutrally stable when uncontrolled. We shall choose configuration parameters to ensure this.

The coupled roll-yaw equations (from Ref. 3.21) are

$$\begin{bmatrix} \theta_1 \\ \theta_1' \\ \theta_2 \\ \theta_2' \end{bmatrix} = \begin{bmatrix} 0 & 1 & 0 & 0 \\ -\alpha_1 & 0 & 0 & 1 - \alpha_1 \\ 0 & 0 & 0 & 1 \\ 0 & -(1 - \alpha_2) & -4\alpha_2 & 0 \end{bmatrix} \begin{bmatrix} \theta_1 \\ \theta_1' \\ \theta_2 \\ \theta_2' \end{bmatrix} + \begin{bmatrix} 0 & 0 \\ 1 & 0 \\ 0 & 0 \\ 0 & 1 \end{bmatrix} \begin{bmatrix} u_1 \\ u_2 \end{bmatrix}$$

$$(3.155)$$

where $\alpha_1 \equiv \dfrac{I_3 - I_2}{I_1}$

$$\alpha_2 \equiv \dfrac{I_3 - I_1}{I_2}$$

$$(3.156)$$

and time is normalized to the orbital period.[2] The characteristic equa-

---

[1] Such comparisons should really be made by first stating in mathematical terms the exact performance criterion required for the design. However, Frederickson's work preceded the construction of optimizing controls that make more exact comparisons possible.

[2] That is, $\tau = \omega_0 t$, where ω_0 is the orbital frequency and τ is dimensionless.

tion of system (3.155) is

$$(s^2 + \alpha_1)(s^2 + 4\alpha_2) + (1 - \alpha_1)(1 - \alpha_2)s^2 = 0 \qquad (3.157)$$

with the configuration parameters limited by the inequalities

$$0 < \alpha_1 < 1 \qquad\qquad\qquad\qquad\qquad (3.158a)$$
$$0 < \alpha_2 < \alpha_1 \qquad\qquad\qquad\qquad\qquad (3.158b)$$

With this restriction on α_1 and α_2, the solution to Eq. (3.157) is two pairs of imaginary roots, $\pm j\omega_1$ and $\pm j\omega_2$, where

$$0 < \omega_1 < 1 \qquad\qquad\qquad\qquad\qquad (3.159a)$$
$$1 < \omega_2 < 2 \qquad\qquad\qquad\qquad\qquad (3.159b)$$

In Ref. 3.7 α_1 and α_2 are given as functions of ω_1 and ω_2. If we let

$$\mathbf{y} = B\mathbf{\theta} \qquad\qquad\qquad\qquad\qquad (3.160)$$

where

$$B = \begin{bmatrix} \dfrac{\alpha_1}{\omega_1} & 0 & 0 & \dfrac{\omega_1(\omega_2{}^2 - 4\alpha_2)}{4\alpha_2(1 - \alpha_2)} \\[3mm] 0 & 1 & \dfrac{4\alpha_2 - \omega_2{}^2}{1 - \alpha_2} & 0 \\[3mm] 0 & \dfrac{\omega_2(\alpha_1 - \omega_1{}^2)}{\alpha_1(1 - \alpha_1)} & \dfrac{4\alpha_2}{\omega_2} & 0 \\[3mm] \dfrac{\omega_1{}^2 - \alpha_1}{1 - \alpha_1} & 0 & 0 & 1 \end{bmatrix} \qquad (3.161)$$

we get

$$\mathbf{y}' = \begin{bmatrix} 0 & \omega_1 & 0 & 0 \\ -\omega_1 & 0 & 0 & 0 \\ 0 & 0 & 0 & \omega_2 \\ 0 & 0 & -\omega_2 & 0 \end{bmatrix} \mathbf{y} + \begin{bmatrix} 0 & c_2 \\ 1 & 0 \\ c_1 & 0 \\ 0 & 1 \end{bmatrix} \mathbf{u} \qquad (3.162)$$

where $c_1 = \dfrac{\omega_2(\alpha_1 - \omega_1{}^2)}{\alpha_1(1 - \alpha_1)}$ $(3.163a)$

$$c_2 = \dfrac{\omega_1(4\alpha_2 - \omega_2{}^2)}{4\alpha_2(\alpha_2 - 1)} \qquad\qquad\qquad (3.163b)$$

The greater the value of c_1 and c_2, the stronger is the coupling between the roll and yaw motions.

    Two examples were investigated, one of strong and one of weak coupling, with the two sets of two differential equations of first order coupled essentially through the control vector $\mathbf{u}^T = (u_1, u_2)$. It is difficult at this point to guess a good switching function. Actually, this study was undertaken with the intent of minimizing the settling times, but it provides some guidance for a simpler control with a linear switching

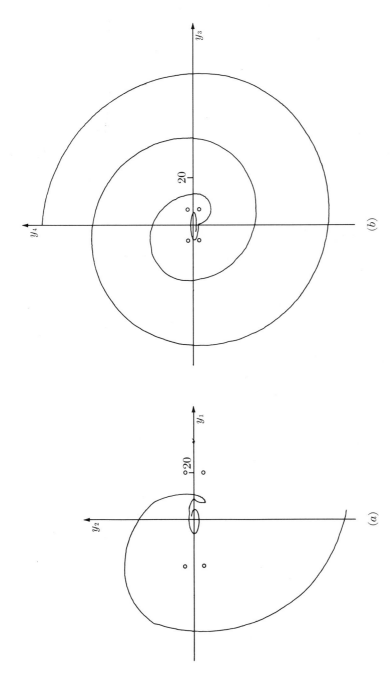

Fig. 3.34 Fourth-order plant with two control inputs. Example with strong coupling. (a) $y_1 y_2$ plane; (b) $y_3 y_4$ plane.

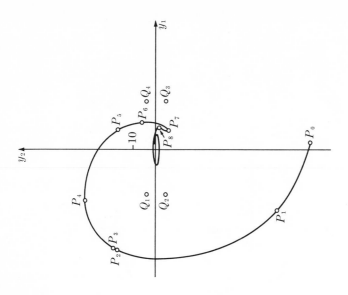

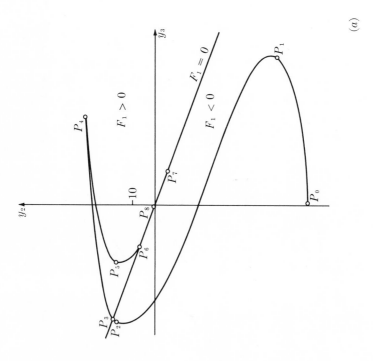

(a)

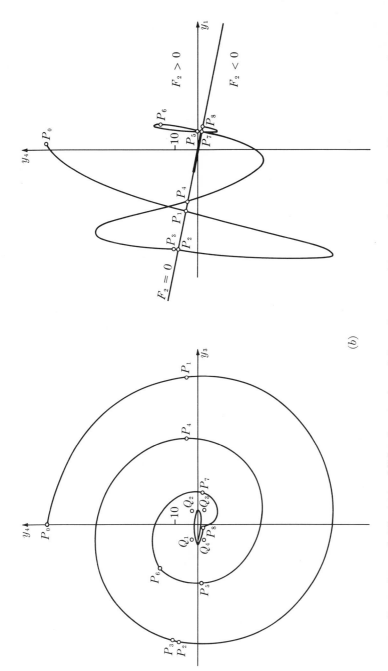

Fig. 3.35 Same plant as in Fig. 3.34; additional projections of the trajectory. (a) y_1y_2 and y_3y_2 planes; (b) y_3y_4 and y_1y_4 planes.

function F.   A suggestion was

$$u_1 = -N_1 \text{ sgn } (y_2 + c_1 y_3)$$
$$u_2 = -N_2 \text{ sgn } (y_4 + c_2 y_1)$$

(3.164)

The result of zeroing a disturbance is shown in Fig. 3.34; the construction of the two parts of this figure is clarified by Fig. 3.35.   Figure 3.36 shows the chatter behavior of the coupled switching functions.   It is to be expected (and the plots show it) that the switching functions of Eq. (3.164) are more effective at large than in the immediate neighborhood

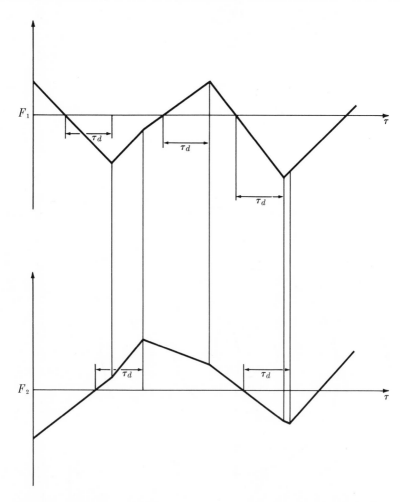

Fig. 3.36 The effect of the switching of one controller on the other switching function when both are chattering.

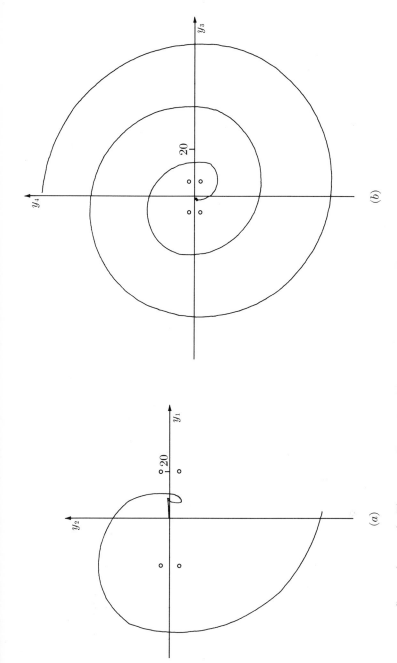

(a)

(b)

Fig. 3.37 Same plant as in Fig. 3.34. Example with strong coupling; reinforced damping in the chatter region. (a) y_1y_2 plane; (b) y_3y_4 plane.

153

of the space origin. Experience with second-order systems suggested

$$F_1 = y_2 + c_1 y_3 + m_1 y_1$$
$$F_2 = y_4 + c_2 y_1 + m_2 y_3$$

and these switching functions indeed improve the behavior near the origin, as Fig. 3.37 shows. For details of determining chatter region and decay of the average motion see Ref. 3.7.

One observation is interesting: With several control inputs that depend on linear switching functions it is possible to zero a disturbance in finite time. With one control input, strictly speaking, infinite time is needed to reach the finite small limit cycle around the origin. But with two or more chattering relays the motion will reach its final state when the system, with one relay chattering, reaches the chatter region of the next (see Ref. 3.7).

REFERENCES

3.1   Lass, Harry: *Elements of Pure and Applied Mathematics*, McGraw-Hill Book Company, New York, 1957.

3.2   Flügge-Lotz, I., and H. A. Titus, Jr.: Optimum and Quasi-optimum Control of Third-order Systems, *Stanford Univ. Div. Eng. Mechan. Tech. Rept.* 134, October, 1962.

3.3   Kurzweil, F., Jr.: The Analysis and Synthesis of Non-linear Continuous and Sampled-data Systems Involving Saturation, *Stanford Electron. Lab. Tech. Rept.* 2101-1, November, 1959.

3.4   Flügge, W.: *Handbook of Engineering Mechanics*, McGraw-Hill Book Company, New York, 1962.

3.5   Zadeh, L. A., and Charles A. Desoer: *Linear System Theory: The State Space Approach*, McGraw-Hill Book Company, New York, 1963.

3.6   Truxal, J. G.: *Automatic Feedback Control System Synthesis*, McGraw-Hill Book Company, New York, 1955.

3.7   Flügge-Lotz, I., and M. Maltz: Analysis of Chatter in Contactor Control Systems, with Applications to Dual-input Plants, *Stanford Univ. Dept. Aeron. Astronaut. Rept.* 155, June 1963. (An abbreviated version was published in *Automatica*, vol. 2, pp. 255–274, 1965.)

3.8   Flügge-Lotz, I., and A. Anton Frederickson, Jr.: Contactor Control of Higher Order Systems Whose Transfer Functions Contain Zeros, prepared for Boeing Airplane Company under Boeing Prime Contract AF33(600)-35030, *Stanford Univ. Div. Eng. Mechan. Tech. Rept.* 119, June 1959.

3.9   Flügge-Lotz, I.: Synthesis of Third-order Contactor Control Systems, *Proc. First Intern. Congr. Intern. Federation Autom. Control*, Moscow, 1960, vol. 1, pp. 390–397, Butterworth & Co. (Publishers), Ltd., London, 1961.

3.10 Flügge-Lotz, I., and T. Ishikawa: Investigation of Third-order Contactor Control Systems with Zeros in Their Transfer Functions, *NASA Tech. Note* D-719, January, 1961.

3.11 Alimov, Yu. I.: On the Application of Lyapunov's Direct Method to Differential Equations with Ambiguous Right Sides, *Automation Remote Control*, vol. 22, no. 7, pp. 713–725, December 1961.

3.12 Weissenberger, S.: Stability Analysis of Relay Control Systems Via the Direct Method of Lyapunov, presented at the Joint Automatic Control Conference, 1965, Rensselaer Polytechnic Institute, *J. Basic Eng., Trans. ASME, Ser. D*, pp. 419–428, June 1966.

3.13 Weissenberger, S.: Stability Analysis of Relay Control Systems Via the Direct Method of Lyapunov, *Stanford Univ. Dept. Aeron. Astronaut. Rept.* 222, March 1965. (This is a more detailed version of Ref. 3-12.)

3.14 Hamel, B.: Contribution à l'étude mathématique des systèmes de réglages par tout-ou-rien, *Serv. Tech. Aeron.*, CEMV 17, 1949, and Étude mathématique des systèmes à plusieurs degrés de liberté décrits par des équations linéaires avec un terme de commande discontinu, *Proc. J. Etudes Vibrations AERA, Paris*, 1950.

3.15 Zypkin, Ja. S.: *Theorie der Relaissysteme der automatischen Regelung*, translated from the Russian by W. Hahn and R. Herschel, R. Oldenbourg KG, Munich, 1958. (The name is often spelled Tsypkin in the English literature.)

3.16 Aizerman, M. A.: *Theory of Automatic Control*, chap. V, B, Pergamon Press, New York, 1963. (The original Russian version appeared in 1958.)

3.17 Gille, J. C., M. J. Pélegrin, and P. Decaulne: *Feedback Control Systems: Analysis, Synthesis and Design*, McGraw-Hill Book Company, New York, 1959.

3.18 Flügge-Lotz, I., and T. Ishikawa: Investigation of Third-order Contactor Control Systems with Two Complex Poles without Zeros, *NASA Tech. Note* D-428, 1960

3.19 Flügge-Lotz, I.: *Discontinuous Automatic Control*, Princeton University Press, Princeton, N.J., 1953.

3.20 Frederickson, A. A.: "Contactor Control of Higher Order Systems Whose Transfer Functions Contains Zeros," doctoral dissertation, Stanford University, Department of Electrical Engineering, Stanford, Calif., 1959.

3.21 DeBra, D. B., and R. H. Delp: Rigid Body Attitude Stability and Natural Frequencies in Circular Orbit, *J. Astronaut. Sci.*, vol. 8, no. 1, pp. 14–17, 1961.

4
Optimal control that leads to contactor control

4.1 INTRODUCTION

In many cases the major goal of a control-system design, such as reducing a disturbance of a system to zero, may be subject to further conditions, such as avoidance of an oscillatory state, avoidance of undershoot, or a time limit on zeroing the disturbance. The theory of linear systems with linear controls usually provided ample rules for accommodating such requests, many based on former experiences and some based on theoretical observations. About a decade ago in certain fields the idea arose of developing an exact formulation of the problem to include these parameters. For instance, a given system (plant) is to go from one well-defined state to another state either in minimum time or in a given time T, with minimum fuel consumption, and in both cases with bounded controls. These problems turned up in fields such as missile and satellite motion and automation of chemical processes. Soon it was discovered that the optimal control was in many cases a discontinuous control if the control effort was bounded, and as a result new emphasis was put on the study of relay controls.   Moreover, saturating amplifiers in linear control systems often caused a system to behave nearly like a relay system.   Since there was a willingness in other engineering fields as well to work at nonlinear problems, a totally new way of dealing with control problems emerged.

The following discussions provide derivation of the laws of optimal controls, followed by a number of interesting examples.   These derivations and applications of the theorems are intended primarily for practicing engineers; hence the treatment may not always satisfy the mathematician because it does not rigorously cover all possible cases.   In general, the most important cases are discussed and sources of further information are indicated.

4.2 FORMULATION OF OPTIMAL-CONTROL PROBLEMS

4.2.1 The main problem

Consider a system described by n variables, which may be called x^i, with $t = 1, 2, \ldots, n$, and controlled by control functions u^j, with $j = 1, 2, 3, \ldots, r$ and $r \leq n$.   Its behavior is determined by a set of first-order differential equations.   With vector notation we can write

$$\dot{x}^i = f^i(\mathbf{x}, \mathbf{u}) \tag{4.1}$$

where t denotes the time and the dot indicates differentiation with respect to time.   It is obvious that this is a special case of the more general problem

$$\dot{x}^i = f^i(\mathbf{x}, \mathbf{u}, t)$$

We shall treat systems which satisfy Eq. (4.1).[1]

If $\mathbf{u} = \mathbf{u}(t)$ is known and appropriate initial conditions are given, the system of Eq. (4.1) can be integrated in a unique way when the Lipschitz conditions are satisfied.[2]

---

[1] The treatment makes extensive use of an unpublished Air Force report AFOSR TN 1489 by I. Flügge-Lotz and H. Halkin, *Stanford Univ. Div. Eng. Mech. Rept.* 130, 1961.

[2] For the reader who is not familiar with Lipschitz conditions, the book *Ordinary Differential Equations* by G. Birkhoff and G.-C. Rota, Ginn and Company, Boston, 1962, is recommended as a reference.   Lipschitz conditions are concerned with the uniqueness of solutions of differential equations of first order.   Example: If $y' = F(x,y)$ and the Lipschitz condition

$$|F(x,y) - F(x,z)| \leq \mathfrak{L}|y - z|$$

with $\mathfrak{L}$ being a finite positive constant, is satisfied for all points (x,y) and (x,z) having the same x coordinate in a domain D, then a unique solution of the differential equation exists.

The problem under consideration is to select a particular vector function **u** belonging to a given class of functions in order to meet requirements which will be discussed later in detail.

This class of functions is specified by the particular problem. This specification usually takes the form that

$$\mathbf{u}(t) \in \Omega$$

if and only if (i) $\mathbf{u}(t)$ is piecewise continuous and (ii) $g_i(\mathbf{u}) \geq 0$, where $i = 1, \ldots, k$. For instance, if this condition is

$$\sum_{i=1}^{r} u^{i^2} \leq 1$$

Ω will be the unit hypersphere in U^r; if it is

$$|u^i| \leq 1 \qquad i = 1, \ldots, r$$

Ω will be the unit hypercube in U^r; etc. We assume that the initial value $\mathbf{x}(0) = \xi_1$ and the final value $\mathbf{x}(T) = \xi_2$ of the solution of system (4.1) are given. The final time T may be undetermined, may be determined in advance, or may be infinite.

The problem is to find a vector function $\mathbf{u}(t) \in \Omega$ such that (i) there exists a $T > 0$ for which the integration of Eq. (4.1) with the control $\mathbf{u}(t)$ and the initial condition $\xi_1 = \mathbf{x}(0)$ satisfies $\mathbf{x}(T) = \xi_2$, and (ii) a chosen performance criterion

$$\int_0^T f^0(\mathbf{x}, \mathbf{u}(t)) \, dt \tag{4.2}$$

is minimum.

Some particular examples of this performance criterion are as follows:

1. For the case $f^0(\mathbf{x}, \mathbf{u}(t)) = 1$ we shall have

$$\int_0^T f^0(\mathbf{x}, \mathbf{u}(t)) \, dt = T$$

That is, we shall require the process to take place in the minimum time.

2. In the more general case

$$\int_0^T f^0(\mathbf{x}, \mathbf{u}(t)) \, dt$$

can represent, for instance, the total energy consumption or the cost.

3. The particular problem for which T is fixed beforehand can be treated with this formulation by selecting a state variable x^{n*} for which

$$f^{n*} = 1$$
$$x^{n*}(0) = 0$$
$$x^{n*}(T) = T$$

For the general case, if we introduce the new function

$$x^0(t) = \int_0^t f^0(\mathbf{x},\mathbf{u}(t)) \, dt$$

we can add the differential equation

$$\dot{x}^0 = f^0(\mathbf{x},\mathbf{u}(t))$$

to system (4.1) to give the extended system

$$\dot{x}^i = f^i(\mathbf{x},\mathbf{u}(t)) \tag{4.3}$$

where $\mathbf{x} = (x^0, x^1, \ldots, x^n)$
$\quad \mathbf{f} = (f^0, f^1, \ldots, f^n)$
$\quad \mathbf{u} = (u^1, u^2, \ldots, u^r)$

We assume that the functions

$$f^i(\mathbf{x},\mathbf{u}(t)) \qquad i = 0, \ldots, n$$

are defined and are sufficiently differentiable for all

$$(\mathbf{x},\mathbf{u}) \in X^n U^r$$

Hence our problem is to find a function $\mathbf{u}(t) \in \Omega$ such that (i) there exist a $T > 0$ and an $x^0(T) = X^0$ for which the integration of Eq. (4.3) with the control $\mathbf{u}(t)$ and the initial condition $\mathbf{x}(0) = (0,\xi_1)$ satisfies

$$\mathbf{x}(T) = (X^0,\xi_2)$$

and (ii) $X^0 = \int_0^T f^0(\mathbf{x},\mathbf{u}(t)) \, dt$ is minimum.

4.2.2 Other problems

We have described one of the most frequently occurring optimal problems, and its solution will occupy us for some time. However, several other problems should be mentioned.

1. Consider a situation where ξ_1, ξ_2, and the performance criterion are given, but the time of performance is not specified. This problem may not always be well formulated. For instance, if a damped second-order system is to be guided from $\xi_1 \neq 0$ to $\xi_2 = 0$ with minimum fuel consumption $\int_0^T |u| \, dt$, we would conclude at once that $u \equiv 0$ and infinite time

are the optimal solution.[1] If the plant were undamped, the "open time" would lead to the absolute minimum fuel consumption instead of the relative minima associated with different desired performance times T_j.

2. With starting state ξ_1 a given point in the n-dimensional phase or state space, it may be desired to reach a certain $(n-1)$-dimensional surface in the n space in time T with a given performance criterion. This problem arises, for instance, in attempting to reduce a disturbance to a very small magnitude, such as a sphere around the state origin, but not to absolute zero. In fact, examples may show that the cost of reaching absolute zero, instead of a small value $\|\xi_2\|$, is quite great.

3. Another interesting problem arises in using a state-variable transformation in controlling a linear plant with zeros. In Sec. 2.1.2 the control system

$$\ddot{e} = b_1\dot{u} + u$$

was considered, and the state variables $e_1 = e$ and $e_2 = \dot{e}_1 - b_1u$ were introduced. If the desired final state is $e = \dot{e} = 0$, the desired final state in the new variables is

$$e_1 = 0$$
$$e_2 + b_1u = 0$$

For optimal control $u(t)$ must be found according to the desired performance criterion. The final state (if T is not fixed in advance) is $e_1 = 0$ and $e_2(t) = -b_1u(t)$, which in this case would be a portion of the e_2 axis (see later example). Hence the problem is similar to example 2; there is not a given endpoint, but the endpoint must be on a given manifold.

4.3 SOLUTION OF THE OPTIMAL-CONTROL PROBLEM: PONTRYAGIN'S MAXIMUM PRINCIPLE

4.3.1 Set of reachable events[2]

Let us consider the $(n+2)$-dimensional space TX^{n+1} of the points $(t, x^0, x^1, \ldots, x^n)$. A reachable event is a point of TX^{n+1} defined by a function $\mathbf{u}(t) \in \Omega$ and a value $\tau \geq 0$ in the following way:

$$t = \tau$$
$$x^i = \xi_1{}^i + \int_0^\tau f^i(\mathbf{x}, \mathbf{u}(t))\, dt \qquad i = 0, 1, \ldots, n$$

subject to the initial conditions $\mathbf{x}(0) = (0, \xi_1)$.

[1] The control is a scalar in this case.
[2] The application of this concept in control theory was introduced independently by E. Roxin (private communication). See also Ref. 4.1.

The set of all reachable points will be called $R(\xi_1)$. We shall assume this set to be dense everywhere and its boundary hypersurface to belong to $R(\xi_1)$. Let us call this boundary hypersurface $S(\xi_1)$.

Example

A system $\dot{x}^1 = u^2$ is to move with the condition

$$\int_0^t u^1 \, dt \to \min \tag{4.4}$$

where u^1 and u^2 are constants and $(u^1)^2 + (u^2)^2 \leq 1$. Thus

$$\dot{x}^0 = u^1 \tag{4.5}$$
$$\dot{x}^1 = u^2$$

where $\mathbf{u} \in \Omega <=> (u^1)^2 + (u^2)^2 \leq 1$
and $\mathbf{x}(0) = (0,0)$
that is, $x^0(0) = 0$ and $x^1(0) = 0$.

The set of reachable events $R(0)$ is here the set of points (t,x^0,x^1) such that

$$x^{0^2} + x^{1^2} \leq t^2 \tag{4.6}$$
$$t \geq 0$$

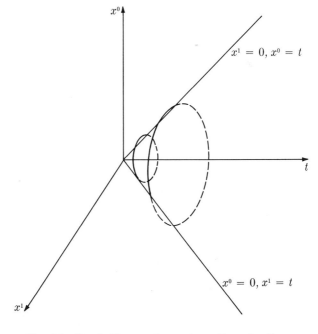

Fig. 4.1 Reachable events, system $\dot{x}^1 = u^2$. For performance criterion, see Eq. (4.4).

In other words $R(0)$ is the interior (including the surface) of the semicone of revolution around the t axis with the generatrix $x^0 = t$. The boundary hypersurface $S(0)$ is in this case the surface of this semicone (see Fig. 4.1).

4.3.2 Principle of optimal evolution

Let us call $G(\xi_1,\xi_2)$ the set of reachable events satisfying the end conditions. By definition, $G(\xi_1,\xi_2)$ is a subset of $R(\xi_1)$. More formally, this is equivalent to

$$G(\xi_1,\xi_2) = \{P: P \in R(\xi_1); (x^1,x^2, \ldots ,x^n)_P = \xi_2\}$$

We shall assume that A is the element of $G(\xi_1,\xi_2)$ with the smallest x^0.[1] We shall assume that such a point exists; in other words, that the infimum of $G(\xi_1,\xi_2)$ with respect to x^0 belongs to $G(\xi_1,\xi_2)$.

By definition, A is the endpoint of the optimal trajectory, and the function $\mathbf{u}(t)$ associated with this trajectory is the solution of our problem. We see immediately that, by definition, A belongs to the boundary hypersurface $S(\xi_1)$ of $R(\xi_1)$. (Proof by contradiction.)

Theorem I

Every event of the optimal trajectory belongs to $S(\xi_1)$.

The proof, by contradiction, is immediate.

This theorem constitutes what we call the *principle of optimal evolution*. In the next paragraph we shall express analytically the construction of trajectories belonging to $S(\xi_1)$.

Examples[2]

1. Returning to the example in Sec. 4.3.1, consider $G(0,a)$, where a is a given value of x^1, to be the set of all points to the right of the right branch of the hyperbola obtained by intersecting the semicone $R(0)$ by the plane $x^1 = a$ (Fig. 4.2). It is obvious that in such a case there is no point of $G(0,a)$ for which x^0 is minimum, so we conclude that this problem has no solution. If we had asked for the reachable events satisfying the end conditions in time T, however, we would have had a solution.

2. Consider the system

$$\begin{aligned}\dot{x}^0 &= u^1 + 1 \\ \dot{x}^1 &= u^2 + 1\end{aligned} \qquad (4.7)$$

---

[1] Remember that x^0 measures the performance.

[2] These examples may appear trivial; however, the author has found it rather difficult to insert more sophisticated examples. Their presentation becomes so difficult that a newcomer to the field would have trouble following them.

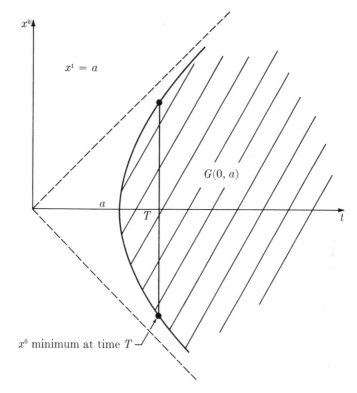

Fig. 4.2 Same system as in Fig. 4.1; x^0 as function of t for fixed $x^1 = a$.

where $\mathbf{u} \in \Omega <=> (u^1)^2 + (u^2)^2 \leq 1$ and u^1 and u^2 are constants. The boundary conditions are

$\xi_1 = 0 \quad$ [or $x^1(0) = 0$]
$\xi_2 = 1 \quad$ [or $x^1(T) = 1$]

The set of reachable events is defined by

$$(x^0 - t)^2 + (x^1 - t)^2 \leq t^2$$
$$t \geq 0 \tag{4.8}$$

that is, by a semicone situated entirely within the octan

$$t \geq 0 \qquad x^0 \geq 0 \qquad x^1 \geq 0$$

$G(0,1)$ is the set of events defined by

$$(x^0 - t)^2 + (1 - t)^2 \leq t^2$$
$$t \geq 0$$

These equations describe the parabola shown in Fig. 4.3.

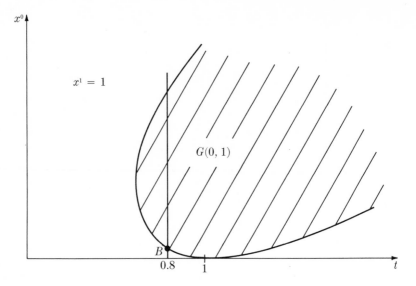

Fig. 4.3   System given by Eqs. (4.7); x^0 as function of t for $x^1 = 1$.

The absolute minimum value for x^0 is $x^0 = 0$, and we see that in this case

$$T = 1$$
$$u^1(t) \equiv -1$$
$$u^2(t) \equiv 0$$

If another value of T is chosen for reaching ξ_2, say $T = 0.8$, a minimum value of $x^0 \neq 0$ is obtained.   This value is marked by point B in Fig. 4.3.

4.3.3   Generalized Huygens' principle

The principle of optimal evolution is closely related to a problem in physics, namely, the propagation of an event happening at a particular point or region in space.   We are speaking of a wavefront to indicate to which parts of the space the event has proceeded in a certain time.   The form of the wavefront depends on the specific laws governing the particular physical problem.

In geometrical optics there is a simple construction based on Huygens' principle which gives the wavefront at $t + dt$ [that is, $W(t + dt)$] when the wavefront at t [that is, $W(t)$] is known (Ref. 4.2).   From every point of $W(t)$ a small circle of radius $c\,dt$, called a *wavelet*, is drawn, and the exterior envelope of the small circles is $W(t + dt)$ (see Fig. 4.4).

This is the procedure in the case of a homogeneous isotropic medium, where c is the light velocity, and the construction can be generalized to

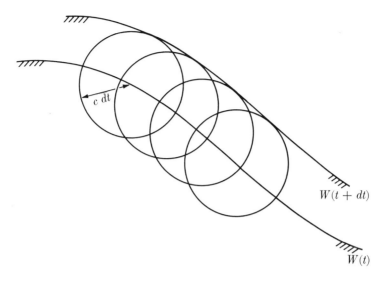

Fig. 4.4 Wavefronts (wavelets indicated).

the case where these wavelets are no longer circular, for instance, for propagation in a homogeneous anisotropic medium.

The extension to the case of wavelets that are connected, continuous, and differentiable has been studied extensively (theory of contact transformation, Hamilton-Jacobi partial differential equation, etc.; see Refs. 4.3 to 4.8). We shall generalize to the case of arbitrary wavelets, that is, wavelets for which the conditions of connectedness, continuity, and differentiability have been dropped.

Examples

1. Let us assume that the wavelet associated with the point A is the line segment BC (see Fig. 4.5). The construction of the new

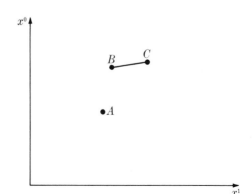

Fig. 4.5 Wavelet of special form, $\overline{BC}$ belonging to point A.

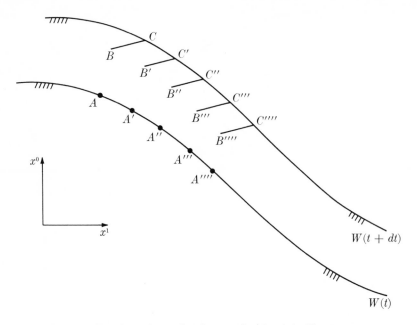

Fig. 4.6 Wavefront formation for wavelet shown in Fig. 4.5.

wavefront is described in Fig. 4.6. Starting with a wavefront
$A\ A'\ A''\ \ldots$, we obtain the new wavefront $C\ C'\ C''\ \ldots$.
2. Now let us assume that the wavelet associated with the point A
is represented by two points B and C (see Fig. 4.7). The construction of the new wavefront is described in Fig. 4.8. In this particular problem we can consider the intersection of the boundary hypersurface $S(\xi_1)$ by a hyperplane $t = \tau$ as a wavefront $W(\tau)$. Then the
wavefront $W(\tau + dt)$ can be constructed by the method described
above. In fact, this will allow us to construct the whole surface
$S(\xi_1)$ from the point $(0,\xi_1)$, which is the intersection of $S(\xi_1)$ by the
hyperplane $t = 0$.

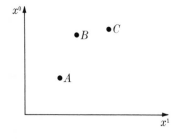

Fig. 4.7 Wavelet belonging to point A consists
of two points B and C.

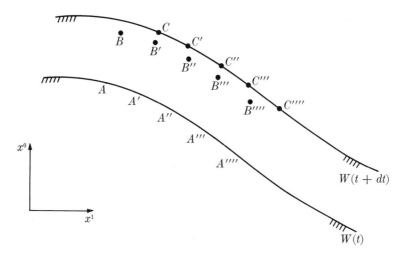

Fig. 4.8 Wavefront formation for wavelet shown in Fig. 4.7.

3. In Example 2 of Sec. 4.3.2 $W(\tau)$ is a circle in the plane (x^0, x^1) with center at (τ, τ) and a radius equal to τ (see Fig. 4.9). Let the wavelet corresponding to a point A be a circle of radius dt and center (dt, dt) relative to A (see Fig. 4.10). The construction of $W(\tau + dt)$ is given in Fig. 4.11. Usually this wavelet is drawn in a space $\dot{X}^n$ without the factor dt; it is then the mapping of Ω (set of allowable $\mathbf{u}$)

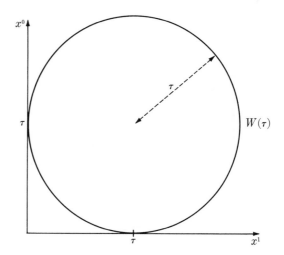

Fig. 4.9 Wavefront for system given by Eqs. (4.7).

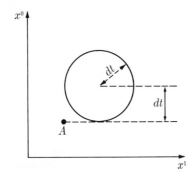

Fig. 4.10 Wavelet belonging to the system of Fig. 4.9.

into $\dot{X}^n$ by the relation

$$\dot{\mathbf{x}} = \mathbf{f}(\mathbf{x},\mathbf{u})$$

The system under discussion is described by the differential equations

$$\begin{aligned}\dot{x}^0 &= u^1 + 1 \\ \dot{x}^1 &= u^2 + 1\end{aligned} \qquad \mathbf{u} \in \Omega <=> (u^1)^2 + (u^2)^2 \leq 1 \qquad (4.9)$$

Thus a circle in the $u^1 u^2$ plane (Fig. 4.12) is mapped into a circle in the $\dot{x}^0 \dot{x}^1$ plane (Fig. 4.13).

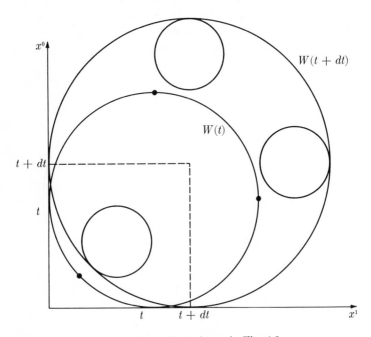

Fig. 4.11 Propagation of wavefront shown in Fig. 4.9.

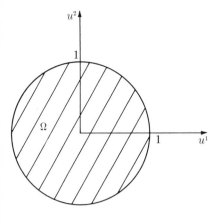

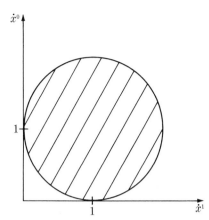

Fig. 4.12 Allowable set of control components for the system given by Eqs. (4.7).

Fig. 4.13 Mapping of the set Ω shown in Fig. 4.12 into the $\dot{x}^0\dot{x}^1$ plane.

In general, the wavelet will vary with x, but since we have assumed that the functions $f^k(\mathbf{x},\mathbf{u})$ are sufficiently differentiable in x^i and u^j, successive construction of wavefronts $W(t)$ is always possible.

4.3.4 Analytic formulation of the principle of optimal evolution

In Fig. 4.14, let A be a point of $W(t)$, where $W(t)$ is differentiable and $\mathbf{p}$ is the *normal* to $W(t)$. Then we must determine the value of $\mathbf{u}$ by which the point A will be transferred to a point B of $W(t + dt)$. If we define $H(\mathbf{x},\mathbf{p},\mathbf{u}) = \langle \mathbf{p} \mid \mathbf{f}(\mathbf{x},\mathbf{u}) \rangle$, that is, as the scalar product of $\mathbf{p}$ and $\mathbf{f}$, then the appropriate control function $\mathbf{u}$ is determined by[1]

$$\mathbf{u}(\mathbf{x},\mathbf{p}) = \operatorname*{argmax}_{u\in\Omega} H(\mathbf{x},\mathbf{p},\mathbf{u}) \tag{4.10}$$

In other words, the point $A \in W(t)$ will be transferred into a point $B \in W(t + dt)$ if and only if we choose the control $\mathbf{u}$ for which $H(\mathbf{x},\mathbf{p},\mathbf{u})$ is maximum.

As justification, we see immediately from Fig. 4.14 that $B \in W(t + dt)$ is the point corresponding to $\max \langle \mathbf{p} \mid \mathbf{f}(\mathbf{x},\mathbf{u}) \rangle$ and that to a C not on $W(t + dt)$ there corresponds a $\mathbf{u}^*$ such that

$$\langle \mathbf{p} \mid \mathbf{f}(\mathbf{x},\mathbf{u}^*) \rangle < \langle \mathbf{p} \mid \mathbf{f}(\mathbf{x},\mathbf{u}) \rangle$$

For the time being, we shall assume that condition (4.10) determines one and only one $\mathbf{u}$.

---

[1] We define the symbol argmax as $X = \operatorname*{argmax}_{x\in\Xi} f(x)$ if and only if $f(X) = \operatorname*{max}_{x\in\Xi} f(x)$.

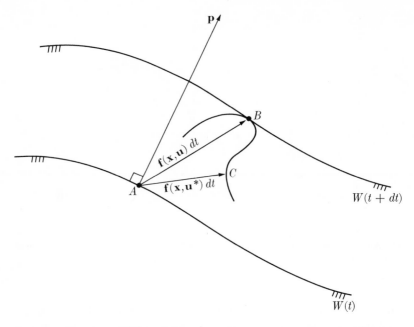

Fig. 4.14   Wavefront $W(t)$ and its propagation; $\mathbf{p}$ = normal to wavefront in point A.

Theorem II

If there exists a control $\mathbf{u}(t)$ transferring $A \in W(t)$ into $B \in W(t + h)$ and $C \in W(t + h + k)$, where h and $k > 0$, then the topology of $W(t + h)$ at B is greater than or equal to the topology of $W(t)$ at A.

The topology of a wavefront W at a point P is defined as the set of properties (such as existence, continuity, or differentiability) of W in the neighborhood of P.   The topology at B is said to be greater than or equal to the topology at A if all such properties of $W(t)$ at A are also properties of $W(t + h)$ at B.

The validity of Theorem II is easily checked in the previous examples.   Its practical importance will be discussed in Sec. 4.3.10.

Corollary

If $W^*(t + dt)$ is the hypersurface obtained from $W(t)$ by using for all its points the same control $\mathbf{u}$ that transfers $A \in W(t)$ into $B \in W(t + dt)$ (see Fig. 4.15), then, by definition, $W^*(t + dt)$ and $W(t + dt)$ intersect at the point B, and by Theorem II, $W^*(t + dt)$ and $W(t + dt)$ are even tangent at the point B.   In particular, if $W(t)$ admits a normal

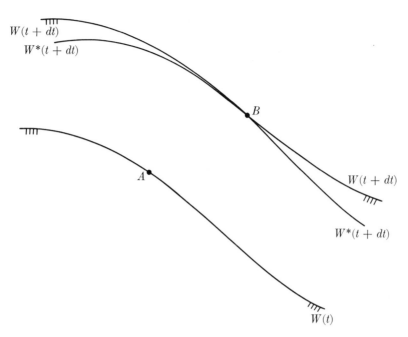

Fig. 4.15   Illustration of Theorem II and Corollary II.

$\mathbf{p}(A)$ at A, then, by definition, $W^*(t + dt)$ also admits a normal $\mathbf{p}(B)$ at B.   Moreover, $W(t + dt)$ will also have a normal $\mathbf{p}(B)$ at B.

4.3.5   Generalized hamiltonian formulation

The results obtained in Sec. 4.3.4 allow us to construct a trajectory belonging to $S(\xi_1)$ if we know the $\mathbf{p}$ normal to $W(t)$ for all points of the trajectory.   Hence we shall now establish a system of differential equations for $\mathbf{p}$.

Let us define

$$\begin{aligned}
\langle \mathbf{p} \mid (\delta\mathbf{x})_i \rangle &= 0 \qquad i = 1, 2, \ldots, n \\
\langle \mathbf{p} \mid (\delta\mathbf{x})_0 \rangle &= -1
\end{aligned} \tag{4.11}$$

where the $(\delta\mathbf{x})_i$ are n independent vectors tangent to $W(t)$ at point A and $(\delta\mathbf{x})_0$ is an arbitrary vector independent of the $(\delta\mathbf{x})_i$ and directed toward the inside of $W(t)$.[1]   We shall choose the same control vector for the

---

[1] These new independent vectors are chosen for mere convenience.   It is much easier to express the normal to the wavefront with their help than with vector components Δx^i which would be parallel to the coordinate axes.   Since we know the change of x^i with time $[\dot{x}^i = f^i(\mathbf{x}, \mathbf{u})]$, we can obtain the change of Δx^i by linearization of that equation.   This will allow us to compute $(\delta\mathbf{x})_i$ easily.

point $\mathbf{x}$ and for all the $n + 1$ points $\mathbf{x} + (\delta\mathbf{x})_i$, with $i = 0, 1, 2, \ldots, n$, which we shall assume to be in the neighborhood of $\mathbf{x}$.

We shall require the invariance along a trajectory of relations (4.11). In virtue of the preceding corollary, we have[1]

$$\langle \mathbf{p} \mid (\delta\mathbf{x})_i \rangle^{\cdot} = 0 \qquad i = 0, 1, 2, \ldots, n$$

That is, $\langle \dot{\mathbf{p}} \mid (\delta\mathbf{x})_i \rangle + \langle \mathbf{p} \mid (\delta\mathbf{x})_i^{\cdot} \rangle = 0$

But $(\delta\mathbf{x})_i^{\cdot} = A(\delta\mathbf{x})_i$

where $A_{jk} = \dfrac{\partial f^j}{\partial x^k}$

Hence $\langle \dot{\mathbf{p}} \mid (\delta\mathbf{x})_i \rangle + \langle \mathbf{p} \mid A(\delta\mathbf{x})_i \rangle = 0$

or $\qquad \langle \dot{\mathbf{p}} \mid (\delta\mathbf{x})_i \rangle + \langle \tilde{A}\mathbf{p} \mid (\delta\mathbf{x})_i \rangle = 0$

where $\tilde{A}$ is the transpose of A, a real matrix. Hence

$$\langle \dot{\mathbf{p}} + \tilde{A}\mathbf{p} \mid (\delta\mathbf{x})_i \rangle = 0 \qquad i = 0, 1, \ldots, n$$

that is, $\qquad \dot{\mathbf{p}} + \tilde{A}\mathbf{p} = 0$

since the $(\delta\mathbf{x})_i$ are $n + 1$ independent vectors in the space X^{n+1}. Therefore

$$\dot{\mathbf{p}} = -\tilde{A}\mathbf{p} \tag{4.12}$$

This last relation can be written in the form

$$\dot{p}_i = -\sum_j \tilde{A}_{ij} p_j$$

But $\quad \tilde{A}_{ij} = A_{ji} = \dfrac{\partial f^j}{\partial x^i}$

Hence $\quad \dot{p}_i = -\sum_j \dfrac{\partial f^j}{\partial x^i} p_j$

If we define

$$H(\mathbf{x},\mathbf{p},\mathbf{u}) = \langle \mathbf{p} \mid \mathbf{f}(\mathbf{x},\mathbf{u}) \rangle = \sum_i p_i f^i(\mathbf{x},\mathbf{u})$$

we see that

$$\dot{x}^i = f^i(\mathbf{x},\mathbf{u})$$

is strictly equivalent to

$$\dot{x}^i = \frac{\partial H(\mathbf{x},\mathbf{p},\mathbf{u})}{\partial p_i}$$

and that $\dot{p}^i = -\sum_j \dfrac{\partial f^j}{\partial x^i} p_j$

---

[1] The dot indicates differentiation with respect to time.

is strictly equivalent to

$$\dot{p}_i = - \frac{\partial H(\mathbf{x},\mathbf{p},\mathbf{u})}{\partial x^i}$$

The complete integration along a trajectory on $S(\xi_1)$, that is, the integration of the state variable and its associated normal, is given by

$$\dot{x}^i = \frac{\partial H(\mathbf{x},\mathbf{p},\mathbf{u})}{\partial p_i}$$

$$\dot{p}_i = - \frac{\partial H(\mathbf{x},\mathbf{p},\mathbf{u})}{\partial x^i} \qquad (4.13)$$

$$\mathbf{u} = \underset{u\in\Omega}{\mathrm{argmax}}\, H(\mathbf{x},\mathbf{p},\mathbf{u})$$

The components p_i of the normal to the wavefront are mostly called the *adjoint* variables of the controlled system.

The results given in Eqs. (4.13) form what is known as *Pontryagin's maximum principle*.

4.3.6 Pontryagin's maximum principle

The derivation just developed is a geometric interpretation of the vector function $\mathbf{p}$ introduced by Pontryagin et al. in formulating the maximum principle. This interpretation of $\mathbf{p}$ as the normal to the boundary hypersurface $S(\xi_1)$ of the set of reachable events $R(\xi_1)$ allows us to overcome, with the help of Theorem II, most of the difficulties that arise in applying the maximum principle to a particular problem. These difficulties are generally of two natures:

1. How to choose the initial value of the vector function $\mathbf{p}$, that is, $\mathbf{p}(0)$
2. What is to be done when the relation

$$\mathbf{u} = \underset{u\in\Omega}{\mathrm{argmax}}\, H(\mathbf{x},\mathbf{p},\mathbf{u})$$

does not determine a unique value for $\mathbf{u}$

The value of the geometric interpretation in resolving these questions will be shown in Sec. 4.3.9 on synthesis of the solution.

4.3.7 Control with nonzero inertia

In the general formulation of the problem in Sec. 4.2.1 we defined $\mathbf{u}(t)$ to belong to the class Ω only if $\mathbf{u}(t)$ is piecewise continuous and $g_i(\mathbf{u}) \geq 0$, with $i = 1, \ldots, k$; that is, if $\mathbf{u} \in \Omega$. For some problems, however, the restriction that $\mathbf{u}(t)$ be piecewise continuous is not strong enough. The rate of change of the control itself may be bounded (for instance, for control devices with nonzero inertia), and this condition should be reinforced to read "$u_i(t)$ is continuous and $\dot{u}_i(t) \leq M$." From the theoretical standpoint it is very easy to transform a problem with such a reinforced condition into a new problem with usual condition for $\mathbf{u}(t)$.

Example

If $u_i(t)$ is to be continuous with $\dot{u}_i(t) \leq M$, we must replace $u_i(t)$ by a new control variable $u_k(t)$ and consider $u_i(t)$ as a new state variable with the associated differential equation

$$\dot{u}_i(t) = u_k(t)$$

4.3.8 Chattering

To ensure that the solution proposed in Sec. 4.3.5 satisfies the requirements expressed in the general formulation of the problem, we must still check that the control function $\mathbf{u}(t)$ obtained by this method belongs to Ω, or that $\mathbf{u}(t)$ is piecewise continuous and $\mathbf{u} \in \Omega$.

The condition $\mathbf{u} \in \Omega$ is satisfied by construction, but it may happen that the condition of piecewise continuity is not. In this event the control function given by Pontryagin's maximum principle is an oscillating function of infinite frequency characterized only by its mean value, and the problem has no solution, mathematically speaking. It corresponds to a variational problem with a bounded minimizing sequence whose infimum does not belong to the sequence.

Example

Find the shortest continuous and differentiable curve joining two given points A and B of a plane such that the tangents to the curve at A and B have given directions, at least one of which is different from $\overline{AB}$.

From a practical standpoint such a pseudo solution is not without interest: it gives the infimum of $x^0(T)$, a value perhaps impossible to actually attain but which can be approached increasingly from above. When such a case arises in a specific problem, the problem must be reformulated, and the reinforced condition for $\mathbf{u}(t)$ given in Sec. 4.3.7 must be used.

4.3.9 Synthesis of the solution

4.3.9a *Special cases of wavefronts.* The maximum principle leads to a solution which is a relatively strong minimum but not necessarily an absolute strong minimum. For example, the two points A and B of $W(t)$ (see Fig. 4.16), which are not in the same neighborhood on $W(t)$, can be transferred to the same point C of $W(t + dt)$ (see Fig. 4.17). The

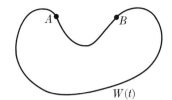

Fig. 4.16 Wavefront $W(t)$ of particular character.

trajectory t passing through point D, for instance, will give a relatively strong minimum but not an absolute strong minimum.[1]   In the following developments we shall assume that such cases do not arise.

The next problem is to analyze the situation at a point A of $W(t)$, where $W(t)$ is not differentiable.

Example

Consider the wavefront of Fig. 4.18 and its corresponding wavelet in Fig. 4.19.   In such a case the maximum principle applied to P_L will give the control vector corresponding to point B; applied to P_R it will give the control vector corresponding to point C.

We see immediately that a control vector corresponding to any point D on the boundary of the wavelet between B and C will also transfer point A to $W(t + dt)$.   Hence the transformation of $W(t)$ into $W(t + dt)$ is not pointwise one to one.

[1] For example,

$$\dot{x}^1 = u^1(\sin^2 x^1 + \sin^2 x^2)$$
$$\dot{x}^2 = u^2(\sin^2 x^1 + \sin^2 x^2)$$

where $\mathbf{u} \in \Omega <=> (u^1)^2 + (u^2)^2 \leq 1$.

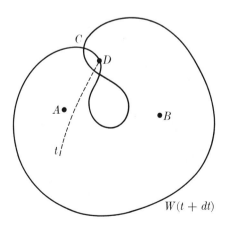

Fig. 4.17 Propagation of wavefront shown in Fig. 4.16.

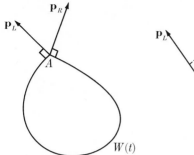

Fig. 4.18 Wavefront which is not differentiable at point A.

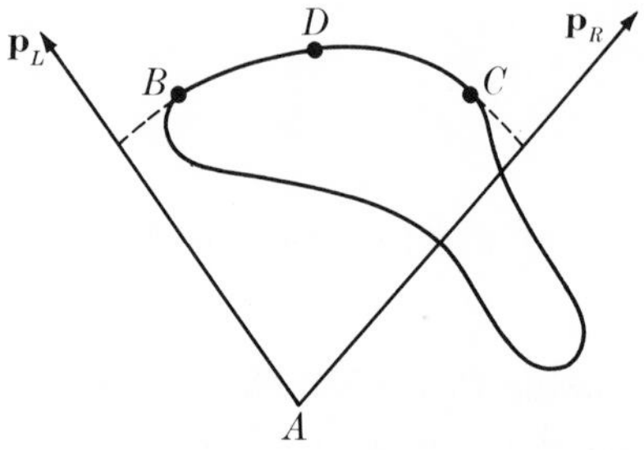

Fig. 4.19 Propagation at point A of Fig. 4.18.

Such a problem can also arise in the case of a differentiable wavefront at A if the relation

$$\mathbf{u} = \operatorname*{argmax}_{u \in \Omega} H(\mathbf{x}, \mathbf{p}, \mathbf{u})$$

does not determine a unique control $\mathbf{u}$.

Example

Consider the wavefront of Fig. 4.20 and wavelet at A of Fig. 4.21. In this case the controls corresponding respectively to B and C will both transfer A into $W(t + dt)$.

4.3.9*b* *Special behavior of trajectories.* If we consider the set of trajectories obtained by choosing all possible values of $\mathbf{p}(0)$ and all possi-

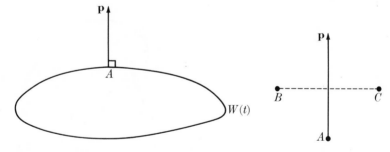

Fig. 4.20 Wavefront.

Fig. 4.21 Wavelet shape at point A of Fig. 4.20, which transfers point A into two points B and C.

Fig. 4.22 Behavior of trajectories; branching points.

ble values of the control vector satisfying the maximum principle, we obtain a generalized field of trajectories corresponding to the set of all rays in geometric optics.   This generalized field may contain

1. Branching points (see Fig. 4.22)
2. Disparition points (see Fig. 4.23)
3. Indifference regions

That is, the field may contain a subset of X^{n+1}, where all trajectories passing through all its points and corresponding to all possible controls belong to the generalized field.

Example

$\dot{x}^0 = 1$
$\dot{x}^1 = u$

with $x^1(0) = 0$

and $|u| \leq 1 <=> u \in \Omega$

It is easy to see that the wavefront $W(t)$ is determined by

$x^0(t) = t$
$|x^1(t)| \leq t$

(see Fig. 4.24) and that if $A \in W(t)$, any $|u| \leq 1$ will transfer A to $W(t + dt)$.

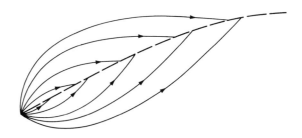

Fig. 4.23 Behavior of trajectories; disparition points.

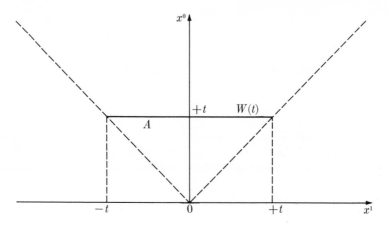

Fig. 4.24 Behavior of trajectories; indifference regions.

4.3.10 Embedding method

We now turn to a general method for avoiding the difficulties that arise with a nondifferentiable wavefront. In the formulation given earlier the wavefront at $t = 0$ [that is, $W(0)$] is reduced to the single point $(0,\xi_1)$. Let us now assume that $\bar{W}(0)$ is an n-dimensional circular manifold[1] of center $(0,\xi_1)$ and radius ϵ, with ϵ a small positive quantity. The orientation of this $\bar{W}(0)$ is completely determined by its normal $\mathbf{p}(0)$. By applying the maximum principle to this new starting wavefront $\bar{W}(0)$ we may obtain $\bar{W}(t)$ for any $t \geq 0$. From Theorem II (see Sec. 4.3.4), we know that $\bar{W}(t)$ is differentiable at A, a point of $\bar{W}(t)$ corresponding to point $(0,\xi_1)$ of $\bar{W}(0)$.

In general, trajectories comprising the set of points of $\bar{W}(t)$ corresponding to $(0,\xi_1)$ of $\bar{W}(0)$ for all $t \geq 0$ will belong to the generalized field defined in Sec. 4.3.9b, and the whole field will be the set of all such trajectories corresponding to all possible choices of $\bar{W}(0)$ [that is, of $\mathbf{p}(0)$]. This method gives a good interpretation of the initial choice of $\mathbf{p}(0)$, and

---

[1] By an n-dimensional circular manifold of center $(0,\xi_1) = y^0, y^1, \ldots, y^n$ and of radius ϵ in the space X^{n+1}, we mean the set of points such that

$$\sum_{i=0}^{n} p_i(x^i - y^i) = 0$$

$$\sum_{i=0}^{n} (x^i - y^i)^2 \leq \epsilon^2$$

where the vector $\mathbf{p}$ is the characteristic orientation of the manifold. For example, if $n = 2$, the circular manifold is an ordinary circular disk of radius ϵ.

its application will greatly facilitate the solution of most practical problems.

4.3.11 Singular controls

Examples of optimal controls will be treated in Sec. 4.4. Example 4.4.2 will show the reader a particular difficulty, which may occur when looking for the extremum of the hamiltonian: Maximizing the hamiltonian may not provide us with a well-defined expression for the optimal control, especially if the hamiltonian is a linear function of the control function $u(t)$ or of its absolute value $|u(t)|$. For a detailed treatment the reader is referred to secs. 6.22 and 6.23 in Ref. 4.9 and also to Ref. 4.10. In this section only a short description of the difficulty will be given (singular controls are in general not discontinuous controls of the simple bang-bang or coast type).

For a time-invariant system

$$\dot{\mathbf{x}}(t) = \mathbf{f}[\mathbf{x}(t)] + \mathbf{b}[\mathbf{x}(t)]u(t) \tag{4.14}$$

with $|u(t)| \leq 1$ for all $t > 0$, and the initial state $\mathbf{x}(0) = \xi_1$ and the final state $\mathbf{x}_f = 0$, the cost functional may be

$$J(\mathbf{x},u) = \int_0^T \{f^0[\mathbf{x}(t)] + b^0[\mathbf{x}(t)]u(t)\} \, dt \tag{4.15}$$

The hamiltonian is given by

$$H = \sum_{i=0}^n f^i p_i + u \sum_{i=0}^n b^i p_i \tag{4.16}$$

The hamiltonian is linear in u. The equations for the adjoint variables p_i are given by

$$\dot{p}_i = -\frac{\partial H}{\partial x^i} = -\sum_{j=0}^n p_j \frac{\partial f^j}{\partial x^i} - u \sum_{j=0}^n p_j \frac{\partial b^j[\mathbf{x}(t)]}{\partial x^i} \qquad i = 0,1,2, \ldots ,n \tag{4.17}$$

Maximizing Eq. (4.16) we obtain

$$u(t) = + \operatorname{sgn} \left\{ \sum_{i=0}^n b^i[\mathbf{x}(t)]p_i(t) \right\} \tag{4.18}$$

As long as $\Sigma b^i p_i \neq 0$, the control function $u(t)$ is defined. However, if there should be finite time intervals for which $\Sigma b^i p_i = 0$, then Eq. (4.16) does not give information about the behavior of $u(t)$.

If we consider the same time-invariant system, but the cost functional

$$J(u) = \int_0^T \{f^0[\mathbf{x}(t)] + b^0[\mathbf{x}(t)]|u(t)|\} \, dt \tag{4.19}$$

the problem is somewhat more difficult.   In this case $u(t)$ is given by a function often called *coast function*.

$$
u(t) = \begin{cases} \text{sgn} \left\{ \sum_{i=0}^{n} b^i[\mathbf{x}(t)]p_i(t) \right\} & \text{for } |\{\cdots\}| \geq 1 \\ 0 & \text{for } -1 < \{\cdots\} < +1 \end{cases}
\tag{4.20}
$$

If the expression in braces should be equal to $+1$ or -1 for a finite time interval, one would again not get information about $u(t)$ in this interval.

4.3.12 Concluding remarks concerning optimal control

There are, of course, other methods of deriving optimal-control laws (see Refs. 4.11 to 4.13).   Note that the ordinary calculus of variations is not among them; a close look at an essential peculiarity of this problem will indicate some possible difficulties with this method.   If the control vector or control variable is only piecewise continuous and is limited in magnitude, we cannot admit arbitrary variations around the optimal phase-point trajectory, and hence we cannot be sure that the minimum of the performance criterion $I(x,u)$ is given by differentiation. Figure 4.3 shows a good example.

At this time we may return briefly to the difficulties posed by some design missions.   For instance, recall problem 2 in Sec. 4.2.2, where the final state is described as a point (unknown) lying on a given $(n-1)$st-order surface.   The wavefront must finally come in contact with this $(n-1)$-dimensional surface, which means that at the contact point (if there is a unique solution) the normal to the wavefront must coincide with the normal of the final surface (transversality condition).   An important question here, as in a problem of type 3 in Sec. 4.2.2, is whether the final state is stable or whether an additional control $\bar{u}(t)$ must be designed for $t > T$ to keep the phase point in this desired position.   This same problem will turn up in the examples treated in Secs. 5.2.5 and 5.2.6.

A problem not treated here is the optimal control of systems with bounded phase or state variables.   This problem is treated in chap. VI of Ref. 4.11.   Imagine that the phase variables of a second-order plant are restricted by the conditions[1]

$$
|x^1| \leq |x_b^1| \qquad \text{and} \qquad |x^2| \leq |x_b^2|
$$

If we compute the optimal control for a given performance criterion without taking care of these restrictions, we may find that the phase trajectory hits the boundary S_b in a certain point.   Then we face the problem of what control to apply that will observe the performance criterion and never transgress the given boundary.   This problem is

---

[1] A very simple example is the controlled landing of an airplane.   It starts at the initial point $P_i(x^1,x^2)$ and is supposed to reach the point $P_f = (0,0)$ without ever passing through points with negative altitude x^2 because $x^2 \equiv 0$ represents the solid ground of the landing strip.

studied in principle; however, applying the rules (the so-called jump conditions) is not very easy because in general we do not know in advance how often the hypersurface S_b of at most $(n - 1)$ order is hit in a problem of nth order.

There is an interesting possibility of avoiding this difficulty by modifying the performance criterion and forcing the trajectory to practically stay in the bounded region. For instance, if the performance criterion

$$J = \int_0^T f^0(\mathbf{x},\mathbf{u}(t))\, dt \rightarrow \text{minimum}$$

is desired, we replace it by

$$J = \int_0^T \{\psi(\mathbf{x}) + f^0(\mathbf{x},\mathbf{u}(t))\}\, dt \rightarrow \text{minimum}$$

This function ψ (often called a "penalty" function) may be a function of the state variables which is practically zero in the interior of the hypersurface S_b that bounds the region of the restricted state variables and increases rapidly to very high values outside this region. Figure 4.25

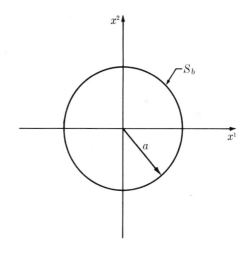

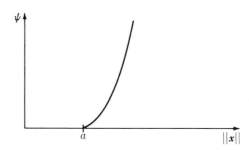

Fig. 4.25 Optimal control with bounded state variables; S_b = boundary; ψ = penalty function.

shows an example for a second-order plant; Ref. 4.14 contains examples of synthesis of such controls for a sixth-order plant (attitude control of a satellite).

4.4 SIMPLE EXAMPLES OF OPTIMAL CONTROL

Let us now apply these geometric and analytic considerations to some simple systems.

4.4.1 Time-optimal control

The system[1] is

$$\ddot{x}(t) = u(t) \tag{4.21}$$

with an initial state given by x_0 and $\dot{x}_0$ and a final state given by $x_f = 0$ and $\dot{x}_f = 0$. It is desired to reach the final state in minimum time. That is,

$$I = \int_0^T |dt| = T \to \min \tag{4.22}$$

where $|u| \leq 1$ \hfill (4.23)

First we replace the second-order system by a system of two first-order differential equations,

$$\dot{x}_1 = x_2 \tag{4.24}$$
$$\dot{x}_2 = u$$

and add $\dot{x}_0 = 1$ as a differential equation which measures the performance. The hamiltonian is given by

$$H = \sum_0^2 p_i f_i = p_0 1 + p_1 x_2 + p_2 u \tag{4.25}$$

The equations for the adjoints are

$$\dot{p}_0 = -\frac{\partial H}{\partial x_0} = 0$$

which yields $p_0 = $ const, and

$$\dot{p}_1 = -\frac{\partial H}{\partial x_1} = 0 \to p_1 = p_{10}$$
$$\dot{p}_2 = -\frac{\partial H}{\partial x_2} = -p_{10} \to p_2 = -p_{10}t + p_{20} \tag{4.26}$$

The magnitude of p_0 does not influence the process of maximizing H by a choice of $u(t)$. We see immediately that H will be kept at its largest value at each instant t by a choice of $u = \operatorname{sgn} p_2(t)$. In this case the term

[1] This system was considered in Sec. 2.1.1.

p_2u is always positive and as large as possible; it is added to the value $p_0 1 + p_1 x_2$. The relation

$$u = \text{sgn}\ (-p_{10}t + p_{20}) \tag{4.27}$$

indicates that as soon as p_{10} and p_{20} are found, there is at most one value of t_s in which u jumps from 1 to -1 or vice versa. Hence the time-optimal control is a discontinuous (relay) control.

The next step is to determine p_{10} and p_{20} such that the system

$$\dot{x}_1 = x_2$$
$$\dot{x}_2 = u$$

satisfies the given initial and final conditions. One way would be to establish equations for the two possible portions of the trajectory, specifying the switching instance t_s and solving for t_s and u_0 (the value of the control in the first portion if there are two portions). But a geometric consideration allows us to avoid this tedious procedure. Since the final point is the origin of the $x_1 x_2$ system, the final portion of the trajectory must be a portion of the zero trajectory. Figure 4.26 shows that there

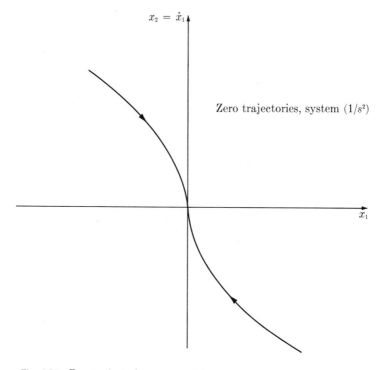

Zero trajectories, system $(1/s^2)$

Fig. 4.26 Zero trajectories; system $1/s^2$.

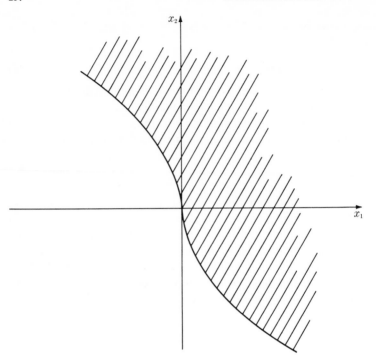

Fig. 4.27   Time-optimal control for system $1/s^2$; $u = -1$ in shaded region.

are two parabolic branches which lead to the origin, one in the fourth and one in the second quadrant. From this we conclude that if the initial point $\mathbf{x}(0)$ does not lie incidentally on one of those branches, then the switching point must lie on them. If the initial point lies on a zero trajectory, then $p_{10} = 0$. Figure 2.16f showed a phase trajectory starting in P_i and reaching the origin after switching on the zero trajectory.

The geometric consideration immediately gives the locus of all possible switching points and therefore allows the immediate design of a feedback control. If the initial point lies in the shaded region of Fig. 4.27, the motion starts with $u_0 = -1$ and switches to $u_1 = 1$ at the switching line (composed of two parabola branches); if the motion starts in the unshaded region, the process starts with $u_0 = 1$. This control can be realized in different ways. We can compare the value x_{20} with the x_2 of the switching line at x_{10} and then decide on u; or we can construct a screen which provides a visual indication of whether the initial point is in the shaded or unshaded area.

4.4.2 Minimum-fuel control

Consider the same plant, but with a performance criterion

$$I = \int_0^T |u|\, dt \qquad |u| \leq 1$$

The initial error and error derivative of the disturbed system is to be reduced to zero in a given time T with a minimum control cost. It is assumed that the cost of the control action is proportional to $|u|$ (for example, control by cold gas jets). The system and its hamiltonian are described by

$$\begin{aligned}
\dot{x}_0 &= |u| \\
\dot{x}_1 &= x_2 \\
\dot{x}_2 &= u \\
\dot{x}_3 &= 1 \qquad \text{with } x_3(0) = 0,\; x_{3_f} = T \\
H &= p_0|u| + p_1 x_2 + p_2 u + p_3 \cdot 1
\end{aligned} \qquad (4.28)$$

The adjoint function $\mathbf{p}^T = (p_0, p_1, p_2, p_3)$ has $\dot{p}_0 = 0$, as expected, hence $p_0 = \text{const.}$ In agreement with the geometric interpretation of our problem, the adjoint component $p_0(T)$, or p_0 at the final time T, must be negative or zero. A choice of zero is impossible because it would remove the influence of the performance criterion from the hamiltonian. Since the differential equations for all p_i

$$\begin{aligned}
\dot{p}_1 &= -\frac{\partial H}{\partial x_1} = 0 \\
\dot{p}_2 &= -\frac{\partial H}{\partial x_2} = -p_1 \\
\dot{p}_3 &= -\frac{\partial H}{\partial x_3} = 0
\end{aligned} \qquad (4.29)$$

are linear and homogeneous, we may choose $p_0 = -1$. The solutions for p_1 and p_2 are then

$$\begin{aligned}
p_1 &= p_{10} \\
p_2 &= -p_{10}t + p_{20}
\end{aligned} \qquad (4.30)$$

Determining the extremum of H entails finding the extremum of

$$H^* = -|u| + p_2 u$$

which is given by

$$u = \begin{cases} \text{sgn } p_2 & |p_2| \geq 1 \\ 0 & -1 < p_2 < +1 \end{cases} \qquad (4.31)$$

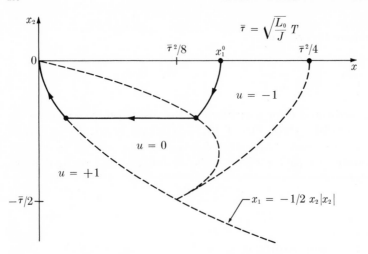

Fig. 4.28 Plant $1/s^2$; optimal switching loci for minimum gas consumption.

Again, a discontinuous control yields optimum performance. Figure 4.28 shows a phase trajectory for initial error only, with an initial-error rate of zero. As the figure indicates, T must be chosen greater than T_{min}, but the chosen time will determine the rate level for which $u = 0$. The figure also shows that errors larger than a certain number $\bar{\tau}^2/4$, where $\bar{\tau}$ is the total dimensionless transition time, cannot be zeroed with the admissible controls (maximum value of $|u|$).

Since, for example, gas jets are most conveniently used with the

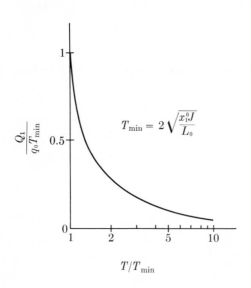

Fig. 4.29 Plant $1/s^2$; fuel consumption versus time allowed for zeroing an error.

valves either fully open or fully closed, this theoretical result of a discontinuous control is a welcome one. Many details of this problem are discussed in Ref. 4.15, particularly the influence of transition time on the total gas consumption. Figure 4.29 shows the total gas consumption[1] Q_1 for zeroing an error (where the initial-error derivative is zero). Q_1 is made dimensionless with $q_0 T_{min}$, which is the constant gas-flow rate q_0 multiplied by the minimum settling time.

This example is an important illustration of some difficulties that may arise in some further optimization problems. Consider an initial point lying in the interior of that region for which the best choice is $u = 0$ (Fig. 4.30). The trajectory $P_i A O$ will need a fuel consumption proportional to $|x_2(P_i)|$. If we had chosen the path $P_i B C O$, the fuel consumption would be the same, but the time for zeroing the disturbance would be different. Thus there are infinitely many ways to reach the origin from P_i with the same amount of fuel, and because of the infinite number of

---

[1] Reference 4-2 may be consulted for a practical design of a feedback solution.

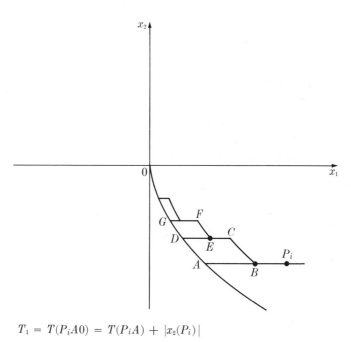

$$T_1 = T(P_i A 0) = T(P_i A) + |x_2(P_i)|$$

$$T_2 = T(P_i B C D 0) = T_i(P_i B) + T(CD) + |x_2(P_i)|$$

$$T_3 = T(P_i B C E F G 0) = T_i(P_i B) + T(CE) + T(FG) + |x_2(P_i)|$$

Fig. 4.30 Plant $1/s^2$; singular control.

possible steps, a number of paths may need the same time for the same fuel consumption (see Fig. 4.30). The maximum principle does indicate these possibilities. The control

$$u = \operatorname{sgn} p_2 = \operatorname{sgn} (-p_{10}t + p_{20})$$

can be said to include these cases if we choose $p_{10} = 0$. It is clear, then, that finding the maximum of the hamiltonian is a necessary, but not a sufficient condition for optimization.

4.4.3 Control of a plant with a zero in the transfer function

Now let us look at the way in which a zero in the plant transfer function influences determination of the optimal control. Consider the time-optimal problem for

$$\ddot{e} = b_1\dot{u} + u \qquad |u| \leq 1, b_1 > 0 \tag{4.32}$$

with initial conditions $e_0 = e(0)$ and $\dot{e}_0 = \dot{e}(0)$ and final conditions $e_f = 0$ and $\dot{e}_f = 0$. If we define $e_1 \equiv e$, we can replace the description of system (4.32) by

$$\begin{aligned}
\dot{e}_1 &= e_2 + b_1u \\
\dot{e}_2 &= u
\end{aligned} \tag{4.33}$$

Initial conditions: $e_{10} = e_1(0) \qquad \dot{e}_{10} = \dot{e}_1(0)$

Final conditions: $e_{1f} = 0$ and $e_{2f} + b_1u_f = 0$ (4.34)

Note that e_{2f} is a point on the e_2 axis, with $-b_1 \leq e_{2f} \leq b_1$, and that we must find this point.

The hamiltonian is given by

$$H = -1 + p_1(e_2 + b_1u) + p_2u \tag{4.35}$$

which requires the control law $u = \operatorname{sgn} (b_1p_1 + p_2)$ for minimum settling time. For this value of u the functional H will reach its extreme value at any time $t \leq t_f$. The time t_f is still to be determined. The differential equations for the p_i are

$$\begin{aligned}
\dot{p}_1 &= -\frac{\partial H}{\partial e_1} \rightarrow p_1 = p_{10} = \text{const} \\
\dot{p}_2 &= -\frac{\partial H}{\partial e_2} \rightarrow p_2 = -p_{10}t + p_{20}
\end{aligned} \tag{4.36}$$

where p_{20} is an integration constant. The control function u is discontinuous and has at most one switching.

Since u is constant between the beginning of motion and switching or between switching and the end of the state-point motion, the original system equation can easily be integrated in these intervals:

$$\ddot{e} = \dot{e}u$$

because $\dot{u} = 0$, and

$$\frac{\dot{e}^2}{2} = u(e - e_\nu)$$

where e_ν is a constant.   In the new coordinates this result is expressed as

$$\frac{(b_1u + e_2)^2}{2} = u(e_1 - e_{1\nu}) \tag{4.37}$$

We see immediately that the state point moves on parabolas whose axes are parallel to the e_1 axis.

Let us start at the point P_{i1} in Fig. 4.31.   In this figure two zero trajectories are indicated; these are zero trajectories in the e_1e_2 system. From the chosen initial point P_{i1} the state point proceeds with $u = -1$ to P_s and then on a zero trajectory to $(e_{1f} = 0, e_{2f} = 0)$; however, only if u jumps at this moment from 1 to zero can the state point stay at this point.   Now let us consider an initial point P_{i2}.   The state point proceeds with $u = -1$ to point P_{s2}; at this point $e_1 = 0$ (one of the final conditions), and $e_{2f} + b_1u_f$ can be made zero if u changes.   It is only

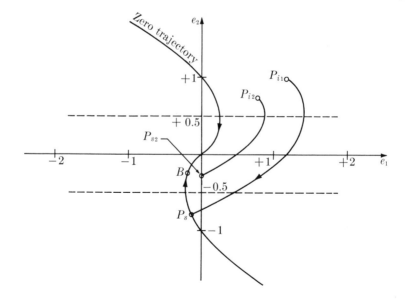

Fig. 4.31   Time-optimal control for a plant of second order with zero in the transfer function.

necessary to keep $e_1 \equiv 0$; that is,

$$e_2 + b_1 u = 0$$

or, from Eq. (4.33), $e_2 + b_1 \dot{e}_2 = 0$.

With $e_2 = C e^{(-1/b_1)(t-t_s)}$

and $\quad u = \dfrac{-C}{b_1} e^{(-1/b)(t-t_s)}$ (4.38)

the relations $e \equiv 0$, and $\dot{e} \equiv 0$ apply for all times $t > t_s$.

The original goal[1] of reaching the point $(e_f = 0,\ \dot{e}_f = 0)$ was certainly achieved much faster than if the state point had proceeded past P_{s2} to reach the zero trajectory in B. Hence $P_{i2}P_{s2}$ represents the solution; however, the final point is not an equilibrium point of the system.

4.4.4 Control of a second-order plant from a given phase point to a point on a given line in the phase plane

This case will be described only briefly because it is discussed in full detail in Ref. 4.11, pp. 50–52. The plant transfer function is again $1/s^2$. A time-optimal control is desired which leads from a given initial error and error derivative to a point with $e = 0$. This means that in the phase plane $(e, \dot{e})$ the endpoint must be a point on the $\dot{e}$ axis. The solution depends very much on the initial location of the phase point with respect to the zero trajectories. Figure 4.32 shows possible control patterns. In Fig. 4.32c two possible solutions are traced, but it can easily be shown that the lower trajectory requires less time to reach its goal than the upper one.

4.4.5 Time-optimal control of a plant with only real poles

We now consider an nth-order system as given by Eq. (3.1), with $b_i \equiv 0$ for $i = 1, 2, \ldots, n - 1$ and $|u| \leq 1$. However, the coefficients a_i of the derivatives and of the function c (output) are such that the characteristic equation of the system has only real roots (the earliest treatment of this problem is in Ref. 4.16). This means that, in the representation (3.18) of this system,

$$\mathbf{x}' = \Lambda \mathbf{x} + G^{-1} D u$$ (4.39)

$G^{-1}D$ is a column vector $\hat{\mathbf{g}}$ with the components $\hat{g}_i$. It is possible by simple renumbering to arrange the system such that $\lambda_{j+1} > \lambda_j$. Now let us assume that at $t = 0$ the system has the components (deviations from an equilibrium state) $x_j(0) = x_{j0}$ and that we want to zero these

---

[1] This example was first treated by H. Hubbs in his doctoral dissertation, Stanford University, Department of Electrical Engineering, Stanford, Calif., 1962.

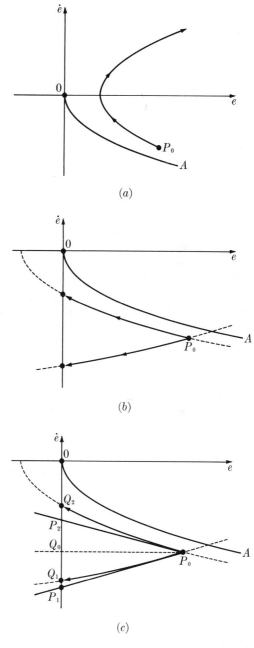

Fig. 4.32 Plant $1/s^2$. Time-optimal control; desired final state $e = 0$. Influence of the location of the initial point on the possibility of a solution.

components in minimum time. The hamiltonian is given by

$$H = -1 + \Sigma p_j f^j = -1 + \Sigma p_j(\lambda_j x^j + \hat{g}_j u) \tag{4.40}$$

and the differential equation for the adjoints is

$$\dot{p}_j = -\lambda_j p_j \tag{4.41}$$

It is obvious that the maximum value of H will be obtained for

$$u = \text{sgn } \Sigma p_j \hat{g}_j = \text{sgn } F(t) \tag{4.42}$$

where the p_j are exponential functions and the $\hat{g}_j$ are constants. Because $\lambda_{j+1} > \lambda_i$, we can easily conclude that the function $F(t)$ will have at most $n - 1$ zero points. Hence we can zero any initial disturbance with at most $n - 1$ switchings. This agrees with results for the second-order systems considered earlier. Unfortunately, however, such a simple result does not exist if some of the roots λ_j are complex, a fact that is often overlooked.

4.4.6 Bushaw's problem

The following problem, the best-known example of a minimum-settling-time problem, was first solved in 1953 by Bushaw (see Ref. 4.17) by topological methods rather than by means of Pontryagin's maximum principle. The reader interested in his derivation should look either at the original paper or at the well-done description in H. S. Tsien's book (Ref. 4.18, pp. 150–159).

Bushaw considered the system

$$e'' + 2\zeta e' + e = u(t) \tag{4.43}$$

where the control input $u(t)$ satisfies $|u| \leq 1$ and $|\zeta| < 1$. The characteristic roots are $\lambda_{1,2} = -\zeta \pm i\nu$, with $\nu = \sqrt{1 - \zeta^2}$.

In the earlier treatment of this system (Sec. 2.1.1) we used oblique coordinates in the phase plane to facilitate the study of trajectories. System (4.43) can be described by two first-order equations for $e^1 = e$ and $e^2 = e'$.

$$\begin{aligned} \frac{de^1}{dt} &= e^2 \\ \frac{de^2}{dt} &= -e^1 - 2\zeta e^2 + u \end{aligned} \tag{4.44}$$

or $$\frac{d}{dt}\begin{bmatrix} e^1 \\ e^2 \end{bmatrix} = \begin{bmatrix} 0 & 1 \\ -1 & -2\zeta \end{bmatrix} \begin{bmatrix} e^1 \\ e^2 \end{bmatrix} + \begin{bmatrix} 0 \\ 1 \end{bmatrix} u \tag{4.45}$$

These coupled differential equations can be transformed by

$$\begin{bmatrix} x^1 \\ x^2 \end{bmatrix} = \begin{bmatrix} 1 & \zeta \\ 0 & \nu \end{bmatrix} \begin{bmatrix} e^1 \\ e^2 \end{bmatrix} \tag{4.46}$$

into a more convenient form (see Chap. 3):[1]

$$\frac{d}{dt}\begin{bmatrix} x^1 \\ x^2 \end{bmatrix} = \begin{bmatrix} -\varsigma & +\nu \\ -\nu & -\varsigma \end{bmatrix}\begin{bmatrix} x^1 \\ x^2 \end{bmatrix} + \begin{bmatrix} \varsigma \\ \nu \end{bmatrix}u \tag{4.47}$$

The hamiltonian for the time-optimal problem is

$$
\begin{aligned}
H &= -1 + \Sigma p_i f^i \\
&= -1 + p_1(-\varsigma x^1 + \nu x^2 + \varsigma u) + p_2(-\nu x^1 - \varsigma x^2 + \nu u) \tag{4.48}
\end{aligned}
$$

The maximum value of H for the admissible set u is given by

$$u = \operatorname{sgn}(p_1\varsigma + p_2\nu) \tag{4.49}$$

Since

$$
\begin{aligned}
\dot{p}_1 &= +p_1\varsigma + \nu p_2 \\
\dot{p}_2 &= -\nu p_1 + p_2\varsigma
\end{aligned}
$$

we obtain $\ddot{p}_1 = 2\varsigma\dot{p}_1 + p_1 = 0$

Therefore

$$
\begin{aligned}
p_1 &= Ce^{\varsigma t}\cos(\nu t - \delta^*) \\
p_2 &= -Ce^{\varsigma t}\sin(\nu t - \delta^*)
\end{aligned}
\tag{4.50}
$$

From Eq. (4.49) we obtain

$$u(t) = -\operatorname{sgn}F(t) = -\operatorname{sgn}[C\cos(\nu t - \delta^* - \sigma)]$$

with $\cos\sigma = -\varsigma$. In view of the yet undetermined δ^*, we can write this without loss of generality as

$$u(t) = -\operatorname{sgn}[\cos(\nu t - \delta)] \tag{4.51}$$

Figure 4.33 shows $u(t)$. It is apparent that, with the exception of

[1] A note to the reader who studied Chaps. 2 and 3 carefully: If we use oblique e^1e^2 axes we get trajectories composed of portions of logarithmic spirals. If we want to work with a rectangular frame, we must replace the simple relation between e^1 and e^2 (that is, $de^1/dt = e^2$) by the more complicated one given in Eq. (4.47) for x^1 and x^2.

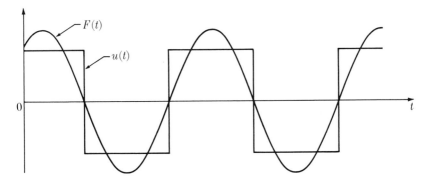

Fig. 4.33 Plant $1/(s^2 + 2\varsigma s + 1)$; minimum settling-time problem; switching function $F(t)$ and control input $u(t)$.

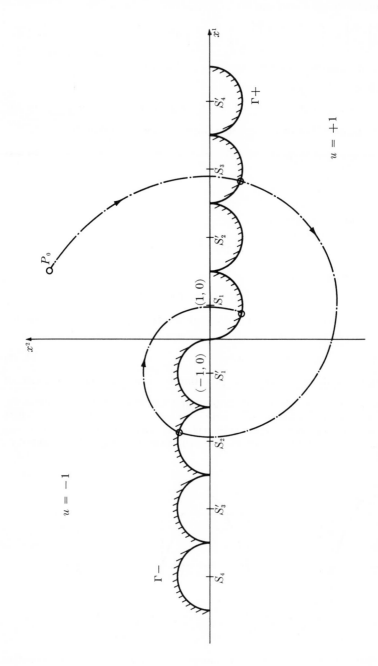

Fig. 4.34 Plant $1/(s^2 + 1)$; switching curve in the x^1x^2 plane.

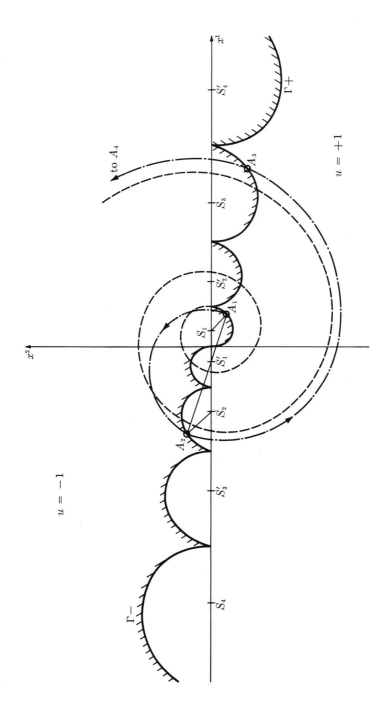

Fig. 4.35 Plant $1/(s^2 + 2\zeta s + 1)$; switching curve for $0 < \zeta < 1$ in the $x^1 x^2$ plane.

the first and last interval, the length of the interval between switchings is $\nu t^* = \pi$. The distance of the initial point from the origin will influence the number of switchings. In principle we should now determine that δ which in each case determines the sequence of switching points. However, we might also consider determining the locus of all possible switching points in the $x^1 x^2$ plane and then drawing trajectories. This can be done easily merely by showing that Eq. (4.49) leads to Bushaw's construction. Figure 4.34 shows a trajectory for the case $\zeta = 0$. The value δ determines the location of A_1, the last switching point on the zero trajectory; the trajectory consists of portions of circles around $x^1 = 1$ and $x^2 = -1$. It is obvious in this case that the switching law (4.51) is observed for the festoon switching locus.

For $\zeta \neq 0$ we can show that the locus of all switching points is also

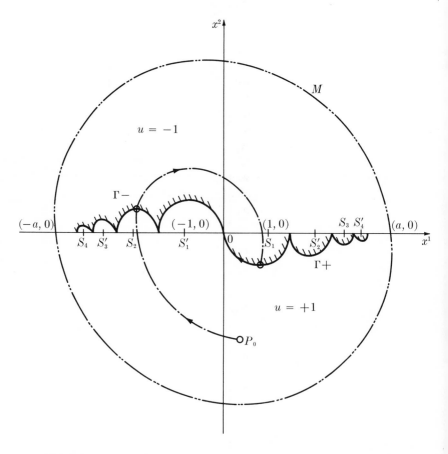

Fig. 4.36   Plant $1/(s^2 + 2\zeta s + 1)$; switching curve for $-1 < \zeta < 0$ in the $x^1 x^2$ plane.

a festoon curve but now made up of spiral segments instead of half circles. The dashed curve in Fig. 4.35 is a spiral around the origin of the x^1x^2 plane which is cut by the x^1 axis in portions which are used for constructing the festoon curve. A backward-drawn trajectory is shown; that is, one started at $(x^1 = 0, x^2 = 0)$ and moved toward the initial state, which could be any point on the trajectory. The simple construction indicated in the figure demonstrates that the switching law (4.51) applies for any A_1 chosen on a zero-trajectory branch.

As in the case for $\zeta = 0$, the festoon curve divides the entire x^1x^2 plane into two half-planes for $0 < \zeta < 1$. The situation is quite different, however, for $-1 < \zeta < 0$ (see Fig. 4.36); here the festoon curve ends at two symmetrically located points on the x^1 axis. A careful investigation shows that if the uncontrolled system is an unstable plant, there is a periodic motion M which encloses that region containing all the initial disturbances which can be zeroed.

If a system can be designed to realize the festoon curves, then $u(t)$ can be replaced by $u(x^1,x^2)$, and a true feedback control is possible. Imagine, for instance, that in an x^1x^2 plane the space above the festoon curve is white and the space below it is black, and that an optical device that senses this color difference picks up $x^1(t)$ and $x^2(t)$ and governs the relay. Another method might be to apply Pontryagin's maximum principle to determine the correct switching locus and then approximate this locus in some form which is highly accurate only near the origin (see Fig. 4.37). Many such devices have been explored. The designer will have to decide what expense, degree of complexity and weight are feasible for a given project. With digital control, for instance, a rather high degree of accuracy is possible in principle because the exact switching locus is known.

4.4.7 Time-optimal control of a third-order plant

Consider a system with the transfer function

$$\frac{1}{s(s^2 + 2\zeta s + 1)} \tag{4.52}$$

and $|\zeta| < 1$. Minimum settling time for instantaneous disturbances is required by a control $|u| \le 1$. We can interpret this as the example of Sec. 4.4.6, with the change that position control is replaced by rate control.

Application of Pontryagin's maximum principle leads to the following development. First we introduce new coordinates

$$\begin{bmatrix} x^1 \\ x^2 \\ x^3 \end{bmatrix} = \begin{bmatrix} 0 & 1 & \zeta \\ 0 & 0 & \nu \\ 1 & 2\zeta & 1 \end{bmatrix} \begin{bmatrix} e^1 \\ e^2 \\ e^3 \end{bmatrix} \tag{4.53}$$

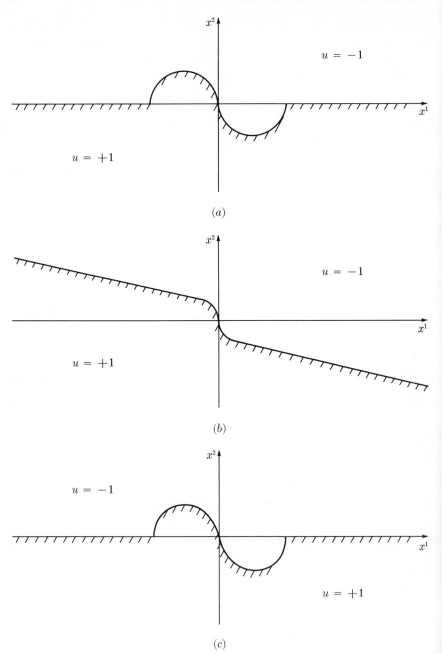

Fig. 4.37 Minimum settling-time problem. Approximate switching curves for (a) plant $1/(s^2 + 1)$; (b) and (c) plant $1/(s^2 + 2\zeta s + 1)$ with $0 < \zeta < 1$.

where $e^2 = (e^1)'$ and $e^3 = (e^2)'$. Then the system is described by

$$\frac{d}{dt}\begin{bmatrix} x^1 \\ x^2 \\ x^3 \end{bmatrix} = \begin{bmatrix} -\zeta & \nu & 0 \\ -\nu & -\zeta & 0 \\ 0 & 0 & 0 \end{bmatrix}\begin{bmatrix} x^1 \\ x^2 \\ x^3 \end{bmatrix} + \begin{bmatrix} \zeta \\ \nu \\ 1 \end{bmatrix} u \qquad (4.54)$$

and the adjoint system is described by

$$\frac{d}{dt}\begin{bmatrix} p_1 \\ p_2 \\ p_3 \end{bmatrix} = \begin{bmatrix} \zeta & \nu & 0 \\ -\nu & \zeta & 0 \\ 0 & 0 & 0 \end{bmatrix}\begin{bmatrix} p_1 \\ p_2 \\ p_3 \end{bmatrix} \qquad (4.55)$$

The maximum value of the hamiltonian is given by

$$u(t) = -\operatorname{sgn} F = \operatorname{sgn}[C^* e^{-\zeta t} - \cos(\nu t - \delta)] \qquad (4.56)$$

where C^* and δ are constants to be determined such that the phase point tends from $\mathbf{x}(0)$ toward $\mathbf{x}_f = 0$. Naturally, we wish to express $u(t)$ as $u(x^1, x^2, x^3)$; that is, we want to determine the switching surface in the $x^1 x^2 x^3$ space.

Figure 4.38 shows the function $F(t)$ for a given pair (C^*, δ). It is immediately evident that there may be many switchings, with perhaps one very large first interval. Mih Yin (Ref. 4.19) has shown that for $\zeta \equiv 0$ the switching surface can be built up of curves whose projections are shown in a sample in Fig. 4.39. The third coordinate is given by the fact that $\dot{x}^3 = u$ for each trajectory portion. Thus the switching surface

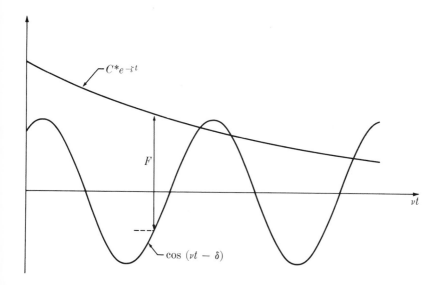

Fig. 4.38 Switching function $F(t)$ for time-optimal control of the plant $1/[s(s^2 + 2\zeta s + 1)]$.

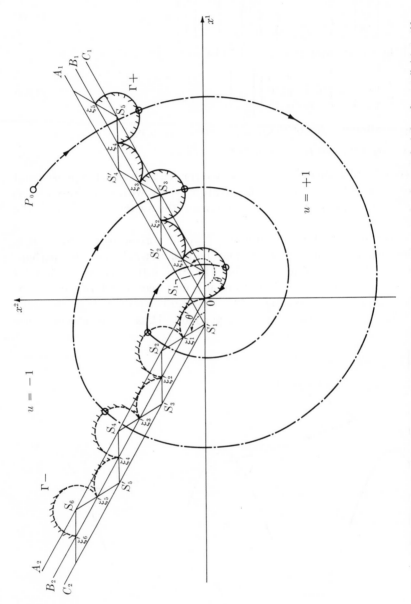

Fig. 4.39 Illustration for visualization of the switching surface for time-optimal control of the plant $1/[s(s^2 + 1)]$.

is highly complicated. For one initial disturbance all switching points lie on one such curve, but it is necessary to find the C^* and δ which determine θ and A in such a way that the phase point will go from its initial location P_0 to the origin. Mih Yin has suggested an iteration procedure to find these constants. It is obvious that a simple realization of such a switching surface is not possible. The surface has a *main* structure and a *fine* structure, reminiscent of a corrugated surface.

Particularly interesting is the location of the switching points when at $t = 0$ there is an error, but no error rate or error acceleration. In this case the projection of the point P_0 with the coordinates ($x^1(0) = 0$, $x^2(0) = 0$, $x^3(0) \neq 0$) into the x^1x^2 plane coincides with the origin of this plane, which is also the projection of the final point, ($x_f^1 = x_f^2 = x_f^3 = 0$). Clearly, fast reduction of a large error will require large intervals with the same u; short intervals with opposite u are needed only to adjust the x^1x^2 components. Hence the projection of the two branches Γ_+ and Γ_- of the switching-curve projection (see Fig. 4.39) will overlap (see Fig. 4.40). For this system with one pole at zero, initial error and step input lead to the same response. Figure 4.41 shows projections of

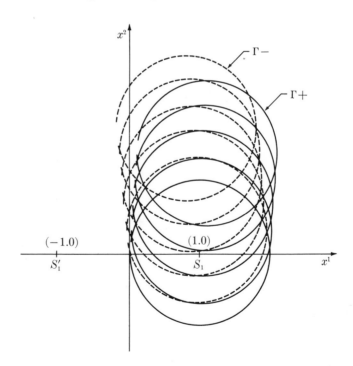

Fig. 4.40 Plant $1/[s(s^2 + 1)]$; the projection of the switching curve for $C^* = 0.9962 = \cos 5°$ in the x^1x^2 plane.

optimal trajectories; the initial error is denoted.   Note how exactly the switching curve would have to be realized for a truly time-optimal trajectory.   It is true that such an optimal trajectory would have no oscillatory character, but the price is high.

Mih Yin has investigated suboptimal controls, and also the approximation of the switching surface for a plant with the transfer function

$$\frac{1}{s(s^2 + 2\zeta s + 1)}$$

and $\zeta \neq 0$.   The case with the real pole at γ {transfer function $1/[(s + \gamma)$

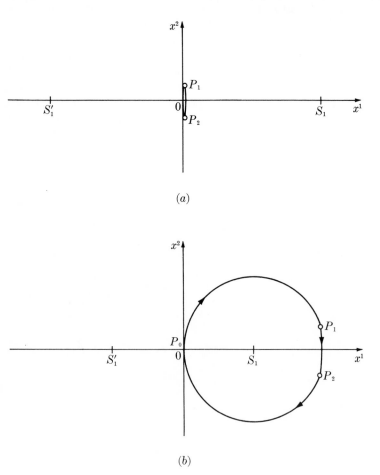

(a)

(b)

Fig. 4.41   Plant $1/[s(s^2 + 1)]$; some of the possible trajectories for $C^* = 0.9962$ and for various step inputs.   (a) $x_0{}^3 = -0.017$ $(-1°)$.   (b) $x_0{}^3 = -5.59$ $(-320.5°)$.

$(s^2 + 2\zeta s + 1)]\}$ instead of at zero has been studied extensively (see Refs. 4.20 and 4.21). Titus started this investigation, and Flügge-Lotz and Titus developed a suboptimal control that could be realized with digital means. Kashiwagi (Ref. 4.21) has tested the region $\gamma_1 < \gamma < \gamma_2$ and $0 < |\zeta| < |\zeta_1|$, for which this suboptimal scheme gives good results. It is essentially based upon the idea that farther from the origin only the main structure of the switching surface is important, and the fine structure needs attention only near the origin (if this is the final state). All investigations were for positive ζ.

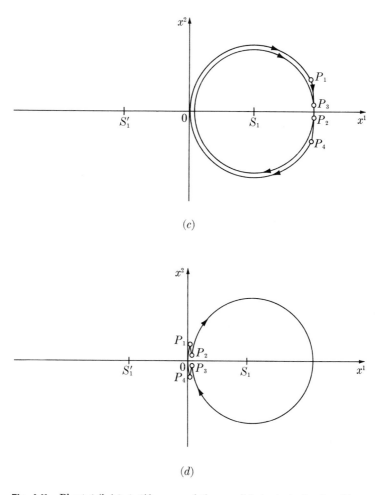

Fig. 4.41   Plant $1/[s(s^2 + 1)]$; some of the possible trajectories for $C^* = 0.9962$ and for various step inputs.   (c) $x_0{}^3 = -11.95$ ($-685°$).   (d) $x_0{}^3 = -6.24$ ($-357.5°$).

This example has shown quite clearly that time-optimal control for systems higher than second order becomes sufficiently complicated that the value of such an exact time-optimal solution may be marginal. This may be the point at which to change over to digital control for simpler realization of the switching surfaces. There have been several attempts to realize switching surfaces by patching the complicated surfaces out of plane and parabolic portions (see, for example, Refs. 4.22 and 4.23).

4.4.8 Minimum-fuel control for a plant with a transfer function $1/(s^2 + 1)$

The optimal control of the system

$$\ddot{e} + e = u \qquad (4.57)$$

with the performance measure $\int_0^T |u|\, dt \to \min$ and the condition $|u| \leq 1$ is a very interesting case. If the objective is to zero the error and its derivative in a chosen time T, for certain times T particularly simple solutions exist. Craig (Ref. 4.24) has studied this problem in detail. He first proceeded as usual to write down the system of first-order differential equations

$$\dot{\mathbf{x}} = \begin{bmatrix} 0 & 1 \\ -1 & -2\zeta \end{bmatrix} \mathbf{x} + \begin{bmatrix} 0 \\ 1 \end{bmatrix} u \qquad (4.58)$$

which for $\zeta = 0$, $x_1 = e$, and $x_2 = \dot{e}$ is equivalent to Eq. (4.57). The adjoint system is given by

$$\dot{\mathbf{p}} = \begin{bmatrix} 0 & 1 \\ -1 & 2\zeta \end{bmatrix} \mathbf{p} \qquad (4.59)$$

The hamiltonian

$$H = p_1 x_2 + p_2(u - 2\zeta x_2 - x_1) - |u| \qquad (4.60)$$

attains a maximum value for

$$u = \begin{cases} \operatorname{sgn} p_2 & |p_2| \geq 1 \\ 0 & |p_2| < 1 \end{cases} \qquad (4.61)$$

Equation (4.59) leads to

$$p_2 = P_m e^{\zeta t} \sin(\nu t + \theta) \qquad \nu = \sqrt{1 - \zeta^2} \qquad (4.62)$$

and we see that the control is of the *bang-bang* type. The switching instances depend on P_m and θ; these two constants must be determined such that

$$x_1(0) = x_{10}$$
$$x_2(0) = x_{20}$$
and $\quad x(T) = x_2(T) = 0$

For $\zeta = 0$ we see that $p_2 = P_m \sin{(t + \theta)}$ and that, except for the last, and maybe the first, interval, the distance between switching points (the interval length) is fixed (see Fig. 4.42a). Figure 4.42b shows a special solution for which the last interval $\overline{EF}$ is equal to $\overline{CD} = \overline{AB}$. An intensive investigation of $p_2(t)$ curves and corresponding trajectories soon shows that for this case all switching points lie on straight lines in the $x_1 x_2$ plane (Fig. 4.42c). Of course, all we can do is choose an infinite number of discrete T values which allow such an arrangement, but these times T probably provide enough design freedom.[1]

4.4.9 Fuller's problem

The performance criterion for this example is that a disturbance be zeroed while the mean-square error is kept to a minimum. In 1960 Fuller (Ref. 4.25) investigated the second-order system $e'' = u/a$ and computed the relay control $u(t)$, with $|u| = 1$, for which

$$\int_0^\infty e^2\, dt \to \min \tag{4.63}$$

while e and e' move from given initial values e_0 and e_0' toward the values (0,0). The positive number a can be taken as 1 without loss of generality because a change in time scale transforms $e'' = u/a$ into $e^{\circ\circ} = u$.

In this work, presented at the First International Conference of Automatic Control in Moscow, Fuller used geometric considerations, rather than Pontryagin's maximum principle, to arrive at the conclusion that the solution was composed of portions of similar parabolas. It turned out that the origin was actually reached in a finite time T. He later showed (Ref. 4.26) that this result could have been found with Pontryagin's maximum principle. The example is treated here because it shows a very special feature which should serve as a warning that even when an optimal control is known to be a discontinuous control, it may not be always easy or even possible to compute the switching-point locus through a study of backward trajectories beginning in the origin of the state space.

Let us consider this problem in our usual framework. The differential equation

$$e'' = u \tag{4.64}$$

can be replaced by

$$\begin{aligned} e' &= e_1' = e_2 \\ e_2' &= u \end{aligned} \tag{4.65}$$

We shall impose the condition $|u| \leq 1$; that is, we shall not start with the assumption that a relay control should be used. The performance

---

[1] See Sec. 5.2.1 for a discussion of this scheme for building suboptimal controls.

criterion is

$$J = \int_0^\infty e^2 \, dt \to \min \tag{4.66}$$

The initial conditions are

$$e(0) = e_0 \tag{4.67a}$$
$$e'(0) = e_0' \tag{4.67b}$$

The final conditions,

$$e_1(\infty) = 0 \tag{4.68a}$$
$$e_2(\infty) = 0 \tag{4.68b}$$

do not preclude reaching the final state at the time $T < \infty$.

The hamiltonian for this problem is given by

$$H = \psi_0 e_1{}^2 + \psi_1 e_2 + \psi_2 u \tag{4.69}$$

and the differential equations for the adjoints are

$$\psi_0' = -\frac{\partial H}{\partial e_0} = 0 \tag{4.70a}$$

$$\psi_1' = -\frac{\partial H}{\partial e_1} = 2\psi_0 e_1 \tag{4.70b}$$

$$\psi_2' = -\frac{\partial H}{\partial e_2} = \psi_1 \tag{4.70c}$$

It is evident that $u = \operatorname{sgn} \psi_2$ makes the hamiltonian assume its maximum value and that therefore the optimal control is a relay control.

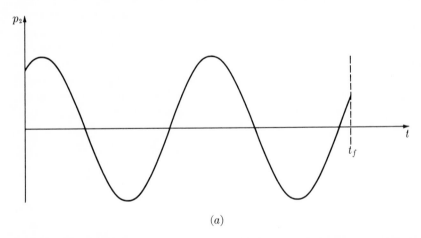

(a)

Fig. 4.42 Minimum-fuel control; plant $1/(s^2 + 1)$. (a) Time intervals between switching points given by $p_2(t)$.

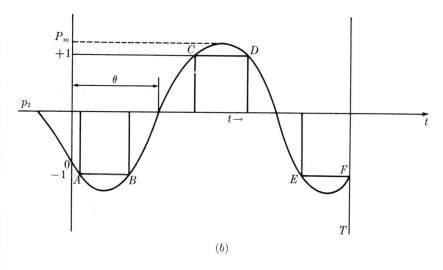

(b)

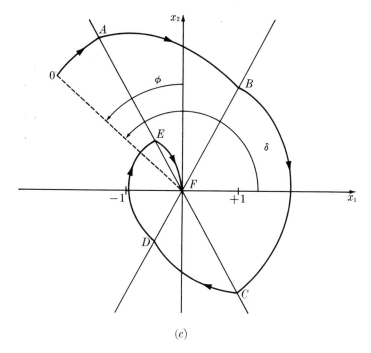

(c)

Fig. 4.42 Minimum-fuel control; plant $1/(s^2 + 1)$. (b) Special case of switching-point sequence. (c) Trajectory for special case (b).

Since the completion time for this mission is not known, we need information about the behavior of the adjoints at the final state. The adjoints are the components of the normal to the wavefront by which disturbances of the system propagate. At the natural end of the process the wavefront normal must be normal to all possible trajectories; that is, the last wavefront must be an envelope of trajectories, or

$$\Sigma \psi_i f_i = 0 \tag{4.71}$$

The differential equations for the adjoints are coupled to the system equations, with the exception of the first one, $\psi_0 = 0$; it thus follows that ψ_0 is constant. Since, ψ_0 must also be negative at the absolute minimum of the performance criterion, we can set $\psi_0 = -1$ without loss of generality [see Eqs. (4.70)]. In addition, ψ_0 is a component of the normal to the wavefront and is related to the performance criterion; therefore all the other components must be zero. $\psi_1(T) = 0$ and $\psi_2(T) = 0$ if T is the still undetermined time for reaching ($e_1 = 0$, $e_2 = 0$).

Since $u = \text{const} = (\pm 1)$, the system equations can be integrated easily between two switching points. The simplest manner is to integrate

$$e'' = u$$

to yield

$$\frac{e_2{}^2}{2} = u(e_1 - e_{1v})$$

where e_{1v} is an integration constant. This means that the phase trajectories are composed of parabolas, just as in the case of the minimum-settling-time control. However, we must still find the location of the switching points, determined by $\psi_2(t) = 0$.

If we decide to write e_1 and e_2 as function of t, for the nth interval, with $t_n < t < t_{n+1}$, we get

$$e_{2n} = u_n(t - t_n) + e_{2n}(t_n) \tag{4.72}$$

$$e_{1n} = u_n \frac{(t - t_n)^2}{2} + e_{2n}(t_n)(t - t_n) + e_{1n}(t_n) \tag{4.73}$$

$e_1(t)$ and $e_2(t)$ are continuous functions, but de_2/de_1 is discontinuous in all switching points. It is obvious that the adjoints ψ_1 and ψ_2, which are continuous functions of t, can be computed from Eqs. (4.70), but this would be a somewhat tedious procedure.

Fuller found it simpler to get information about the location of the switching points in the e_1e_2 plane (Ref. 4.26) by starting from one switching point to compute the next one. From his original treatment of the problem (Ref. 4.25) he knew that the switching points for the relay-control problem were located on the curve

$$e_1 + h e_2 |e_2| = 0 \tag{4.74}$$

with $h \approx 0.4446$ (4.75)

Therefore he assumed that from the initial point (e_{10}, e_{20}) he had reached the first switching point lying on the curve of Eq. (4.74). For this switching point $\psi_2 = 0$. He then demonstrated by integrating the differential equations for e_1, e_2, ψ_1, and ψ_2 that the next switching point would also lie on this curve if h were chosen as

$$h = \frac{1}{2} \frac{\sqrt{\sqrt{33} - 1}}{6} = 0.4446 \tag{4.76}$$

It immediately followed that all switching points would lie on this curve. For the time T for reaching ($e_1 = 0$, $e_2 = 0$) Fuller used the relations

$$\Delta t_{s,n} = t_{s,n+1} - t_{s,n} = \left(1 + \sqrt{\frac{1 - 2h}{1 + 2h}}\right) e_2{}^n \tag{4.77}$$

and $e_2{}^{n+1} = g e_2{}^n$ (4.78)

with

$$g = \frac{1}{4}[3 + \sqrt{33} - \sqrt{26 + 6\sqrt{33}}] \approx 0.24$$

to demonstrate that there are infinitely many switching points but that $\Sigma \Delta t_n$ is finite (geometric progression).

It is interesting to compare the switching locus for the criterion

$$J = \int_0^T e_1{}^2 \, dt \qquad (T \text{ not given})$$

with the switching-point locus for minimum settling time. For the latter case the switching locus is identical with the zero trajectories. This is not so for our present problem (see the dashed curve of Fig. 4.43). It is obvious that the desired final state, even for a perfect relay, can be reached only with a motion similar in its last stage to chatter, except that this chatter is inherent in the ideal problem and is not caused by relay imperfection.

As this example shows, a study of trajectories in backward time will not always reveal information about the locus of switching points. Of course, if our requirement for a final state were only a very small circle around the origin of the $e_1 e_2$ plane instead of the origin itself, some information could be gleaned from a backward time study.

Halkin (Ref. 4.27) has shown that Fuller's problem is identical with the study of solutions of the differential equation

$$z^{(4)} = -\operatorname{sgn} z \tag{4.79}$$

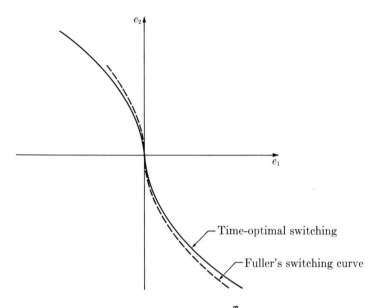

Fig. 4.43   Plant $1/s^2$; performance criterion $\int\limits_{0}^{\infty} e^2\, dt \to$ min.

4.4.10   Time-optimal control of a nonlinear system

Our next example illustrates the fact that Pontryagin's maximum principle gives necessary conditions for optimality, but not sufficient conditions.   The controlled system is described by

$$\ddot{e} + \sin e = u(t) \tag{4.80}$$

with $u(t)$ a piecewise continuous function, $|u| \le A$ for all $t \in (-\infty, +\infty)$, and $A \ge 1$.

If we were to linearize this system, we would obtain $\ddot{e} + e = u$ and, with $|u| \le 1$, have a special case of the example of Sec. 4.4.6.   The nonlinear problem was recently treated by Almuzara (Ref. 4.28).

The nonlinear system of first-order equations that replaces Eq. (4.80) is given by

$$\begin{aligned}
\dot{e}_1 &= e_2 \\
\dot{e}_2 &= u - \sin e_1
\end{aligned} \tag{4.81}$$

The hamiltonian for this system with a time-optimal criterion is

$$H(\mathbf{p}, \mathbf{e}, u) = p_1 e_2 + p_2 u - p_2 \sin e_1 \tag{4.82}$$

The adjoint variables p_1 and p_2 satisfy the equations

$$\begin{aligned} \dot{p}_1 &= -p_2 \cos e_1 \\ \dot{p}_2 &= -p_1 \end{aligned}$$

(4.83)

which allow the formation of an equation for p_2,

$$\ddot{p}_2 - p_2 \cos e_1 = 0$$

(4.84)

The hamiltonian assumes its maximum value for

$$u^*(t) = A \operatorname{sgn} p_2(t)$$

(4.85)

where $\operatorname{sgn} p_2(t) = \begin{cases} 1 & p_2 > 0 \\ -1 & p_2 < 0 \end{cases}$

(4.86)

It can be shown that between switchings, that is, when u^* is constant, the following equation for p_2 holds:

$$e_2{}^2 \frac{d^2 p_2}{de_1{}^2} + (u^* - \sin e_1) \frac{dp_2}{de_1} + \cos e_1 \, p_2 = 0$$

(4.87)

This is a second-order differential equation for p_2 which has the point $M(e_{1m},0)$, the intersection point of the considered trajectory with the e_1 axis, as its only singular point. This equation can be integrated (for details see Ref. 4.28); we shall examine here only the results of a rather long, but not too difficult mathematical investigation.

Before these results are presented it is appropriate to look at an essential difference between this problem and the linearized one, $\ddot{e} + e = u$. If e is growing and becomes very large, $\sin e$ is still bounded by $|\sin e| \leq 1$; that is an indication that the system $\ddot{e} + \sin e = u$ exhibits for large e a behavior which might be closer to that of $\ddot{e} = u$ than $\ddot{e} + e = u$. The time-optimal solution for the system $\ddot{e} = u$ exhibits at most one switching; we shall see that the time-optimal solution of $\ddot{e} + \sin e = u$ exhibits at most two switchings, while it is known that the solution for $\ddot{e} + e = u$ may have very many switchings.

We can show that the zero trajectories γ_+ and γ_- are time-optimal solutions (see Fig. 4.44). However, a new feature appears; the phase points for which $p_2(t) = 0$ are candidates for switching points, but not all may be true switching points. As a result, $p_2(t) = 0$ is a necessary but not a sufficient condition. The curves $\Sigma_R{}^k$ in Fig. 4.44 are loci for $p_2(t) = 0$. However, a detailed investigation shows that only the upper part $\Sigma_{R_a}{}^k$ of each curve $\Sigma_R{}^k$ contains true switching points (dividing points $\rho_R{}^j$, $\rho_R{}^i$, and $\rho_R{}^{i+1}$). The lower part $\Sigma_{R_b}{}^k$ is not a locus of true switching points and must be replaced by new curves (see Fig. 4.45) which are the loci of all points from which the origin can be reached by two different trajectories in the same time. These curves are called *indifference curves* and carry the symbol $\Sigma_{R_e}{}^j$. In Fig. 4.46 two trajectories are traced, one

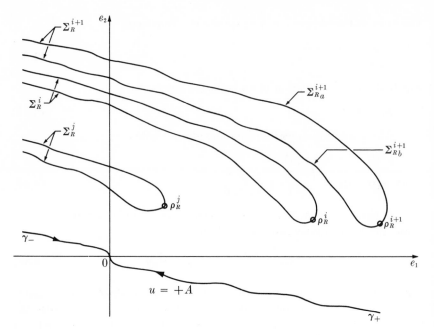

Fig. 4.44 Time-optimal control; system $\ddot{e} + \sin e = u(t)$, with $|u| \leq A$; zero trajectories; and loci, which are "candidates" for switching points.

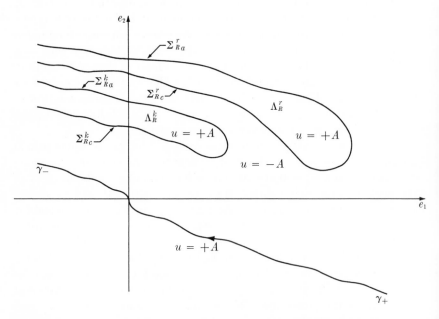

Fig. 4.45 System of Fig. 4.44; true switching curves and indifference curves.

beginning at P_1 and the other at P_2, and on the boundary of $\Lambda_R{}^1$ the point $\rho_R{}^1$ which divides the upper, switching-point part from the lower, indifference-point part is marked. We can easily imagine point P_2 being moved toward $\Sigma_{R_e}{}^1$ and trace the two trajectories that require equal time to reach the origin (the numbers on $\Sigma_{R_e}{}^1$ indicate time). One has two switching points and the other has only one switching point. It is obvious that points on the indifference curves are *starting points;* a motion can start at these points in two directions, but these points cannot be reached from any other point in the plane. Figures 4.46 to 4.48 show how with a changing value of A the first region $\Lambda_R{}^1$ moves out, and we can easily imagine how for increasing A the situation of the system $\ddot{e} = u$ is approached.

It is interesting to compare the time required to zero a disturbance in a nonlinear system with that required to zero the same disturbance in the linearized system (see Figs. 4.49 to 4.58). Note that generally if $e_{20} > 0$ there are some zones for which the nonlinear case allows a faster zeroing than the linear case and other zones for which the zeroing is slower; if $e_{20} < 0$ the zeroing in the nonlinear case is generally faster.

Something must be said about the origin of the corners that appear in the curves associated with the nonlinear case. Let e_{2cr} be the value of e_2 such that the straight line $e_2 = e_{2cr}$ is tangent to the $\Sigma_{R_e}{}^i$ curve and $2\theta = 2\pi$ the period of $\sin e$. Then for $e_{20} > e_{2cr}$ there will be two corners in every interval $2i\theta \leq e_1 \leq 2(i + 1)\theta$, which correspond to the points at which the straight line $e_2 = e_{20}$ intersects the curves $\Sigma_{R_a}{}^i$ and $\Sigma_{R_e}{}^i$; however, if $e_{20} \leq e_{2cr}$, there is only one corner corresponding to the intersection point of $e_2 = e_{20}$ with the γ_+ curve.

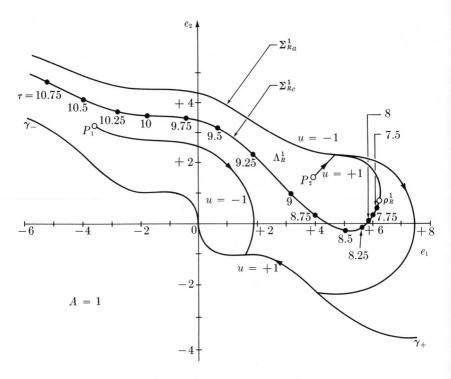

Fig. 4.46 System of Fig. 4.44; dependence of first switching and indifference loci on magnitude of A. $A = 1$; two sample trajectories are shown.

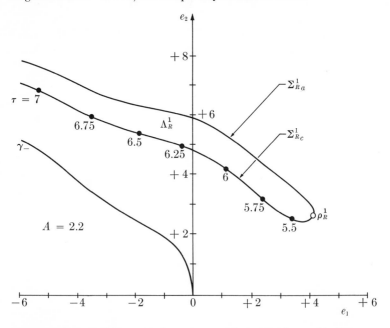

Fig. 4.47 System of Fig. 4.44; dependence of first switching and indifference loci on magnitude of A. $A = 2.2$.

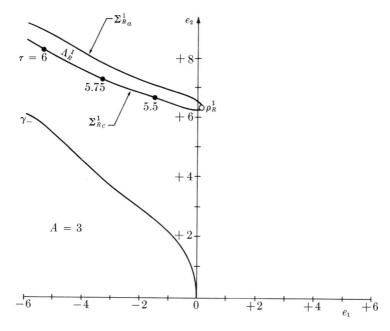

Fig. 4.48   System of Fig. 4.44; dependence of first switching and indifference loci on magnitude of A. $A = 3$.

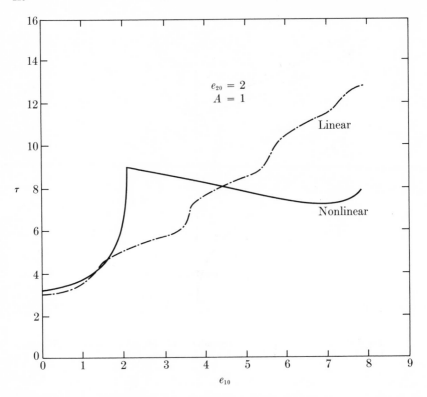

Fig. 4.49   Comparison of minimum settling times for systems

$$\ddot{e} + e = u(t) \qquad \text{and} \qquad \ddot{e} + \sin e = u(t)$$

Initial value $e_{20} = 2$, $A = 1$.

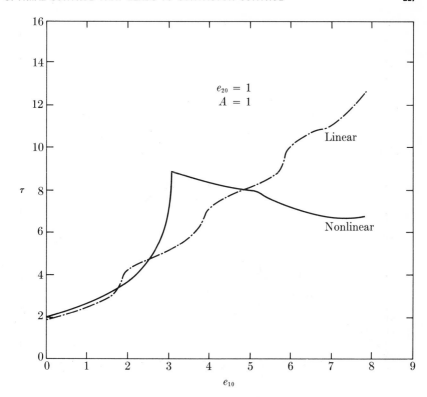

Fig. 4.50 Comparison of minimum settling times for systems

$$\ddot{e} + e = u(t) \qquad \text{and} \qquad \ddot{e} + \sin e = u(t)$$

Initial value $e_{20} = 1$, $A = 1$.

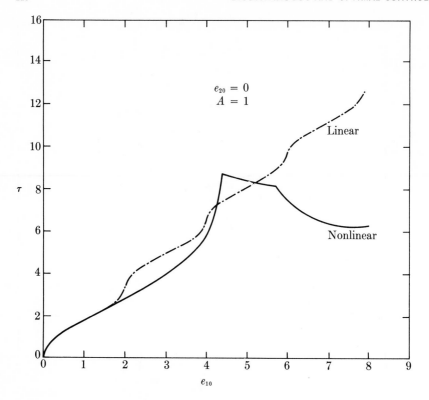

Fig. 4.51   Comparison of minimum settling times for systems

$$\ddot{e} + e = u(t) \qquad \text{and} \qquad \ddot{e} + \sin e = u(t)$$

Initial value $e_{20} = 0$, $A = 1$.

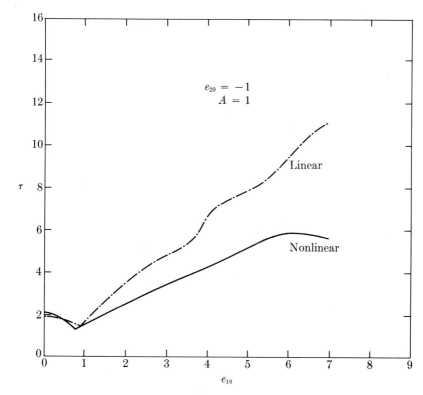

Fig. 4.52 Comparison of minimum settling times for systems

$$\ddot{e} + e = u(t) \qquad \text{and} \qquad \ddot{e} + \sin e = u(t)$$

Initial value $e_{20} = -1$, $A = 1$.

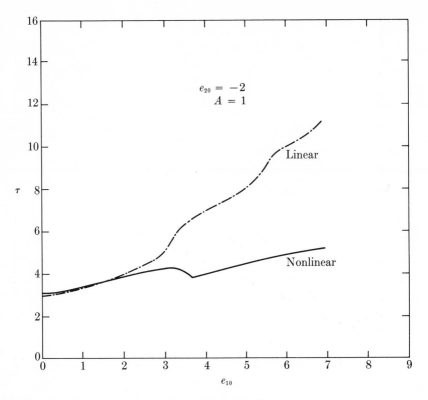

Fig. 4.53   Comparison of minimum settling times for systems

$$\ddot{e} + e = u(t) \qquad \text{and} \qquad \ddot{e} + \sin e = u(t)$$

Initial value $e_{20} = -2$, $A = 1$.

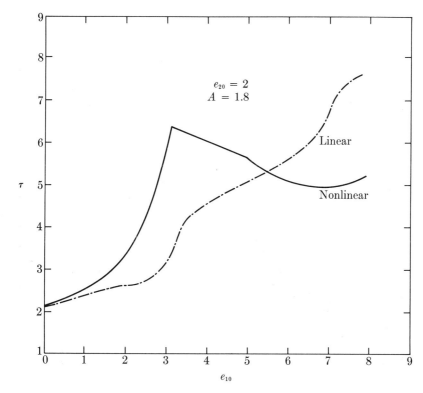

Fig. 4.54 Comparison of minimum settling times for systems

$$\ddot{e} + e = u(t) \qquad \text{and} \qquad \ddot{e} + \sin e = u(t)$$

Initial value $e_{20} = 2$, $A = 1.8$.

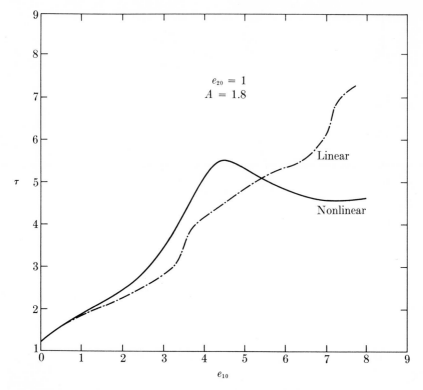

Fig. 4.55   Comparison of minimum settling times for systems

$$\ddot{e} + e = u(t) \qquad \text{and} \qquad \ddot{e} + \sin e = u(t)$$

Initial value $e_{20} = 1$, $A = 1.8$.

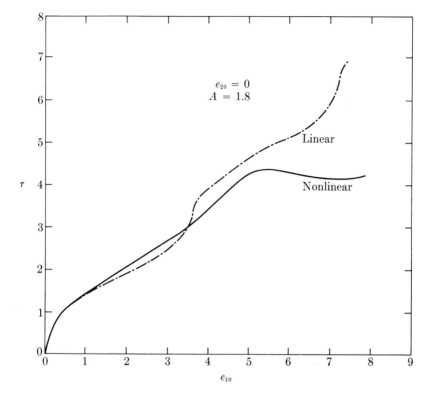

Fig. 4.56 Comparison of minimum settling times for systems

$$\ddot{e} + e = u(t) \qquad \text{and} \qquad \ddot{e} + \sin e = u(t)$$

Initial value $e_{20} = 0$, $A = 1.8$.

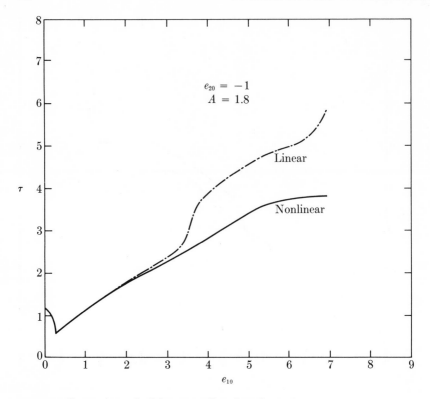

Fig. 4.57 Comparison of minimum settling times for systems

$$\ddot{e} + e = u(t) \qquad \text{and} \qquad \ddot{e} + \sin e = u(t)$$

Initial value $e_{20} = -1$, $A = 1.8$.

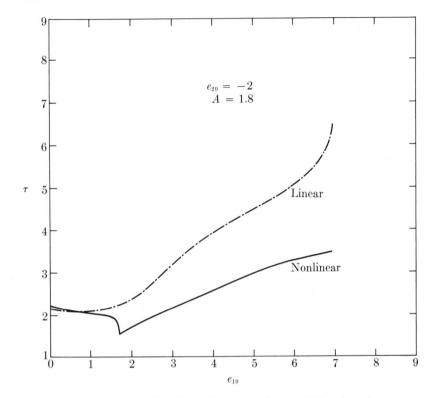

Fig. 4.58 Comparison of minimum settling times for systems

$$\ddot{e} + e = u(t) \qquad \text{and} \qquad \ddot{e} + \sin e = u(t)$$

Initial value $e_{20} = -2$, $A = 1.8$.

REFERENCES

4.1   Roxin, E. D.: Reachable Zones in Autonomous Differential Systems, *Bol. Soc. Mat. Mex.*, vol. 5, no. 1, pp. 125–135, 1960.

4.2   Hadamard, J.: Le principe de Huygens, *Bull. Soc. Math. France*, vol. 52, pp. 610–640, 1924.

4.3   Bliss, G. A.: *Lectures on the Calculus of Variations*, University of Chicago Press, Chicago, 1946.

4.4   Bushaw, D. W.: Optimal Discontinuous Forcing Terms, in S. Lefschetz (ed.), *Contributions to the Theory of Nonlinear Oscillations*, vol. IV, Princeton University Press, Princeton, N.J., 1958.

4.5   Carathéodory, C.: *Variationsrechnung und Partielle Differentialgleichungen Erster Ordnung*, B. G. Teubner Verlagsgesellschaft mbH, Leipzig, 1935.

4.6   Hille, E., and R. S. Philipps: *Functional Analysis and Semi-groups*, American Mathematics Society, Colloquium Publications, 1957.

4.7   Lie, S., and G. Scheffers: *Geometrie der Berührungstransformation*, B. G. Teubner Verlagsgesellschaft mbH, Leipzig, 1896.

4.8   Synge, J. L.: Classical Dynamics, in Band III/1 *Handbuch der Physik*, in S. Flügge (ed.), Springer-Verlag OHG, Berlin, pp. 1–225, 1960.

4.9   Athans, M., and P. L. Falb: *Optimal Control: An Introduction to the Theory and Its Applications*, McGraw-Hill Book Company, New York, 1966.

4.10   Kelley, H. J., R. E. Kopp, and H. G. Moyer: Singular Extremals, in G. Leitmann (ed.), *Topics in Optimization*, Academic Press Inc., New York, 1967.

4.11   Pontryagin, L. S., V. G. Boltianskii, R. V. Gamkrelidze, and E. F. Mishchenko: *The Mathematical Theory of Optimal Processes*, Interscience Publishers, Inc., New York, 1962.

4.12   Rozenoer, L. I.: L. S. Pontryagin's Maximum Principle in the Theory of Optimal Systems, *Automation Remote Control*, vol. 20, pp. 1288–1302, 1405–1421, 1517–1532, October, November, December, 1959.

4.13   Kalman, R. E.: The Theory of Optimal Control and the Calculus of Variations, *Res. Inst. Advanced Studies Tech. Rept.* 6-13, 1961. (Also published in R. Bellman (ed.), *Mathematical Optimization Techniques*, University of California Press, Berkeley, Calif., 1963.)

4.14   Boykin, W. H., Jr., and I. Flügge-Lotz: On the High-Accuracy Control of Satellites in Elliptic Orbits, *Stanford Univ. Dept. Aeron. Astron. Tech. Report.* 322, July, 1967.

4.15   Flügge-Lotz, I., and H. Marbach: Some Attitude Control Systems for Different Performance Criteria, *J. Basic Eng., Trans. ASME, Ser. D*, vol. 85, pp. 165–176, 1963.

4.16   Bogner, I., and L. F. Kazda: An Investigation of Switching Criteria for Higher Order Contactor Servomechanisms, *AIEE Trans.*, vol. 73, part II, pp. 118–127, 1954.

4.17   Bushaw, D.: Optimal Discontinuous Forcing Terms, *Contributions to the Theory of Nonlinear Oscillations*, vol. IV, Princeton University Press, Princeton, N.J., 1958. (This is an abbreviated version of Bushaw's doctoral dissertation, which was finished in 1953.)

4.18   Tsien, H. S.: *Engineering Cybernetics*, McGraw-Hill Book Company, New York, 1954.

4.19 Flügge-Lotz, I., and Mih Yin: On the Optimum Response of Third-order Contactor Control Systems, AFOSR TN 60-476, *Stanford Univ. Div. Eng. Mechan. Tech. Rept.* 125 April, 1960. (An abbreviated version was published in *J. Basic Eng., Trans. ASME, Ser. D,* vol. 83, pp. 59–64, 1961.)

4.20 Flügge-Lotz, I., and H. A. Titus, The Optimum Response of Full Third-order Systems with Contactor Control, *J. Basic Eng., Trans. ASME, Ser. D,* vol. 5, p. 554, 1962.

4.21 Flügge-Lotz, I., and H. A. Titus, Jr., Optimum and Quasi-optimum Control of Third- and Fourth-order Systems, *Autom. Remote Control: Proc. Second Intern. Congr. Intern. Federation Autom. Control,* Basel, 1963, Butterworth-Oldenbourg publishers. (This is an abbreviated version of *Stanford Univ. Div. Eng. Mechan. Tech. Rept.* 134, October, 1962.)

4.22 Frederick, D. K.: Piecewise-linear Switching Functions for Quasi-minimum Time Contactor Control Systems, *Stanford Univ. Dept. Aeron. Astronaut. Tech. Rept.* 178, December, 1963. (An abbreviated version was presented in Preprints of papers at the Joint Automatic Controls Conference, Seattle, Wash., 1966.)

4.23 Gragg, B. B.: Computation of Approximately Optimal Control, *Stanford Univ. Dept. Aeron. Astronaut. Tech. Rept.* 179, January, 1964.

4.24 Flügge-Lotz, I., and Andrew Craig: The Choice of Time for Zeroing a Disturbance in a Minimum-fuel Consumption Control Problem, *J. Basic Eng., Trans. ASME, Ser. D,* vol. 87, 1965.

4.25 Fuller, A. T.: Relay Control Systems Optimized for Various Performance Criteria, *Proc. First Intern. Congr. Intern. Federation Autom. Control, Moscow,* 1960, Butterworth & Co. (Publishers), Ltd. London, 1962, vol. I, p. 510.

4.26 Fuller, A. T.: An Example of Pontryagin's Method in the Optimization of Non-linear Control Systems, 25.4.1961, Cambridge University, Cambridge, England (dittoed report), published in a revised version as Study of an Optimum Nonlinear Control System, *J. Electron. Control,* vol. 15, pp. 63–71, 1963. (Additional material to this problem, not used here, is Further Study of an Optimal Non-linear Control System, *J. Electron. Control Section,* vol. 17, no. 3, pp. 283–300, 1964.)

4.27 Halkin, H.: On the Differential Equation $z^{(4)} = -\operatorname{sgn} z$, 25.4.61 Rept. AF33 (657)-8559 NASr-103 (to be published).

4.28 Almuzara, José Luis Garciá: "Minimum Time Control of a Nonlinear System," doctoral dissertation, Stanford University, Department of Aeronautics and Astronautics, Stanford, Calif., May, 1966.

4.29 Almuzara, José L. Garciá, and I. Flügge-Lotz: Minimum Time Control of a Nonlinear System, *J. Differential Equations,* to be published in 1968.

5
Synthesis of optimal on-off controllers, suboptimal control, and related problems

5.1 INTRODUCTION

Thus far we have considered primarily the zeroing of a single disturbance, where the final state was in each case the origin of the coordinate system. Even when the final point is not the origin, a coordinate transformation easily reduces many problems to the form of those we have discussed. However, we must also consider the case where a second disturbance occurs before the first one is zeroed. The general case would be that of one object moving in pursuit of another moving object, with the pursuing object to meet the pursued one under given conditions. In this case the programmed control is inadequate and a feedback control is needed. In other words, the control must depend on the present and final state of the system, and not just on its initial and final state.

The design of an optimal feedback control will not be easy in many cases. For practical reasons the design will often only approximate the optimal-control law. Since we cannot expect truly optimal performance by such a design, we shall call many of them *suboptimal* controls. How-

228

ever, the performance of such designs often comes rather close to the optimal performance.

We should also keep in mind that optimal discontinuous controls will exhibit features which are due to the imperfections of relays. Therefore reaching of the equilibrium state after a disturbance may show a behavior of the system which resembles the behavior we experienced when we studied examples of discontinuous control with linear switching functions.

5.2 SUBOPTIMAL CONTROLS DESIGNED AS FEEDBACK CONTROLS

5.2.1 A second-order plant

Let us return to the example of Sec. 4.4.8. It has been decided that the zeroing is to be accomplished in times T which allow switching points to lie on straight lines through the origin. Such a design is truly optimal for certain infinite sets of initial conditions but not for all initial conditions (all points of the x_1x_2 phase plane). The angle these lines

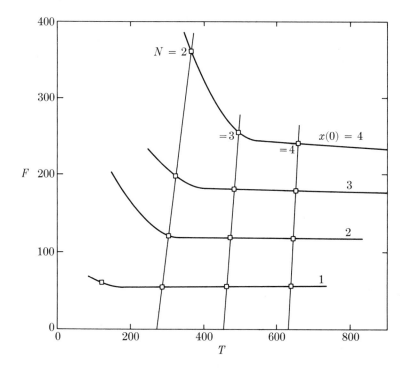

Fig. 5.1 Plant $1/(s^2 + 1)$; effect on fuel consumption of time for solution.

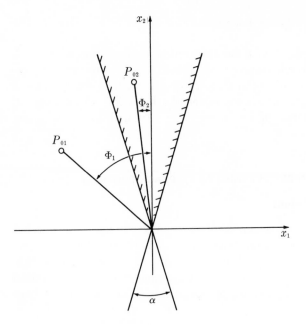

Fig. 5.2 Plant $1/(s^2 + 1)$; region of control application. P_{01} is outside the sector of control application; P_{02} is inside the sector of control application.

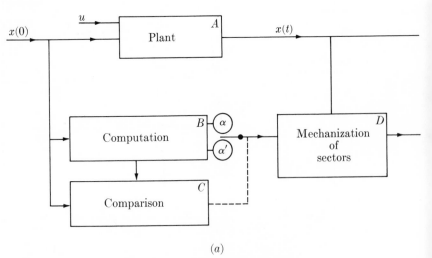

(a)

Fig. 5.3 Plant $1/(s^2 + 1)$. (a) Control system schematic.

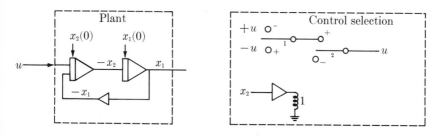

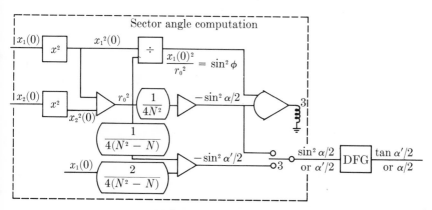

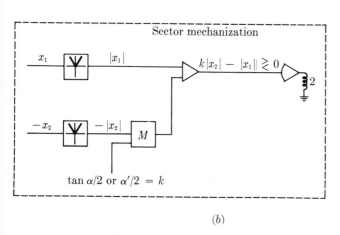

(b)

Fig. 5.3 Plant $1/(s^2 + 1)$. (b) Analog simulation block diagram.

form with the x_2 axis can be determined in different ways. First, a diagram will show how the fuel consumption depends on the magnitude of the disturbance $|\mathbf{x}_0| = r_0 = \sqrt{x_{10}^2 + x_{20}^2}$ and on the time T allowed for zeroing. Figure 5.1 shows such a diagram relating the number N of applications of fuel action to the time T. The maximum value of $|\mathbf{x}_0|$ is generally known for a proposed control system, so either the number N or the time T may be chosen for the design. A fixed value of N gives the simplest design. If the initial point P_{01} lies outside a sector of control application the sector width α is given by

$$\sin \alpha/2 = \frac{r_0}{2N} \tag{5.1}$$

with the requirement that $r_0/2N \le 1$ (see Fig. 5.2). If the initial point P_{02} lies inside in a sector of control application α' is given by

$$\sin^2 \frac{\alpha'}{2} = \frac{r_0^2 - 2r_0 \sin \phi}{4(N^2 - N)} \qquad N = 2, 3, 4 \ldots \tag{5.2}$$

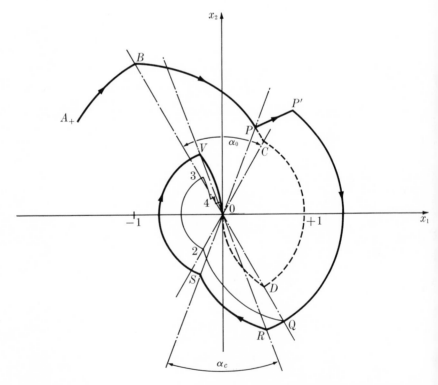

Fig. 5.4 Plant $1/(s^2 + 1)$; minimum-fuel consumption control; disturbance trajectory.

For the derivation of these formulas see Ref. 5.2. Figure 5.3 shows the control system schematically and in detail.

If the design is a compromise solution based upon statistics of the expected inputs, a fixed sector width may be chosen. In this case chatter motion must be expected at the end of the trajectory; however, these oscillations between $u = |N|$ and $u = 0$ are less wasteful than oscillations in a system with one linear switching function. If repeated disturbances are expected the sector angle can be recomputed at selected instances. Figure 5.4 shows the effect of such a sampling. Compare trajectory $ABPP'QO$ to $ABPP'RVO$. In Ref. 5.2 the design of a suboptimal system for a plant with transfer function $1/(s^2 + 2\zeta s + 1)$ is also discussed.

5.2.2 A fourth-order plant

The control of the attitude of satellites has put emphasis on the control of plants of fourth and sixth order. If the satellite is in a circular orbit and disturbances from the desired attitude are small, the sixth-order system can usually be decoupled into a second-order system governing the motion around the pitch axis and a fourth-order system governing the motion around the roll and yaw axes. We shall examine this roll-yaw system as an example of a fourth-order controlled system; for the derivation of the equations see De Bra (Ref. 5.4).

If ψ and ϕ denote yaw and roll angle, and I_1, I_2, and I_3 are the moments of inertia about the yaw, roll, and pitch axes, then the coupled roll and yaw motions are described by

$$
\begin{aligned}
\ddot{\psi} + \frac{I_3 - I_2}{I_1}\, n^2\psi - \left(1 - \frac{I_3 - I_2}{I_1}\right) n\dot{\phi} &= \frac{T_{c\psi}}{I_1} \\
\ddot{\phi} + 4\frac{I_3 - I_1}{I_2}\, n^2\phi + \left(1 - \frac{I_3 - I_1}{I_2}\right) n\dot{\psi} &= \frac{T_{c\phi}}{I_2}
\end{aligned}
\tag{5.3}
$$

where n denotes the orbital frequency and $T_{c\psi}$ and $T_{c\phi}$ are the applied controlling torques. We introduce a new time variable $\tau = nt$ and a vector

$$
\mathbf{Y}^T = (\psi, \mathring{\psi}, \phi, \mathring{\phi})
\tag{5.4}
$$

where $\mathring{\phi}$, for example, stands for $d\phi/d\tau$. In addition, we use the abbreviations

$$
\frac{T_{c\psi}}{n^2 I_1} = u_1
$$

$$
\frac{T_{c\phi}}{n^2 I_2} = u_2
\tag{5.5}
$$

$$
\frac{I_3 - I_2}{I_1} = \alpha_1
$$

$$
\frac{I_3 - I_1}{I_2} = \alpha_2
\tag{5.6}
$$

The admissible control values are $|u_1| \leq U_1$ and $|u_2| \leq U_2$, since gas jets will be used for controlling the attitude of the satellite.

With this simplified notation we obtain the system equations

$$
\begin{bmatrix} Y_1 \\ Y_2 \\ Y_3 \\ Y_4 \end{bmatrix}^{\circ} = \begin{bmatrix} 0 & 1 & 0 & 0 \\ -\alpha_1 & 0 & 0 & (1-\alpha_1) \\ 0 & 0 & 0 & 1 \\ 0 & (\alpha_2-1) & -4\alpha_2 & 0 \end{bmatrix} \begin{bmatrix} Y_1 \\ Y_2 \\ Y_3 \\ Y_4 \end{bmatrix} + \begin{bmatrix} 0 \\ u_1 \\ 0 \\ u_2 \end{bmatrix} \tag{5.7}
$$

It is possible to uncouple the modes of motion by introducing a linear transformation $\mathbf{X} = B\mathbf{Y}$, where

$$
B = \begin{bmatrix} \dfrac{\alpha_1}{\omega_1} & 0 & 0 & \dfrac{\omega_1(\omega_2{}^2 - 4\alpha_2)}{4\alpha_2(1-\alpha_2)} \\[2ex] 0 & 1 & \dfrac{4\alpha_2 - \omega_2{}^2}{1-\alpha_2} & 0 \\[2ex] 0 & \dfrac{\omega_2(\alpha_1 - \omega_1{}^2)}{\alpha_1(1-\alpha_1)} & \dfrac{4\alpha_2}{\omega_2} & 0 \\[2ex] \dfrac{\omega_1{}^2 - \alpha_1}{1-\alpha_1} & 0 & 0 & 1 \end{bmatrix} \tag{5.8}
$$

and ω_1 and ω_2 are the roots of the characteristic equation

$$
s^4 + [(1-\alpha_1)(1-\alpha_2) + \alpha_1 + 4\alpha_2]s^2 + 4\alpha_1\alpha_2 = 0 \tag{5.9}
$$

We obtain the system

$$
\begin{bmatrix} X_1 \\ X_2 \\ X_3 \\ X_4 \end{bmatrix}^{\circ} = \begin{bmatrix} 0 & \omega_1 & 0 & 0 \\ -\omega_1 & 0 & 0 & 0 \\ 0 & 0 & 0 & \omega_2 \\ 0 & 0 & -\omega_2 & 0 \end{bmatrix} \begin{bmatrix} X_1 \\ X_2 \\ X_3 \\ X_4 \end{bmatrix} + \begin{bmatrix} 0 & \beta_1 \\ 1 & 0 \\ \beta_2 & 0 \\ 0 & 1 \end{bmatrix} \begin{bmatrix} u_1 \\ u_2 \end{bmatrix} \tag{5.10}
$$

where

$$
\beta_1 = \frac{\omega_1(4\alpha_2 - \omega_2{}^2)}{4\alpha_2(\alpha_2 - 1)}
$$

$$
\beta_2 = \frac{\omega_2(\alpha_1 - \omega_1{}^2)}{\alpha_1(1-\alpha_1)}
$$

In other words, the fourth-order system without controls would be decoupled into two second-order systems. Values of moments of inertia which produce a satisfactory pitch-attitude performance require that β_1 and β_2 be positive and smaller than 1 and that $\omega_2/\omega_1 \leq 10$ if $\omega_2 > \omega_1$.

We add $\overset{\circ}{X}_0 = |u_1| + |u_2|$ to the system to indicate that fuel consumption is to be kept to a minimum in zeroing the disturbance in a given time T. Then the hamiltonian of the system is given by

$$
\begin{aligned}
H = {} & p_0(|u_1| + |u_2|) + p_1(\omega_1 X_2 + \beta_1 u_2) + p_2(-\omega_1 X_1 + u_1) \\
& + p_3(-\omega_2 X_4 + \beta_2 u_1) + p_4(-\omega_2 X_3 + u_2) \tag{5.11}
\end{aligned}
$$

The equations for the adjoint functions are given by

$$
\begin{aligned}
\overset{\circ}{p}_0 &= 0 \\
\overset{\circ}{p}_1 &= -\omega_1 p_2 \\
\overset{\circ}{p}_2 &= -\omega_1 p_1 \\
\overset{\circ}{p}_3 &= -(-\omega_2 p_4) \\
\overset{\circ}{p}_4 &= -(-\omega_2 p_3)
\end{aligned}
\tag{5.12}
$$

Since the equations for the adjoints are linear in the adjoints, we can choose for p_0, which must be negative at the final time T, the value -1. Then for maximizing H it is sufficient to consider the function

$$
H^* = -|u_1| - |u_2| + u_1(p_2 + \beta_2 p_3) + u_2(p_4 + \beta_1 p_1) \tag{5.13}
$$

Hence the control law is given by

$$
\begin{aligned}
u_1 &= \begin{cases} U_1 \operatorname{sgn}(p_2 + \beta_2 p_3) & |U_1(p_2 + \beta_2 p_3)| \geq U_1 \\ 0 & |U_1(p_2 + \beta_2 p_3)| < U_1 \end{cases} \\
u_2 &= \begin{cases} U_2 \operatorname{sgn}(p_4 + \beta_1 p_1) & |U_2(p_4 + \beta_1 p_1)| \geq U_2 \\ 0 & |U_2(p_4 + \beta_1 p_1)| < U_2 \end{cases}
\end{aligned}
\tag{5.14}
$$

and, we again have a discontinuous control. From Eqs. (5.12) it follows that

$$
\begin{aligned}
u_1 &= U_1 \operatorname{sgn}[C_1 \cos(\omega_1 \tau + \delta_1) + \beta_2 C_2 \cos(\omega_2 \tau + \delta_2)] \\
u_2 &= U_2 \operatorname{sgn}[C_2 \cos(\omega_2 \tau + \delta_2) + \beta_1 C_1 \cos(\omega_1 \tau + \delta_1)]
\end{aligned}
\tag{5.15}
$$

The constants C_1, C_2, δ_1, and δ_2 must be determined in such a way that the initial error $\mathbf{X}_{\text{in}}$ is reduced in time T to $\mathbf{X}_f = 0$. It is evident from Eqs. (5.15) that this is a difficult task. Before we consider finding these constants, however, it is important to get an idea of the state trajectory. From Eq. (5.10) it follows that between switching points the projections of the trajectories are composed of portions of circles. For a portion passing through a state point $(X_{1S}, X_{2S}, X_{3S}, X_{4S})$ the projections into the $X_1 X_2$ plane and $X_3 X_4$ plane are given by

$$
\begin{aligned}
\left(X_{1S} - \frac{U_1}{\omega_1}\right)^2 + \left(X_{2S} + \frac{\beta_1 U_2}{\omega_1}\right)^2 &= \left(X_1 - \frac{U_1}{\omega_1}\right)^2 + \left(X_2 + \frac{\beta_1 U_2}{\omega_1}\right)^2 \\
\left(X_{3S} - \frac{U_2}{\omega_2}\right)^2 + \left(X_{4S} + \frac{\beta_2 U_1}{\omega_2}\right)^2 &= \left(X_3 - \frac{U_2}{\omega_2}\right)^2 + \left(X_4 + \frac{\beta_2 U_1}{\omega_2}\right)^2
\end{aligned}
$$
$$\tag{5.16}$$

These are equations of circles in the two planes $X_1 X_2$ and $X_3 X_4$. Their centers are determined by the applied control; there are eight circle center-points in each plane (see Fig. 5.5).

As mentioned above, the determination of C_i and δ_i for a special case would be quite a problem. Craig and Flügge-Lotz (Ref. 5.3) ran many optimal solutions on the analog computer in backward time; this

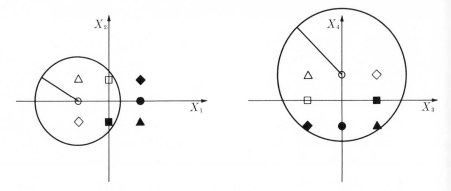

Fig. 5.5 Fourth-order plant with two control inputs; trajectory centers.

collection of samples showed definite trends which might, with the help of simple considerations of probability theory, be used to develop an efficient suboptimal control that corresponds to the use of a fixed-sector method of control application in second-order systems.

5.2.3 Optimal and near-optimal regulation of spacecraft spin axes

This problem has been treated by M. Yin and W. C. Grimmel (Ref. 5.32) and only recently came to the attention of the author. The system is described by the equations

$$I \frac{dw_x}{dt} = (I - I_z)w_y w_z + T_x$$

$$I \frac{dw_y}{dt} = (I_z - I)w_x w_z + T_y$$

$$I_z \frac{dw_z}{dt} = 0$$

where w_x, w_y, w_z = components along the principal axes of inertia of the body angular velocity

I_z = polar moment of inertia

I = moment of inertia about any axis orthogonal to the polar axis

T_x, T_y = control torques.

Since w_z is assumed to be constant, actual investigation is concerned with a second-order system with two control inputs. T_x and T_y are bounded:

$$|T_x| \leq M \quad \text{and} \quad |T_y| \leq M$$

The performance criterion, a measure of fuel consumption for zeroing a deviation $w_x(0)$ and $w_y(0)$ from $w_x = 0$ and $w_y = 0$ in time T, is given by

$$J = \int_0^T (|T_x| + |T_y|)\, dt \to \min$$

The control torques T_x and T_y are discontinuous functions, as one can easily see by investigating the hamiltonian of the system; they can only assume the values $\pm M$ or 0. This means that T_x and T_y are "coast" functions like the one control function in the problem treated in Sec. 5.2.1. Yin and Grimmel studied the location of the switching points in the $w_x w_y$ plane and established charts for the trade-off between fuel consumption and length of time for zeroing deviations from the desired state. These charts show possibilities for developing suboptimal controls; their appearance will remind the reader of Fig. 5.1. The discussion of various feedback designs is very interesting.

5.2.4 A second-order plant with a disturbance to be zeroed with limited control effort in a given time with minimum fuel consumption

The preceding examples have shown the importance of knowing the control input as function of the state variables. In these examples the time for the mission was chosen in advance and then a suboptimal scheme for finding the location of the switching points was determined. Now we want to determine the control at any instant of time, given the phase point and the time to go. This means that the boundaries that are to separate the regions of positive, negative, and zero control should be given in the phase plane as functions of time to go (Refs. 5.5 and 5.6).

Consider again the control system

$$\dot{\mathbf{x}}(t) = \begin{bmatrix} 0 & 1 \\ -1 & 0 \end{bmatrix} \mathbf{x}(t) + \begin{bmatrix} 0 \\ 1 \end{bmatrix} u(t)$$

or $\quad \dot{\mathbf{x}}(t) = A\mathbf{x}(t) + \mathbf{b}u$

$$(5.17)$$

with $|u| \le 1$ and the performance criterion

$$I(\mathbf{x}_0, T_0) = \int_{t_0}^{t_f} |u^*(t)|\, dt \to \min \qquad t_f - t_0 = T_0 \qquad (5.18)$$

The hamiltonian is given by

$$H = p_0|u| + p_1 x_2 + p_2(-x_1 + u) \qquad (5.19)$$

The adjoint function $\mathbf{p}$ is determined by

$$\begin{aligned} \dot{p}_0 &= 0 \\ \dot{p}_1 &= p_2 \\ \dot{p}_2 &= -p_1 \end{aligned} \qquad (5.20)$$

or $p_0 = \text{const}$ and $p_2 = p_{1f} \sin (t_f - t) + p_{2f} \cos (t_f - t)$. Thus the final value of p_2 is p_{2f}, the final value of $p_1 = -p_{1f}$, and the value of p_0 is a constant which has to be smaller than or equal to zero. The value zero must be excluded, however; otherwise the hamiltonian will not depend on the performance criterion. Since any negative value can be chosen without influencing the extremization of H, which is a linear function of the p_i, we choose $p_0 = -1$. The maximum value of the hamiltonian is obtained with $u = \text{sgn } p_2(t)$ for $|p_2| \geq 1$ and $u = 0$ for $|p_2| < 1$.

Figure 5.6 shows the dependence of the control action on the values of the integration constants p_{1f} and p_{2f} and the time to go $T_1 = t_f - t_1$. With the help of this figure we can, for example, trace the boundaries of the regions for the different control action in the $x_1 x_2$ plane (see Fig. 5.7). It is clear that for time to go $T_1 = 3\pi/2$ only a limited region of the $x_1 x_2$ plane contains phase points from which the origin can be reached in this time. The region is limited by the *isochrone* for T_1, which prohibits occurrence of the control-action zero (if either p_{1f} or p_{2f} or both go toward infinity, we have the limiting case that the time of the control-action "0" shrinks to zero). Figure 5.8 shows the limiting isochrones for selected times in a three-dimensional space $x_1 x_2 t$. More details are given in Ref. 5.6.

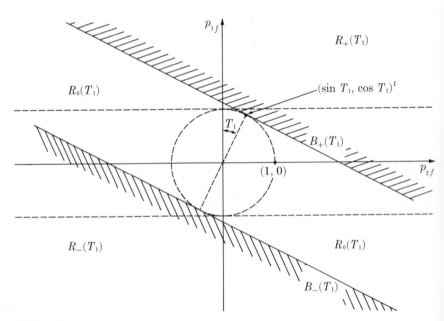

Fig. 5.6 Second-order plant; the adjoint plane p_f for the system with two imaginary roots.

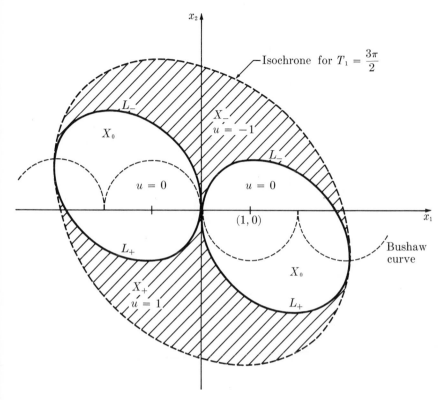

Fig. 5.7 Plant of Fig. 5.6; the optimal control as a function of the instantaneous state for $T_1 = 3\pi/2$.

Obviously, a control system that implemented these switching rules would be very complicated. An average subdivision of the x_1x_2 plane can be developed for certain region of allowed times for zeroing; one was developed by Marbach, but the suboptimal system suggested by Craig (Ref. 5.3) seems preferable.

5.2.5 The main structure of the switching surface

In Sec. 4.4.6 some suggestions were made for approximating the switching curve for a second-order system. The true character of such a curve was observed only near the final state; we worked instead with an average curve starting at some distance from the final state. This idea of a main and a fine structure of the switching surface for an nth-order system is discussed further in Ref. 5.7.

Let us first look at a plant with the transfer function $1/s(s^2 + 1)$. We shall design a suboptimal minimum-settling-time control for the sys-

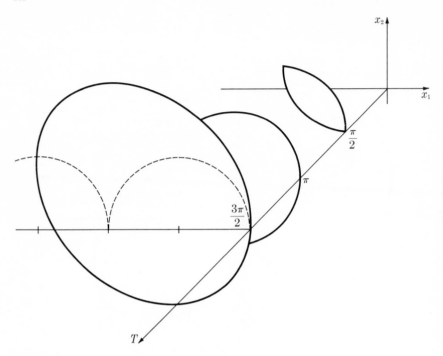

Fig. 5.8 Plant of Fig. 5.6; dependence of the optimal switching curve on the time-to-go variable T.

tem described by

$$e''' + e' = u \tag{5.21}$$

(a second-order velocity-controlled system).[1] In matrix form the system is described by

$$\dot{\mathbf{e}} = \begin{bmatrix} 0 & 1 & 0 \\ 0 & 0 & 0 \\ 0 & -1 & 0 \end{bmatrix} \mathbf{e} + \begin{bmatrix} 0 \\ 0 \\ 1 \end{bmatrix} u \tag{5.22}$$

which may be transformed into the orthogonal form by using

$$\mathbf{e} = \begin{bmatrix} 0 & -1 & 1 \\ 1 & 0 & 0 \\ 0 & 1 & 0 \end{bmatrix} \mathbf{x} \tag{5.23}$$

The canonical form of the system is then given by

$$\dot{\mathbf{x}} = \begin{bmatrix} 0 & 1 & 0 \\ -1 & 0 & 0 \\ 0 & 0 & 0 \end{bmatrix} \mathbf{x} + \begin{bmatrix} 0 \\ 1 \\ 1 \end{bmatrix} u \tag{5.24}$$

[1] A special case of the example in Sec. 4.4.7.

From Pontryagin's maximum principle we obtain the time-optimal control

$$u = \operatorname{sgn} [C_1 + C_2 \cos (t + \delta)] \qquad (5.25)$$

The constants C_1 and C_2 (actually, only the ratio C_1/C_2) and δ depend on the initial conditions. Equation (5.25) indicates that the ratio of the intervals of positive or negative settings of the relay will be constant (except for the first and last intervals).

With the aid of the procedures developed by Flügge-Lotz and Mih Yin (see Sec. 4.4.7) we can draw projections of the curves on the switching surface which contain the switching points for particular initial conditions. The projection of such a curve in the x_1x_2 plane is shown in Fig. 5.9. Note that the alternating tips of the cups lie on the lines Γ_+ and Γ_- emanating from the origin. Other initial conditions result in other pairs of lines Γ_+ and Γ_-; the entire set of these lines for all possible initial conditions forms a ruled surface. The real switching surface is a surface with many bulges (valleys and ridges) having an infinite number of points in common with the ruled surface, which we shall consider as the *main structure*. In Fig. 5.10 the main structure is indicated in the regions at

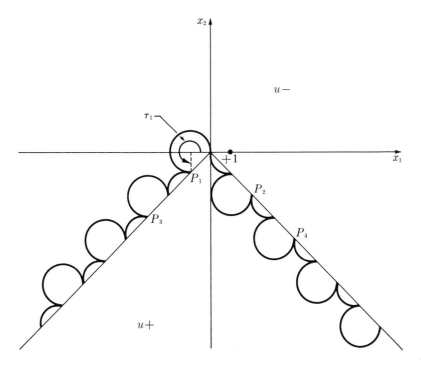

Fig. 5.9 Third-order plant; projection of a curve on the optimum switching surface, on which the switching points for given initial conditions lie.

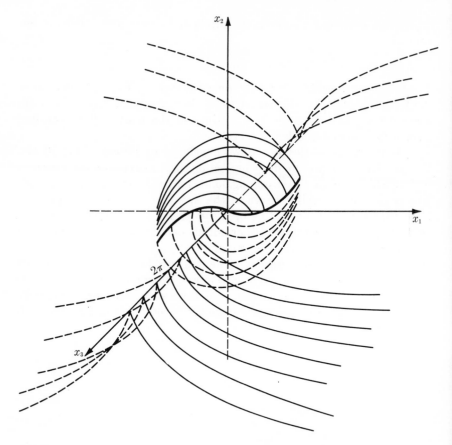

Fig. 5.10   Visualization of the quasi-optimum switching surfaces in the $x_1 x_2 x_3$ space for $(s^3 + s)e(s) = u(s)$.

some distance from the origin.   If this ruled *outer* surface is used as the switching surface $F = 0$, then the control function is given for $x_1 x_3 > 0$ by

$$u = -\operatorname{sgn} F$$
$$= -\operatorname{sgn}\left[2|x_1|x_3 + (\operatorname{sgn} x_2)(x_1{}^2 + x_2{}^2)\arccos\frac{x_1{}^2 - x_2{}^2}{x_1{}^2 + x_2{}^2}\right]$$

and for $x_1 x_3 < 0$ by   (5.26)

$$u = -\operatorname{sgn}\left[2|x_1|(x_3 - \operatorname{sgn} x_3)\pi + (\operatorname{sgn} x_2)(x_1{}^2 + x_2{}^2)\right.$$
$$\left.\arccos\frac{x_1{}^2 - x_2{}^2}{x_1{}^2 + x_2{}^2}\right]$$

Titus' thesis contains a discussion of why the x_1 and x_3 axes cannot be considered part of the switching surface; in the visualization of (Fig. 5.10) we may at least surmise that $F = 0$ is reached but not passed.

Near the origin the exact switching surface, or a very good approximation, should be used. In this case this may be the optimum-time switching surface of the plant $1/s^3$, also indicated in Fig. 5.10. This *inner* switching surface yields a switching law

$$u = -\operatorname{sgn} F = \operatorname{sgn}\left[e_1 + \frac{e_3{}^3}{3} + W e_2 e_3 + W\left(\frac{e_3{}^2}{2} + W e_2\right)^{3\!/\!2} \right]$$

(5.27)

$$\text{where } W = \operatorname{sgn}\left(e_2 + \frac{e_3|e_3|}{2} \right)$$

(5.28)

Equations (5.26) to (5.28) indicate what results are obtained (even after simplification) for suboptimal switching surfaces. There is no doubt that such switching surfaces can be realized only by digital means.

An important point that still needs discussion is where to make the transition from use of the outer to use of the inner switching surface. Wherever this transition is chosen, of course, chatter can occur during a brief period when the phase point is on the wrong side of the exact switching surface.

These switching surfaces have been investigated for a plant with the transfer function

$$\frac{1}{(s + \gamma)(s^2 + 2s\zeta + 1)}$$

and the discussion to the IFAC paper (see Ref. 5.7) indicates some results. For $\gamma = 0$ and $\zeta = 0$ the suggested procedure gives good results; for $\gamma \neq 0$ and $\zeta \neq 0$ it is suggested that the approximate surfaces be used only for $\gamma < 0.5$ and $0 < \zeta < 0.3$ so that the deviation of optimal and suboptimal time for reaching $\|e\| < \Delta$ can be kept below 20 percent.[1]

5.2.6 Optimization procedures that demand high-digital-computing devices

The last section indicated some of the difficulties in realizing an optimal control. Of course, engineers are looking chiefly for simpler methods, one of them being a kind of trial-and-error method based on the knowledge of the type of optimal control for the desired performance. If the optimal control is a discontinuous one, then it is possible to find the switching points by a trial-and-error method. An electronic model of the actual system can be built which runs at a much higher speed than the actual system, tries a number of switching-point sets, chooses the one

---

[1] $\Delta = 0$ will never be reached because of relay imperfections and the simplified inner switching surface.

with the lowest increment of performance integral, and then runs the system with this set for a short time and repeats the process.

Repetition of the process is necessary for two reasons. First, the trial-and-error process may not have been continued long enough to give the exact optimal switching instances, but only a good approximation of them (usually the number of trials in a computer program is limited); hence this trial-and-error process is repeated while the final state is being approached. Second, the system under control may not be time invariant, but may undergo slight changes in its buildup (equivalent to changes of coefficients or coefficient functions in the system equations), and this would really change the control needed for reaching the final state with the best performance.

Let us examine this method in terms of the minimum-fuel–attitude control of a rigid body in an elliptical orbit. Hales (Ref. 5.8) studied the motion of a satellite by using the full nonlinear equations but assuming that the undesired attitude deviations are never larger than 180° (pitch, yaw, or roll angle). This ensured a nonlinear dynamic system, but by limiting the deviations under consideration he avoided such difficulties as the fact that a pitch angle of zero and $2n\pi$ are physically identical. In other words, he eliminated the possibility that the trajectory may start in indifference regions of the state space, from which the final state could be reached in different ways with the same amount of fuel in a given time T. Nor did he consider singular controls (mentioned in Sec. 4.4.2), for which the maximum of the hamiltonian becomes independent of a control u_i.

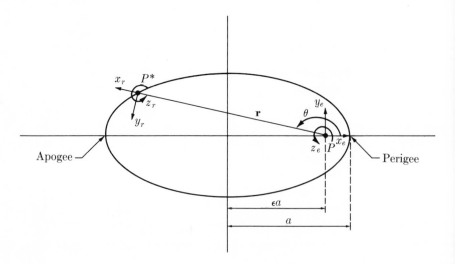

Fig. 5.11 Satellite motion; orbital and inertial reference frames.

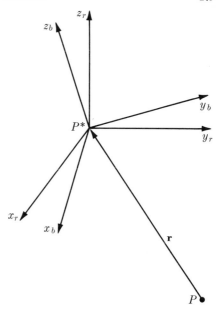

Fig. 5.12 Orbital and body fixed reference frames.

Let us describe Hales' control problem in some detail.   Figure 5.11 shows an elliptical satellite orbit and marks the orbital and inertial reference frames.   Figure 5.12 shows the orbital and body fixed reference frames, where θ is the angle between x_e and x_r and fixes the location of the satellite at time t on the orbit.   The attitude of the satellite can be described with the help of the Euler angles or the Euler parameters, which relate the systems of the body fixed coordinates to the orbital reference-frame coordinates.   Hales preferred the Euler parameters W_1, W_2, W_3, and W_4, with $\sum\limits_{i=1}^{4} W_i^2 = 4$ (see Ref. 5.9).   In addition, the angular velocity of the body with respect to the orbital reference frame is needed:

$$\boldsymbol{\omega}^{B/R} = x_2\mathbf{n}_{xb} + x_3\mathbf{n}_{yb} + x_4\mathbf{n}_{zb} \tag{5.29}$$

where $\mathbf{n}$ denotes a unity vector whose direction is indicated by subscripts. The symbol x_1 is reserved for the performance criterion; the control by gas jets is given by

$$\mathbf{u} = \begin{bmatrix} u_1 \\ u_2 \\ u_3 \end{bmatrix} = u_1\mathbf{n}_{xb} + u_2\mathbf{n}_{yb} + u_3\mathbf{n}_{zb} \tag{5.30}$$

Therefore in state-variable notation, collected in Table 10, we can represent the problem by eight differential equations for $x_1, \ldots, x_8$,[1] con-

[1] $x_5, \ldots, x_8$ correspond to $W_1, \ldots, W_4$.

Table 10   Notation and dimensions for response curves

Plot nomenclature	Original symbols	State notation	Dimensions
T	t	t	sec
Omega 1	x_2	x_2	deg/sec
Omega 2	x_3	x_3	deg/sec
Omega 3	x_4	x_4	deg/sec
$W1$	W_1	x_5	
$W2$	W_2	x_6	
$W3$	W_3	x_7	
J	J	x_1	sec^{-1}
$W4$	W_4	x_8	
$UV1$	u_x	u_1	deg/sec^2
$UV2$	u_y	u_2	deg/sec^2
$UV3$	u_z	u_3	deg/sec^2

taining the still undetermined u_1, u_2, and u_3 for optimal performance

$$\dot{x}_i = f_i(\mathbf{x},\mathbf{u},t) \tag{5.31}$$

The performance criterion

$$x_1 = \int_0^T \sum_{i=1}^3 d_i|u_i|\, dt \to \min \tag{5.32}$$

is what we need.

With this description of physical background for the general mathematical problem, we shall turn to the mathematical optimization procedure, illustrated by figures from Hales' examples.

There is no doubt that solving a system of linear differential equations would be easier than solving system (5.31) with the performance criterion (5.32). Therefore we adopt a method that is well known in general (although not in discontinuous-control studies); we choose a function $\mathbf{u}(t)$ and compute a "nominal" trajectory $\mathbf{x}_n(t)$, which in most cases will meet neither the terminal constraints nor the performance criterion. Then we linearize the equations about this nominal trajectory and improve the performance [that is, change $\mathbf{u}(t)$ by $\delta\mathbf{u}(t)$] in such a way that the terminal constraints are met and the performance-criterion value is lowered. Of course, the initial guess should, if possible, be a good one, and care must be taken that the changes stay within the framework of the linearization. This improvement method for continuous controls is called the *steepest-descent method*. By changing $\mathbf{u}$ at each instance t we create a surface in the state space which contains all trajectories with the parameter $\mathbf{u}(t) + \delta\mathbf{u}(t)$, and we choose $\delta\mathbf{u}(t)$ such that the goal (that is, the lowest performance integral) is approached in the fastest way. The chosen changes $\delta\mathbf{u}$ at all points of the nominal trajectory are related, and this relation can be expressed by a system of linear equations.

Now, in considering a discontinuous control there is no essential difficulty in assuming a discontinuous nominal control $\mathbf{u}_n(t)$ and computing a nominal trajectory $\mathbf{x}_n(t)$.[1] However, if the switching points are wrongly chosen, then at certain times t_i there will be not small changes of $\mathbf{u}_n(t)$, but finite changes of $\mathbf{u}_n(t)$, and it will be necessary to develop a modified method of steepest descent. Such a modified procedure was developed by Hales (Ref. 5.8). As a first step, expressions are derived which relate the effect of a small variation in the initial state with variations in the control history upon the terminal constraints. As we shall see, the notion of influence functions or adjoint variables plays an integral role. To arrive at the desired expression we shall consider small variations in an unbounded control as well as a finite number of *strong variations*[2] in a bounded-control history over a short time period. In addition, we shall make use of an expression for the mean-square variation of the control variable.

The *Mayer formulation* of the general optimization problem is to determine the control $\mathbf{u}(t)$ which minimizes the cost functional

$$x_1 = \phi(\mathbf{u}(t_f)) \tag{5.33}$$

in the interval $t_0 \le t \le t_f$ while satisfying both the system equations $\dot{x}_i = f_i(\mathbf{x},\mathbf{u},t)$ for t in the same interval and the constraint equations[3] $\boldsymbol{\psi} = \boldsymbol{\psi}(\mathbf{x}(t_f)) = 0$, with the quantities $\mathbf{x}(t_0)$, t_0, and t_f given.[4] In this description

$$\mathbf{u}(t) = \begin{bmatrix} u_1(t) \\ \cdots \\ u_m(t) \end{bmatrix}$$

is an m vector of control variables which may be freely chosen within an open or a closed set;

$$\mathbf{x}(t) = \begin{bmatrix} x_1(t) \\ \cdots \\ x_n(t) \end{bmatrix}$$

[1] There may be some special consideration in choosing and programming the integration procedure.

[2] Discontinuities in the control-time history are allowed. When these strong variations in control occur it will not be possible to differentiate and form such expressions as $\partial f_i(\mathbf{x},\mathbf{u},t)/\partial u_j$.

[3] These constraint equations may have the form $x_{if} = 0$ for $i = 2,3, \ldots, k$ and $x_{jf} = c_j$ for $j = k + 1, \cdots$; see Eq. (5.34).

[4] The assumption that t_f is fixed is made to simplify the analysis. This assumption is not restrictive here, as we shall consider minimum-fuel problems, which require a fixed t_f.

is an n vector of state-variable histories which result from given values of $\mathbf{x}(t_0)$ and a choice of $\mathbf{u}_n(t)$;

$$\mathbf{f} = \begin{bmatrix} f_1 \\ \cdot \cdot \cdot \\ f_n \end{bmatrix}$$

is an n vector of known functions of $\mathbf{x}(t)$, $\mathbf{u}(t)$, and t, assumed everywhere differentiable with respect to $\mathbf{x}$ and $\mathbf{u}$ for $\mathbf{u}$ lying in an open set and assumed everywhere differentiable with respect to $\mathbf{x}$ only for $\mathbf{u}$ lying in a closed set; ϕ is the performance index and is a known function of $\mathbf{x}(t)$ and $\mathbf{u}(t)$; and

$$\boldsymbol{\psi} = \begin{bmatrix} \psi_1 \\ \cdot \cdot \cdot \\ \psi_p \end{bmatrix} \tag{5.34}$$

is a p vector of terminal constraint functions, each of which is a known function of $\mathbf{x}(t_f)$, and is assumed everywhere differentiable with respect to $\mathbf{x}$ for $p \leq n$.

5.2.6a. *Unbounded control.* Let us first consider the case where $\mathbf{u}$ is not bounded. With the deviation from the nominal (chosen) $\mathbf{x}_n$ and $\mathbf{u}_n$

$$\begin{aligned} \delta \mathbf{x} &= \mathbf{x} - \mathbf{x}_n \\ \delta \mathbf{u} &= \mathbf{u} - \mathbf{u}_n \end{aligned} \tag{5.35}$$

we can linearize the differential equation $\dot{\mathbf{x}} = \mathbf{f}$ in Eq. (5.31) about $\mathbf{x}_n$ and $\mathbf{u}_n$, and we obtain

$$\delta \dot{\mathbf{x}} = F(t)\, \delta \mathbf{x} + G(t)\, \delta \mathbf{u} \tag{5.36}$$

$$\text{where } F(t) = (\nabla_x \mathbf{f})_{\mathbf{x}_n} = \begin{bmatrix} \dfrac{\partial f_1}{\partial x_1} & \cdots & \dfrac{\partial f_1}{\partial x_n} \\ \cdot \cdot \cdot \cdot \cdot \cdot \cdot \cdot \\ \dfrac{\partial f_n}{\partial x_1} & \cdots & \dfrac{\partial f_n}{\partial x_n} \end{bmatrix}_{\mathbf{x}_n}$$

is an $n \times n$ matrix of partial derivatives evaluated on the nominal state trajectory $\mathbf{x}_n$ and

$$G(t) = (\nabla_u \mathbf{f})_{\mathbf{x}_n} = \begin{bmatrix} \dfrac{\partial f_1}{\partial u_1} & \cdots & \dfrac{\partial f_1}{\partial u_m} \\ \cdot \cdot \cdot \cdot \cdot \cdot \cdot \cdot \cdot \\ \dfrac{\partial f_n}{\partial u_1} & \cdots & \dfrac{\partial f_n}{\partial u_m} \end{bmatrix}_{\mathbf{x}_n}$$

is an $m \times n$ matrix of partial derivatives evaluated on $\mathbf{x}_n$. As stated in Ref. 5.10, the solution to Eq. (5.36) may be written as

$$\delta \mathbf{x}(t) = \Phi(t,t_0)\, \delta \mathbf{x}(t_0) + \int_{t_0}^{t} \Phi(t,\tau)G(\tau)\, \delta \mathbf{u}(\tau)\, d\tau \tag{5.37}$$

where $\Phi(t,t_0)$ is called the state-transition matrix (see, for instance, Ref. 5.11). $\Phi(\cdot\, , \cdot)$ exhibits the following pertinent properties:

$$\frac{d\Phi(t,\tau)}{dt} = F(t)\Phi(t,\tau) \tag{5.38}$$

$$\frac{d\Phi(\tau,t)}{dt} = -\Phi(\tau,t)F(t) \tag{5.39}$$

$$\Phi(t,t) = I \tag{5.40}$$

$$\Phi(t,\xi)\Phi(\xi,\tau) = \Phi(t,\tau) \tag{5.41}$$

Next we need an expression relating the effect of a small variation in state and control to the final variation in state. Letting $t = t_f$ and $t_0 = t$ (where t is a running variable) in Eq. (5.37) leads to

$$\delta \mathbf{x}_f = \Phi(t_f,t)\, \delta \mathbf{x}(t) + \int_{t}^{t_f} \Phi(t_f,\tau)G(\tau)\, \delta \mathbf{u}(\tau)\, d\tau \tag{5.42}$$

A small variation $\delta \psi$ in the terminal constraint leads to the expression

$$\delta \psi = (\nabla_x \psi)_{\mathbf{x}_{n_f}}\, \delta \mathbf{x}_f \tag{5.43}$$

$$\text{where } \nabla_x \psi = \begin{bmatrix} \dfrac{\partial \psi_1}{\partial x_1} & \cdots & \dfrac{\partial \psi_1}{\partial x_n} \\ \cdot\cdot\cdot\cdot\cdot\cdot\cdot\cdot\cdot \\ \dfrac{\partial \psi_p}{\partial x_1} & \cdots & \dfrac{\partial \psi_p}{\partial x_n} \end{bmatrix}$$

Now, if we define

$$\Lambda^T(t_f,t) \equiv (\nabla_x \psi)_{\mathbf{x}_{n_f}} \Phi(t_f,t) \tag{5.44}$$

where the superscript T denotes the transpose operation and $\Lambda^T(t_f,t)$ is a $(p \times n)$ matrix, called the *influence matrix* or *matrix of influence coefficients*. Upon differentiating Eq. (5.44) with respect to t and using Eqs. (5.39) and (5.44), we obtain the adjoint differential equations

$$\dot{\Lambda}^T(t_f,t) = -\Lambda^T(t_f,t)F(t) \tag{5.45}$$

with the boundary conditions at $t = t_f$ [from Eqs. (5.44) and (5.40)]

$$\Lambda^T(t_f,t_f) = (\nabla_x \psi)|_{\mathbf{x}_{n_f}} \tag{5.46}$$

The adjoint equations (5.45) may be integrated in reverse time from $t = t_f$ with boundary conditions (5.46).

Finally, the desired sensitivity relationship between $\delta \mathbf{x}$, $\delta \mathbf{u}$, and $\delta \psi$ is formed by using Eqs. (5.42), (5.43), and (5.44) to give

$$\delta \psi = \Lambda^T(t_f, t) \; \delta \mathbf{x}(t) + \int_t^{t_f} \Lambda^T(t_f, \tau) G(\tau) \; \delta \mathbf{u}(\tau) \; d\tau \tag{5.47}$$

The variable t could be set equal to t_0 [in which case $\delta \mathbf{x}(t_0) \equiv 0$, from Eq. (5.33)], it could be a continuous running variable, or it could possess discrete values t_k, with $k = 1, \ldots, r$, where t_k is contained in $t_0 \leq t_k < t_f$. Allowing t to be a continuous, or "sampled," variable may improve convergence in the steepest-descent method.

The introduced linearization must be watched to see that it remains valid. An equation for the mean-square variation in control V is written as

$$V(t_0) = \int_{t_0}^{t_f} \delta \mathbf{u}^T \; W(\tau) \; \delta \mathbf{u} \; d\tau \tag{5.48}$$

where $W(t)$ is an arbitrary symmetric positive-definite matrix. If the value of V is "small," then the variations in control are "small" and all the assumptions that prompted the development of the sensitivity relationships will remain valid. The selected change in $W(t)$ as a function of time is important in problems in which parameters change widely over the range of the problem solution (see Ref. 5.12). Where there is more than one control variable it is also necessary to decide the *relative* weight of the different control-variable changes at a given instant in time (Ref. 5.13).

5.2.6b   *Bounded control.*   We are interested in problems with bounds on the magnitude of the components of the control vector. We shall assume here that $|u_i| \leq U_i$ for $i = 1, 2, 3$. For certain cost functionals, such as minimum fuel or certain forms of the minimum-fuel problem, the necessary conditions of Pontryagin's maximum principle require that the control u_i be discontinuous and either completely on (at plus or minus) or completely off. Components of the differential constraint $\dot{\mathbf{x}} = \mathbf{f}$ in Eq. (5.31) contain terms such as $|u_i|$ and are therefore not differentiable in those arguments. Hence the concept of *strong variation* is introduced for a finite number of large changes in u_i, each occurring over a short time δt_d. These variations in u_i will cause large variations in the slope of the state trajectories.

The first step in the derivation is to obtain an expression similar to Eq. (5.37) which relates a variation in $\mathbf{x}_n(t_0)$ and a large variation in control, $\delta \mathbf{u}$, to the variation in $\mathbf{x}_n(t)$. First consider the variation in $\mathbf{x}_n$ resulting *only* from a single large variation in control, $\delta \mathbf{u}$, occurring between t_d and $t_d + \delta t_d$. As a result of this variation in control, the new trajectory $\mathbf{x}$ might be generated as in Fig. 5.13. The nominal control switching time

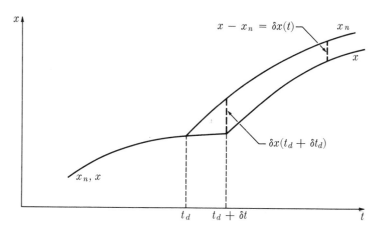

Fig. 5.13 Variation in state resulting from strong variation in control for the scalar case.

$t = t_d$, which causes the discontinuous slope in $\mathbf{x}_n$, is changed to $t = t_d + \delta t_d$. This new switching time represents a new control $\mathbf{u}(t)$ and generates the new trajectory $\mathbf{x}(t)$. Up to time $t = t_d$ the variation in $\mathbf{x}_n$ is zero. As seen from the figure, the expression for $\delta \mathbf{x}$ at $t = t_d + \delta t_d$ may be written (to first order) as

$$\delta \mathbf{x}(t_d + \delta t_d) = [\mathbf{f}(\mathbf{x}_n, \mathbf{u}_n(t_d^-), t_d) - \mathbf{f}(\mathbf{x}_n, \mathbf{u}_n(t_d^+), t_d)] \, \delta t_d \qquad (5.49)$$

Since no further variations in control are encountered, at time $t = t_d + \delta t_d$ the variation $\delta \mathbf{x}$ will be transmitted through time by the state-transition matrix in the form

$$\delta \mathbf{x}(t) = \Phi(t, t_d + \delta t_d) \, \delta \mathbf{x}(t_d + \delta t_d) \qquad t \geq t_d + \delta t_d \qquad (5.50)$$

Since the state trajectories $\mathbf{x}(t)$ or $\mathbf{x}_n(t)$ are continuous and δt_d is small, Eq. (5.50) may be written, with only first-order terms taken into account, as

$$\delta \mathbf{x}(t) = \Phi(t, t_d) \, \delta \mathbf{x}(t_d + \delta t_d) \qquad (5.51)$$

Combining Eqs. (5.49) and (5.51) yields an expression which relates a single strong variation in control to $\delta \mathbf{x}(t)$:

$$\delta \mathbf{x}(t) = \Phi(t, t_d)(\mathbf{f}^- - \mathbf{f}^+) \, \delta t_d \qquad (5.52)$$

where use has been made of the definition

$$\mathbf{f}^\pm = \mathbf{f}(\mathbf{x}_n, \mathbf{u}_n(t_d^\pm), t_d) \qquad (5.53)$$

Next, by assuming that there are more strong variations in control as well as a variation in the initial conditions at $t = t_0$, we obtain an equation similar to Eq. (5.37):

$$\delta\mathbf{x}(t) = \Phi(t,t_0)\ \delta\mathbf{x}(t_0) + \sum_i \Phi(t,t_i)(\mathbf{f}^- - \mathbf{f}^+)\ \delta t_1 \tag{5.54}$$

where the summation is taken over each of the switching points of the control and $t_0 \leq t_i \leq t$.

An expression similar to Eq. (5.42), which relates the effect of a small variation in state and strong variations in control, is derived by letting $t = t_f$ and $t_0 = t$ in Eq. (5.54) to give

$$\delta\mathbf{x}_f = \Phi(t_f,t)\ \delta\mathbf{x}(t) + \sum_i \Phi(t_f,t_i)G(t_i)\ \delta\mathbf{u}(t_i) \qquad t \leq t_i \leq t_f \tag{5.55}$$

The identity

$$G(t_i)\ \delta\mathbf{u}(t_i) \equiv (\mathbf{f}^- - \mathbf{f}^+)\ \delta t_i \tag{5.56}$$

is introduced for analytic and computational convenience.[1] This identity should be used for computing $G(t_i)$.

The last step in this derivation is to write the desired sensitivity relation, which is similar to Eq. (5.47) for the unbounded-control case. Premultiplying Eq. (5.55) by $(\nabla_x\psi)_{\mathbf{x}_{n_f}}$ and using Eqs. (5.43) and (5.44) gives

$$\delta\psi = \Lambda^T(t_f,t)\ \delta\mathbf{x}(t) + \sum_i \Lambda^T(t_f,t_i)G(t_i)\ \delta\mathbf{u}(t_i) \tag{5.57}$$

The presence of the strong variations in $\delta\mathbf{u}$ is reflected in the above summation.

An expression for the mean-square variation in control similar to Eq. (5.48) is written as

$$V(t_0) = \sum_i \delta\mathbf{u}^T(t_i)T_i\ \delta\mathbf{u}(t_i) \tag{5.58}$$

where $T_i = T(t_i)$ and the summation extends over all switching times in the interval $t_0 \leq t \leq t_f$.

5.2.6c *Steepest-descent techniques.* Let us now consider various ways in which the basic sensitivity relationships developed above may be used to derive equations that indicate how the control history is to be changed to meet a desired terminal constraint while minimizing a specific cost functional. We shall examine several alternative paths.

The technique introduced by Kelley (Ref. 5.14) incorporates a penalty-function treatment of the terminal constraints. The new func-

---

[1] We shall not go into the details of digital simulation. Note that the quantity $\delta\mathbf{u}(t_i)$ in the discrete-control case contains an indication of how the switching time is to be changed: $\delta u_j(t_i) = U_j\ \delta t_i$.

tional that is to be minimized is written as

$$J^* = \Phi(\mathbf{x}(t_f)) + \sum_{i=1}^{p} \nu_i \psi_i^2 \tag{5.59}$$

where ν is a $p \times 1$ vector of positive constants. Kelley then minimizes J^*, subject to a given value of an integral similar to $V(t_0)$ of Eq. (5.48). This technique will satisfy the terminal constraint ψ only approximately. Bryson and Denham (Ref. 5.15) minimize the first variation of the original functional ϕ, subject to a specific value of $V(t_0)$ in Eq. (5.48) and to a specific value of $\delta\psi$. The success of this method, as measured by the rate of convergence to a solution of the boundary-value problem, is strongly influenced by the choice of $V(t_0)$.

A further development by Bryson and Denham (Ref. 5.16) and a modification by Rosenbaum (Ref. 5.17) seem to offer the most promise. The integral $V(t_0)$ is minimized subject to the constraint $\delta\psi$, where the vector ψ has been augmented by the cost functional ϕ. Experience has led to the recommendation that no attempt be made to improve the cost functional during the first few iterations until the terminal constraints are met (Ref. 5.17). Upon satisfaction of the terminal constraint, a reduction or increase in the cost functional may be specified and further iterations performed until a satisfactory problem solution is found. The derivation of the desired control equations is found in Appendix 5.1. A computational algorithm is also presented.

Several writers have touched on problems with bounded control, and some have considered moving the switching times to preserve the original bang-bang form of the control-time history (Refs. 5.14, 5.18, and 5.10). One assumption (Ref. 5.10) is that the derivatives $\partial f_i / \partial u_j$ exist; Kelley et al. (Ref. 5.14) make no such assumption. An important set of observations is made in Ref. 5.10: If the switching times are to be treated as control parameters, then there must exist *at least* as many switching times as the $p + 1$ elements of the augmented constraint vector ψ. There must also exist at least as many switching times as in the optimal solution. If two switching times become equal in the limit, then the total number of assumed switching times may become less than the optimal number, which will create an uncontrollable situation. Also, choosing the switching times as control parameters precludes the possibility of finding singular solutions to the two-point boundary-value problem. To make it possible to search out a singular solution, a form of control consistent with singular subarcs must be assumed, an alternative we shall not discuss here.

Some difficulties arise with the computation of the inverse matrices in Eqs. (A5.12) and (A5.21). If t_0 is allowed to become a running variable t, and t approaches t_f, then these matrices will become singular. In addi-

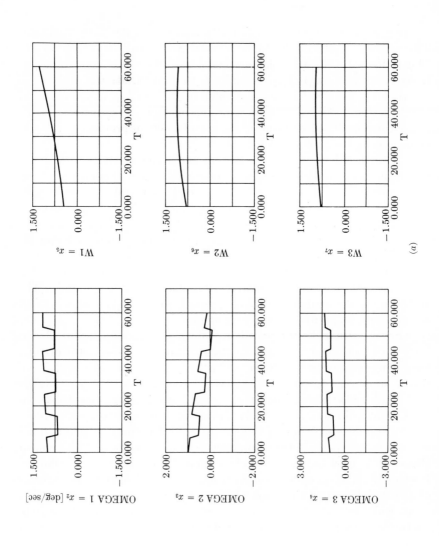

(a)

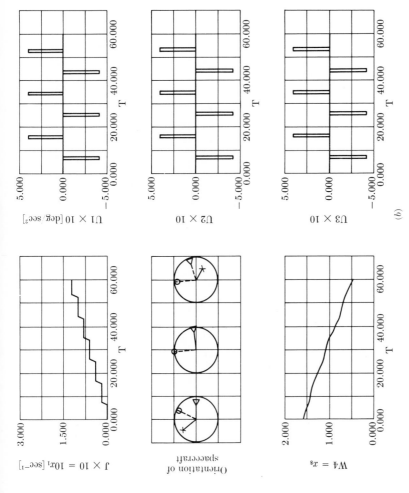

Fig. 5.14 Satellite attitude control; response to an initial guess of control time history. Initial conditions of run $R - 1$. $|u_i| \leq 0.412$ deg/sec^2 (*from Ref.* 5.8).

(b)

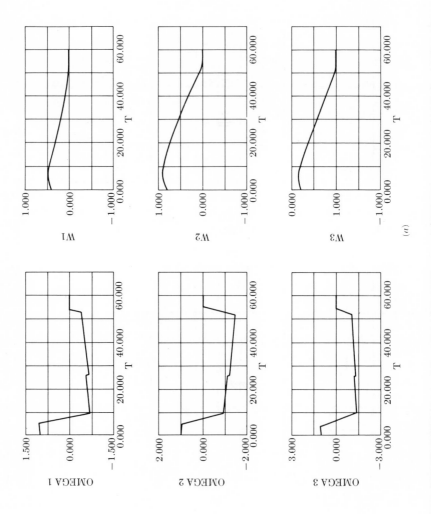

(a)

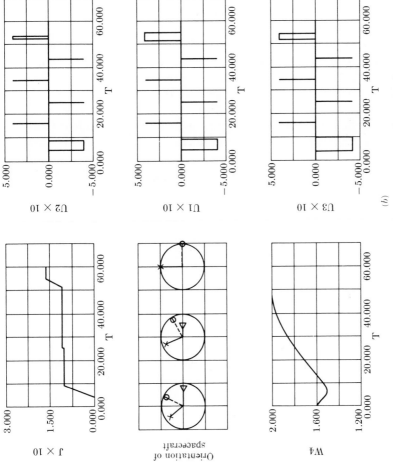

Fig. 5.15 Satellite attitude control; response curves generated by method of steepest-descent from the initial guess demonstrated in Fig. 5.14 (*from Ref. 5.8*).

(b)

tion, as an extremal solution is reached these matrices *may* become singular, with the implication from Eqs. (A5.12) and (A5.21) that it would take an infinite amount of control variation to improve the maximum value of the cost functional (Ref. 5.16). The matrix $D(t_0)$ of Eq. (A5.21) will in most cases not become singular when the optimal solution is reached,[1] because the control has been simulated by a series of pulses and each of the switching times is required to occur at $t = t_i$, with $t_0 \leq t_i \leq t_f$.

5.2.6d *Results.* The two series of diagrams in Figs. 5.14 and 5.15 show the optimization procedure suggested by Hales (Ref. 5.8). For convenience the orientation of the spacecraft is shown by projections of the three body fixed unit vectors, $\mathbf{n}_{xb}$, $\mathbf{n}_{yb}$, and $\mathbf{n}_{zb}$, onto the plane of the unit circle; a vector projected from above or lying in the plane of the unit circle is denoted by a solid line, and a vector projected from below is denoted by a dashed line. The three unit vectors are identified by a circle for $\mathbf{n}_{xb}$, cross for $\mathbf{n}_{yb}$, and a triangle for $\mathbf{n}_{zb}$. No identification is given to a vector if its projection is small, as in the middle circle of Fig. 5.14b.

Nineteen iterations were required to progress from the initial guess in Fig. 5.14 to the final response shown in Fig. 5.15. This case is only one of many examples studied and partially shown in the Hales thesis. Hales gives suggestions for the initial guess and the initial number of pulses. Although the details are beyond the scope of our discussion, some details are given in brief form in Appendix 5.1.

The fact that this control is suboptimal, and not a truly optimal control, is probably best illustrated by the final solution (the solution that reduced the disturbance to zero with the lowest possible control effort). In this solution no control was applied in the direct neighborhood of t_0 and t_f; this is generally not the case in minimum-effort optimal controls.

This example of development of a suboptimal control by an iterative method contains some features not encountered earlier. The system equations mentioned at the beginning of Sec. 5.2.6 but not given in detail contain a direct dependence on θ (see Fig. 5.11), which for small eccentricity is related to time by

$$\theta - \theta_0 = nt + 2en \sin (\theta - \theta_0)$$

where $\theta = \theta_0$ at $t = 0$ and $n = \mu^2/h^3$. μ is the gravitational constant of the earth and h is a constant proportional to the angular momentum of a particle about the center of mass of the earth, $r^2\dot{\theta} = h$. This means that the equations for the attitude control of a satellite in an elliptical orbit

---

[1] Even if the exact optimal switching times are reached, $D(t_0)$ may not become singular.

contain a *forcing term;* in other words, after an initial disturbance is reduced to zero and the control is turned off the attitude will not keep its desired position. The final state obtained is not a state of equilibrium, and the control of this state is a new problem, which for small eccentricities can certainly be handled with linearized system equations.

5.2.7 Suboptimal control of a higher-order system

Let us take another brief look at the physical problem treated in Sec. 5.2.6. For the case in which the attitude deviation stays small enough that a linearization of the system equations is possible, Busch (Ref. 5.19) has developed an efficient suboptimal control for eccentricities $e < 0.125$ by employing the switching law for minimum fuel consumption given by Pontryagin's maximum principle and then running the resulting trajectories in backward time on the analog computer. In particular, he has developed a suboptimal pitch control by determining the location of switching points for various final conditions in reverse time (initial conditions in forward time). The linearized pitch equation is decoupled from the linearized roll and yaw equations and can therefore be studied separately. Owing to the eccentricity of the orbit, there is a forcing term in the differential equation. For an eccentricity as small as $e < 0.125$ the coupled equations for the roll and yaw motions also become simple. The yaw motion is that of a $1/s^2$ plant with not too large a forcing term arising from roll motion. The simplified roll motion is not affected by the yaw motion, and the roll equation has very nearly the same form as the linearized unforced pitch equation.

Busch used the nonclassical Euler angles in establishing the equations of motion θ_1, θ_2, and θ_3 (see Figs. 5.16 and 5.17) and described the general

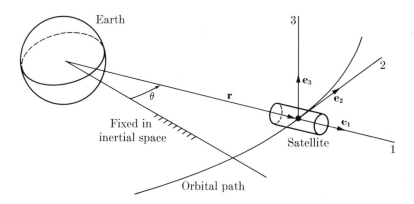

Fig. 5.16 Attitude control of a satellite; attitude reference frame, R.

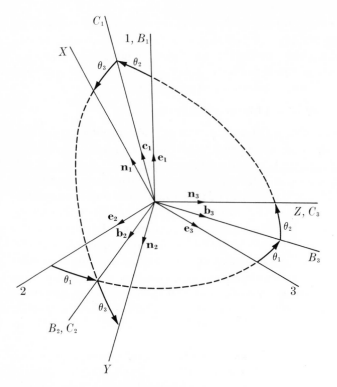

Fig. 5.17   Three-axes Euler angles.

motions by first-order differential equations, with

$$\theta_i = x_{2i-1}$$
$$\theta_i' = x_{2i} \qquad i = 1, 2, 3 \tag{5.60}$$

The moments of inertia of the satellite, I_i, appear in the equations through their parameters

$$k_i = \frac{I_k - I_j}{I_i} \tag{5.61}$$

The motions studied were those caused by disturbances at different stations on the orbit (see Fig. 5.18), with maximum-control components N_i, and a suboptimal solution was found for the pitch motion with the controls indicated in Fig. 5.19.   Figure 5.20 shows a comparison of optimal and suboptimal trajectories.   The number indicating the fuel consumption, J_3, shows that the suboptimal control is quite good.

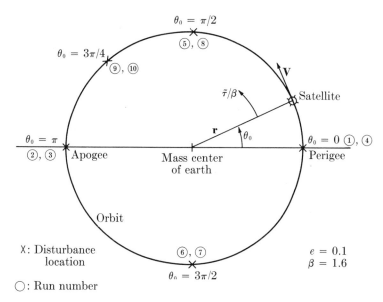

Fig. 5.18 Orbit locations of representative disturbances.

The suboptimal control for the roll and yaw motions was developed by neglecting their coupling. Figure 5.21 indicates the yaw switching lines for

$$u_1 = -\tfrac{1}{2}[\text{sgn}\,(x_2|x_2| + 2x_2) + \text{sgn}\,(x_2 + cx_1)] \qquad (5.62)$$

with $c = 0.25$ for the considered range of eccentricity and

$$u_2 = \begin{cases} -N_2\,\text{sgn}\,x_4 & x_4{}^2 > ax_3 \\ 0 & x_4{}^2 < ax_3 \end{cases} \qquad (5.63)$$

where a is a constant.[1]   Figure 5.22 shows a comparison of optimally and suboptimally controlled roll and yaw motions. The figures show only the so-called "acquisition control." The steady-state control is an additional problem, as was discussed in the preceding section.

This example shows clearly how much simpler the control of linear systems is and how much insight can be gained from a sophisticated study of backward-time trajectories.

5.2.8 Suboptimal control of a high-order system by using only part of the state variables

Often there is need for a simple but efficient control for a higher-order system. The minimum-settling-time control for a second-order system

[1] For the determination of a see Ref. 5.19.

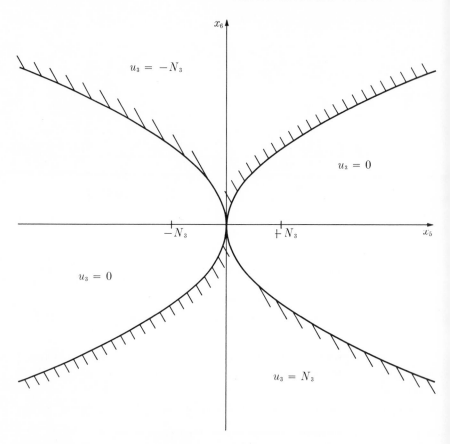

Fig. 5.19 Pitch motion; suboptimal switching lines.

with the transfer function $1/s^2$, for example, is very simple. Practical applications of this control were suggested by J. F. Coales in England and an example is described here by Chestnut et al. (Ref. 5.20), who were interested in automatic aircraft landing, which required a special landing maneuver (indicated in Fig. 5.23 as the reference). At the beginning of the control operation (time is replaced in this figure by horizontal distance) notice that the aircraft is too high above ground and has a horizontal direction of flight. This means that e and $\dot{e}$ are clearly measurable. There is no need to approach the reference curve ($e = 0$) at once, but a definite goal is to minimize the deviation between actual flight trajectory and desired (reference) flight trajectory at some distance before touchdown. The usual symmetrical flight of an uncontrolled aircraft is described by a fourth-order differential equation; however, Chestnut et al.

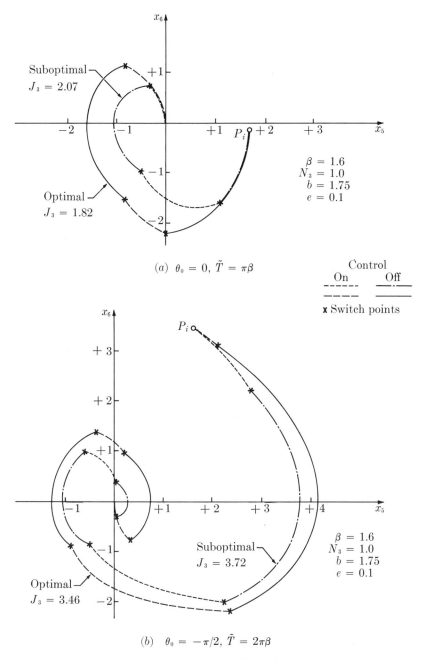

Fig. 5.20 Pitch motion; comparison of optimal and suboptimal trajectories.

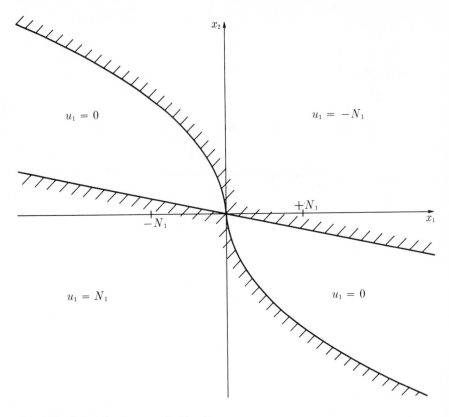

Fig. 5.21   Suboptimal yaw switching lines.

were concerned only with e and $\dot{e}$ and used these variables for control. Since this is not a case of zeroing an initial disturbance, position and velocity must be measured repeatedly and corrected. During this process the aircraft is in progress, so a *prediction* is necessary. Figure 5.24 shows a block diagram of the control system, and Fig. 5.25 shows the predicted trajectory and actual trajectory until at point k of Fig. 5.23 the error and its derivative reach zero; beyond k small hunting (chatter) exists about the reference curve. Figure 5.25 is reminiscent of the minimum-settling-time problem for the plant $1/s^2$. Reference 5.20 shows additional experiments with fast models of different degrees of accuracy of prediction.

This last example illustrates a very primitive "suboptimal" control, which nevertheless borrows an essential idea from the knowledge of the time-dependent behavior of an optimal control.

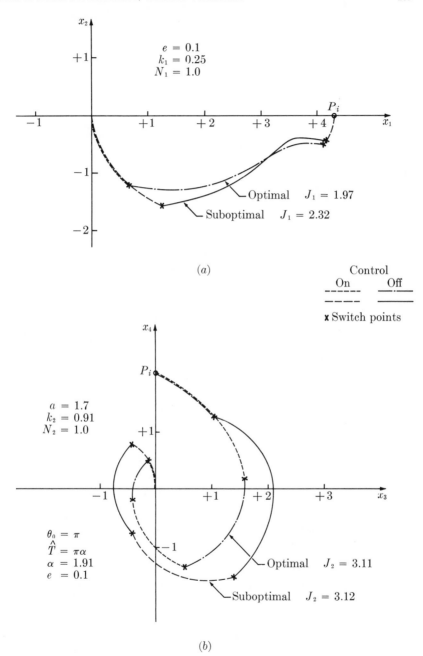

Fig. 5.22 Comparison of optimal and suboptimal trajectories. (*a*) Yaw motion. (*b*) Roll motion.

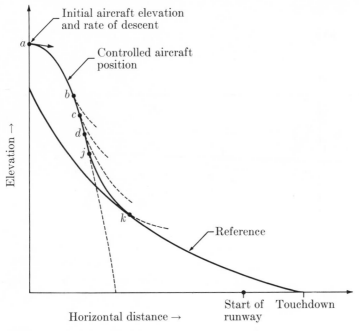

Elevation →

Horizontal distance →

Initial aircraft elevation and rate of descent

Controlled aircraft position

Reference

Start of Touchdown
runway

Fig. 5.23 Predictive control applied to automatic landing of aircraft.

5.3 SATURATING CONTROLS

It is well known that amplifiers used in linear control systems saturate (see Fig. 5.26a) and that this fact must be taken into account in considering the performance of a system. In many cases

$$u = N \tanh \alpha F = N \frac{e^{\alpha F} - e^{-\alpha F}}{e^{\alpha F} + e^{-\alpha F}} = N \frac{1 - e^{-2\alpha F}}{1 + e^{-2\alpha F}}$$

might be considered a good input-output relation for such an amplifier, where the coefficient α is appropriately chosen. However, introduction of this function would undoubtedly make the system nonlinear, and the usual application of the Laplace transform and the frequency-response method would no longer apply.

It seems much simpler to approximate this input-output relation by a broken line (see Fig. 5.26b), which gives for $|F| < |F^*|$ a strictly linear behavior and for $F > F^*$ the behavior of a system with relay control. As a simple example consider Fig. 5.27. The plant has the transfer

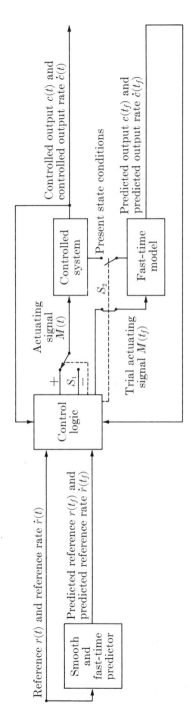

Fig. 5.24 Block diagram of a predictive control system.

267

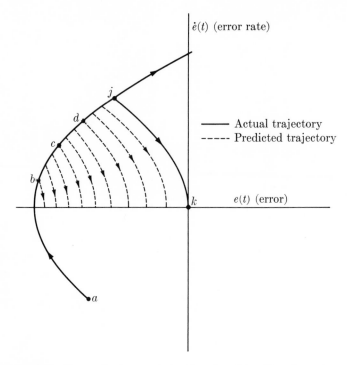

Fig. 5.25   Phase-plane portrait for the aircraft landing shown in Fig. 5.23.

function

$$\frac{1}{(s^2 + 2\zeta s + 1)} \tag{5.64}$$

with $0 < |\zeta| < 1$, $r(\tau) - c(\tau) = e(\tau)$, and $F = e + k_1 e'$. The equations describing the system with only initial disturbances $[r(\tau) \equiv 0 \text{ for } \tau > 0]$ are

$$
\begin{aligned}
r - c &= e \\
-u(\tau) &= c'' + 2\zeta c' + c \\
u(\tau) &= \begin{cases} e + k_1 e' & |F| \leq |F^*| \\ N \operatorname{sgn}(e + k_1 e') & |F| \geq |F^*| \end{cases}
\end{aligned}
\tag{5.65}
$$

The solution in the region $|F| \leq |F^*|$ is given by

$$e'' + (2\zeta + k_1)e' + 2e = 0 \tag{5.66}$$

with the poles

$$-\tfrac{1}{2}(2\zeta + k_1) \pm \sqrt{\tfrac{1}{4}(2\zeta + k_1)^2 - 2} \tag{5.67}$$

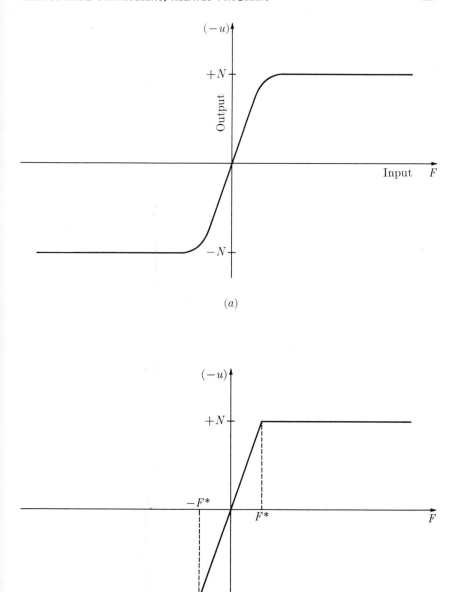

(a)

(b)

Fig. 5.26(*a*) Amplifier characteristic; (*b*) approximate amplifier characteristic.

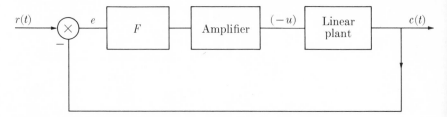

Fig. 5.27 Block diagram of system with saturating amplifier.

Depending on the value of k_1, these poles may be conjugate complex or real.   In both cases the path of the phase point describing the behavior of the system in the phase plane can be drawn easily.   Figure 5.28 shows the phase plane divided by the lines $F = 0$ and $F = \pm F^*$.   Outside the

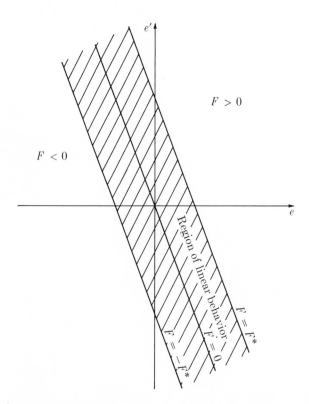

Fig. 5.28 Phase-plane subdivision for control of a second-order plant.

strip $(-F^*, F^*)$ the system follows the equation

$$e'' + 2\zeta e' + e = -N \operatorname{sgn} F \qquad (5.68)$$

If $|\zeta| < 1$, the phase-point trajectory is most easily designed in an inclined coordinate system (see Fig. 5.29); of course, the lines $F = 0$ and $F = \pm F^*$ can also be shown in this system. If the initial point lies in the region $|F| > F^*$, we start in Fig. 5.29 with the design of the trajectory and jump to Fig. 5.28 as soon as we hit one of the lines $|F| = F^*$. If the poles in the linear region are negative real, the trajectory will lead to zero; if they are conjugate complex with negative real part, the phase trajectory may start, say, at a point on F^* and hit the line $-F^*$, in which case we would have to return to Fig. 5.29, etc. In any event, a construction of the entire trajectory is rather simple and requires only a final drawing in either of the diagrams, with the trajectory points transferred point by point from one diagram to the other (there is no simpler way).

With higher-order systems it is best to study the system with contactor control separately from one with linear control. The essential features of the saturating control can generally be obtained from these studies, particularly if the gain of the linear system is high, in which case the system will behave essentially as a contactor-controlled system, except it will not display chatter motion near the origin.

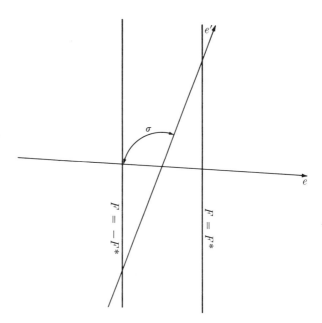

Fig. 5.29   Auxiliary phase plane.

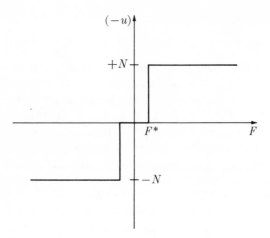

Fig. 5.30 Control element (relay) with dead zone.

5.4 DUAL-MODE CONTROLS

It may be desirable in a design to avoid certain features of discontinuous control, such as a high-frequency steady-state chatter, which influences other parts of a larger system unfavorably (it acts as a kind of exterior noise source). In this case we have two choices. In stable plants we may choose a control element (see Fig. 5.30) with a small dead zone for eliminating the steady-state chatter, or we may intentionally arrange the control to be linear in a certain region of the state space and nonlinear in the rest. This requires a design that allows us to measure, say, $\|\mathbf{e}\|$ and allows the plant (see Fig. 5.31) to be steered by box I or box II. The book by Thaler and Pastel (Ref. 5.22) gives some examples of dual-mode control.

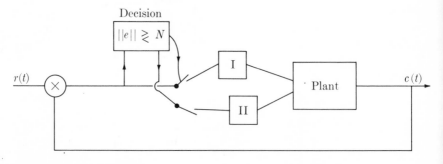

Fig. 5.31 Dual-mode control.

5.5 STABILITY OF CONTACTOR-CONTROLLED PLANTS

Chapter 2 gave several examples of the control of stable and unstable plants with the help of relays, and it was pointed out that a badly chosen relay control can destabilize a stable plant and a well-chosen relay can control an unstable plant in at least a limited region of state space (that is, only disturbances of limited magnitude $\|e\|$ can be zeroed). As discussed, the criterion for determining whether a relay-controlled plant represents a stable system is the occurrence of periodic solutions of finite amplitude, a relatively easy matter to investigate for second-order systems. In Chap. 3 the occurrence of periodic solutions was studied in more detail. However, no directions were given for finding all possible periodic solutions for a higher-order system and any arbitrarily given switching manifold. In fact, it was mentioned that for discontinuous switching functions the task of finding all possible periodic solutions is rather difficult. We must therefore look for a more general criterion to investigate the stability of systems with discontinuous controls.

There is, of course, the powerful method of using a Lyapunov function to test the stability of a system (Refs. 5.23 to 5.27). However, finding a Lyapunov function requires a great deal of ingenuity, and methods such as Zubov's (Ref. 5.28), which show a systematic way to find a Lyapunov function, are restricted to continuous systems.

Since a system with relay control may exhibit chatter in certain regions of the stable space, the system must actually be described by two sets of differential equations, one set for regular motion with regular switching on the switching manifold and another set for the average motion in the chatter region. It is therefore necessary to investigate the behavior of a chosen Lyapunov function in both these regions; the Lyapunov function which has to be a positive-definite function must have a negative-definite derivative with respect to time in the region of regular motion and when the motion is restrained to the switching manifold.

Weissenberger (Ref. 5.29) has investigated the stability of relay-controlled systems with the help of a very simple Lyapunov function; it has an analytic form which was introduced into the literature by Lur'e (Ref. 5.30):

$$V = \tfrac{1}{2}x^t H x + \int_0^F \operatorname{sgn} F \, dF \qquad (5.69)$$

where H is a constant $n \times n$ matrix if x has n components. If F is a linear function of the state variables, this yields

$$V = \tfrac{1}{2}x^t H x + k^t x \operatorname{sgn} k^t x \qquad (5.70)$$

For the sliding region[1] the Lyapunov function takes the simpler form

$$V_s = \tfrac{1}{2}x^t H x \tag{5.71}$$

Weissenberger determined the array of scalars h_{ik} of the matrix H which gave the largest region of stability; he used a steepest-ascent method in which he employed computer methods developed Rodden (Ref. 5.31). For higher-order or nonlinear systems the simple quadratic form, the first part of the left-hand side of Eq. (5.69), may not be the best form for getting good information about the true stability region; however, a discussion of the many possible forms suggested in the rather voluminous literature on Lyapunov functions (see, for example, Higgins' contribution in Ref. 5.27) would require more space than has been devoted to the essential features of the relay control itself. Therefore guidance to the available literature is all that is given here.

REFERENCES

5.1   Flügge-Lotz, I., and Andrew Craig: The Choice of Time for Zeroing a Disturbance in a Minimum-fuel Consumption Problem, *J. Basic Eng., Trans. ASME, Ser. D.*, vol. 87, no. 1, 1965.

5.2   Craig, A., and I. Flügge-Lotz: Realization of Minimum Control-effort Optimal Control, *Stanford Univ. Dept. Aeron. Astronaut., Rept.* 171, October, 1963.

5.3   Craig, Andrew, and I. Flügge-Lotz: Investigation of Optimal Control with Minimum-fuel Consumption Criterion for a Fourth-order Plant with Two Control Inputs: Synthesis of an Efficient Suboptimal Control, *J. Basic Eng., Trans. ASME, Ser. D.*, vol. 87, no. 1, pp. 39–57, 1965.

5.4   De Bra, Daniel: "The Large Attitude Motions and Stability due to Gravity of a Satellite with Passive Damping in an Orbit of Arbitrary Eccentricity about an Oblate Body," doctoral dissertation, Stanford University, Division of Engineering Mechanics, Stanford, Calif., 1962. (See also *Stanford Univ. Dept. Aeron. Astronaut., Rept.* 126, May, 1962.)

5.5   Flügge-Lotz, I., and H. Marbach: The Optimal Control of Linear Systems for a Minimum Control Effort Performance Criterion, *Stanford Univ. Dept. Aeron. Astronaut., Rept.* 153, 1963.

5.6   Flügge-Lotz, I., and H. Marbach: On the Minimum Effort Regulation of Stationary Linear Systems, *J. Franklin Inst.*, vol. 279, no. 4, pp. 229–245, 1965. (An abbreviated version of Ref. 5.5.)

5.7   Titus, H. A., Jr.: "Optimum and Quasi-optimum Control of Third- and Fourth-order Systems," doctoral dissertation, Stanford University Division of Engineering Mechanics, Stanford, Calif., 1962. (For an abbreviated version see I. Flügge-Lotz and H. A. Titus, Jr., in *Autom. Remote Control: Proc. Second Intern. Congr. Intern. Federation Autom. Control, Basel*, 1963, Butterworth-Oldenbourg, London, pp. 363–370.)

---

[1] If the imperfection of the relays is vanishingly small, chatter amplitudes tend toward zero. This state of motion is often called *sliding* (see Sec. 3.3.2). Some mathematicians define this sliding as the continuation of the motion of the system with ideal relays after reaching a point of indecision (endpoint of regular motion).

5.8 Hales, K. A.: "Minimum Attitude Control of a Rigid Body in Orbit by an Extended Method of Steepest Descent," doctoral dissertation, Stanford University, Division of Engineering Mechanics, Stanford, Calif., 1966.

5.9 Whittaker, E. T.: *A Treatise on the Analytical Dynamics of Particles and Rigid Bodies*, 4th ed., Cambridge University Press, London, 1964.

5.10 Denham, W. F., and A. E. Bryson, Jr.: Optimal Programming Problems with Inequality Constraints, part II, Solution by Steepest Ascent, *AIAA J.*, vol. 2, no. 1, 1964.

5.11 Zadeh, L. A., and Charles A. Desoer: *Linear System Theory: The State Space Approach*, McGraw-Hill Book Company, New York, 1963.

5.12 Denham, W. F.: Range Maximization of a Surface-to-surface Missile with In-flight Inequality Constraints, *J. Spacecraft Rockets*, vol. 1, no. 1, 1964.

5.13 Denham, W. F.: private correspondence with K. A. Hales, August 5, 1965.

5.14 Kelley, H. J., R. E. Kopp, and H. G. Moyer: Successive Approximation Techniques for Trajectory Optimization, *Proc. Inst. Aerospace Sci. Symp. Vehicle Systems Optimization, N.Y.*, November, 1961.

5.15 Bryson, A. E., and W. F. Denham: A Steepest-ascent Method for Solving Optimum Programming Problems, *J. Appl. Mech.*, vol. 29, 1962.

5.16 Bryson, A. E., and W. F. Denham: Multivariable Terminal Control for Minimum Mean Square Deviation from a Nominal Path, *Raytheon Rept.* BR-1333, September 20, 1961.

5.17 Rosenbaum, R.: "Convergence Technique for the Steepest-descent Method of Trajectory Optimization, *AIAA J.*, vol. 1, no. 7, 1963.

5.18 Kelley, H. J.: Guidance Theory and External Fields, *IRE Trans. Autom. Control*, AC-7, October, 1962.

5.19 Busch, Ronald: "The Attitude Control of a Satellite in an Elliptic Orbit," doctoral dissertation, Stanford University, Department of Aeronautics and Astronautics, Stanford, Calif., April, 1966. (An abbreviated version appeared in *J. Spacecraft Rockets*, vol. 4, no. 4, pp. 436–442, 1967.)

5.20 Chestnut, H., W. E. Sollecito, and P. H. Troutman: Predictive Control System Application, *AIEE Trans. (Appl. Ind.)*, vol. 80, part II, no. 55, pp. 128–139, 1961.

5.21 Selfand, I. M., and S. V. Fomin: *Calculus of Variations*, Prentice-Hall, Inc., Englewood Cliffs, N.J., 1963.

5.22 Thaler, G. J., and M. P. Pastel: *Analysis and Design of Nonlinear Feedback Control Systems*, pp. 327–331, McGraw-Hill Book Company, New York, 1962. (Dual-mode operation.)

5.23 Liapounoff, M. A.: *Problème général de la stabilité du mouvement*, Princeton University Press, Princeton, N.J., 1949.

5.24 Lefschetz, Solomon: *Stability of Nonlinear Control Systems*, Academic Press, Inc. New York, 1965.

5.25 La Salle, J. P., and Solomon Lefschetz: *Stability by Liapunov's Direct Method with Application*, Academic Press Inc., New York, 1961.

5.26 Hahn, W.: *Theory and Application of Liapunov's Direct Method*, Springer-Verlag OHG, Berlin, 1959. (A translation by S. H. Lehnigk and H. H. Hosenthien was published by Prentice-Hall, Inc., Englewood Cliffs, N.J., 1963.)

5.27 Kazda, L. F. (ed.): *Work Session in Lyapunov's Second Method*, sponsored by the Nonlinear Subcommittee of the AIEE Feedback Control Systems Committee, September, 1960, published by The University of Michigan Industry Program of the College of Engineering, Ann Arbor, Mich.

5.28 Zubov, V. I.: "Methods of A. M. Lyapunov and Their Application," translated from a publication of the Publishing House of Leningrad University, 1957, *U.S. Dept. Commerce, Rept.* AEC-tr-4439, October, 1961.

5.29   Weissenberger, Stein: Stability-boundary Approximations for Relay-control Systems via a Steepest-ascent Construction of Lyapunov Functions, *J. Basic Eng., Trans. ASME, Ser. D*, vol. 88, no. 2, pp. 419–428, 1966.

5.30   Lur'e, A. I.: *Some Non-linear Problems in the Theory of Automatic Control*, translated from the Russian, Her Majesty's Stationery Office, London, 1957. [Or see the German translation, H. Kindler and R. Reissig (eds.), *Einige nichtlineare Probleme aus der Theorie der selbsttätigen Regelung*, Akademie-Verlag GmbH, Berlin, 1957.]

5.31   Rodden, J. J.: "Numerical Applications of Lyapunov Stability Theory," doctoral dissertation, Stanford University, Division of Engineering Mechanics, Stanford, Calif., 1964. (An abbreviated version appears in reprints J.A.C.C., pp. 261–268, Stanford University, 1964.)

5.32   Yin, M., and W. C. Grimmel: *IEEE Trans. Autom. Control*, to be published 1968.

APPENDIX 5.1   DETAILS TO SEC. 5.2.6; OPTIMIZATION WITH THE HELP OF COMPUTING DEVICES

The following equations describe how variations in the terminal conditions and in the initial state $\mathbf{x}(t_0)$ influence control history. Derivations are given both for the conventional method, where the elements of $\mathbf{u}$ are not bounded, and for the extended method, where the u_j are bounded.

1. Conventional method

First let us derive the expression for $\delta\mathbf{u}(t)$. From Eq. (5.35) we saw that computation of $\delta\mathbf{u}(t)$ gives us the new control history $\mathbf{u}(t)$, since $\mathbf{u}_n(t)$ is already known. The technique we shall employ here is to minimize the $V(t)$ defined in Eq. (5.48), subject to the constraint $\delta\psi$ of Eq. (5.47) (see Ref. 5.16). For this purpose we let $t = t_0$ in Eq. (5.47) and consider t_0, $W(t)$, $\delta\psi$, $\delta\mathbf{x}(t_0)$, $\Lambda^T(t_f,t)$, and $G(t)$ as known. The vector ψ contains as its first element the difference between the cost function ϕ and its desired minimum value ϕ_d; therefore ψ becomes a $p + 1$ vector:

$$\psi = \begin{bmatrix} \phi - \phi_d \\ \psi_1 \\ \cdots \\ \psi_p \end{bmatrix} = 0 \tag{A5.1}$$

Note that in most problems the actual value of ϕ_d will not be known beforehand. The matrix $\Lambda^T(t_f,t)$ of Eq. (5.44) now becomes a $(p + 1) \times n$ matrix, since ψ has become a $p + 1$ vector. Since the constraint ψ does not contain time explicitly, the variation in the augmented vector ψ may be written as

$$\delta\psi = \psi(\mathbf{x}(t_f)) - \psi(\mathbf{x}_n(t_f)) \tag{A5.2}$$

where the first term on the right indicates the value of ψ after the *next* iteration and the second term indicates the value of the constraint resulting from the *present* nominal trajectory. If we require constraint (A5.1) to be met (to a first-order approximation) on the next iteration, Eq. (A5.2) becomes

$$\delta\psi = -\psi(\mathbf{x}_n(t_f)) \tag{A5.3}$$

where ψ is as defined in Eq. (A5.1).

Minimization of $V(t_0)$ subject to the integral constraint of Eq. (5.47) is equivalent to an isoperimetric problem in the calculus of variations (Ref. 5.21). Therefore we minimize the new functional V^* as

$$V^* = \int_{t_0}^{t_f} [\delta\mathbf{u}^T W(\tau)\,\delta\mathbf{u} - \mu^T \Lambda^T(t_f,\tau)G(\tau)\,\delta\mathbf{u}(\tau)]\,d\tau$$
$$+ \mu^T[\delta\psi - \Lambda^T(t_f,t_0)\,\delta\mathbf{x}(t_0)] \tag{A5.4}$$

where μ is a $p + 1$ vector of constants. The first variation in Eq. (A5.4) leads to

$$\delta V^* = \int_{t_0}^{t_f} [2\delta\mathbf{u}^T W(\tau) - \mu^T \Lambda^T(t_f,\tau)G(\tau)]\,\delta(\delta\mathbf{u})\,d\tau \tag{A5.5}$$

For an extremum in V^*, $\delta V^* = 0$ for arbitrary variations $\delta(\delta\mathbf{u})$. The integrand of Eq. (A5.5) must vanish, leading to

$$\delta\mathbf{u}(t) = \tfrac{1}{2}W^{-1}(t)G^T(t)\Lambda(t_f,t)\mu \tag{A5.6}$$

where the superscript $^{-1}$ denotes the inverse of a matrix. Substituting Eq. (A5.6) into Eq. (5.47) gives

$$\delta\psi = \Lambda^T(t_f,t_0)\,\delta\mathbf{x}(t_0) + \tfrac{1}{2}C(t_0)\mu \tag{A5.7}$$

with the defining relationship

$$C(t_0) = \int_{t_0}^{t_f} \Lambda^T(t_f,\tau)G(\tau)W^{-1}(\tau)G^T(\tau)\Lambda(t_f,\tau)\,d\tau \tag{A5.8}$$

Thus the vector μ may be written, from Eq. (A5.7), as

$$\mu = 2C^{-1}(t_0)[\delta\psi - \Lambda^T(t_f,t_0)\,\delta\mathbf{x}(t_0)] \tag{A5.9}$$

Finally, the desired expression for $\delta\mathbf{u}(t)$ is written, from Eqs. (A5.6) and (A5.9), as

$$\delta\mathbf{u}(t) = W^{-1}(t)G^T(t)\Lambda(t_f,t)C^{-1}(t_0)[\delta\psi - \Lambda^T(t_f,t_0)\,\delta\mathbf{x}(t_0)] \tag{A5.10}$$

The time t_0 may possess discrete values t_k, or a running continuous variable t may be used.

By defining two more matrices, an $m \times (p + 1)$ matrix

$$L_1(t) \equiv W^{-1}(t)G^T(t)\Lambda(t_f,t) \tag{A5.11a}$$

and a $(p + 1) \times n$ matrix

$$L_2(t_0) \equiv C^{-1}(t_0)\Lambda^T(t_f,t_0) \qquad\qquad (A5.11b)$$

we may write Eq. (A5.10) as

$$\delta \mathbf{u}(t) = L_1(t)C^{-1}(t_0)\ \delta \psi - L_1(t)L_2(t_0)\ \delta \mathbf{x}(t_0) \qquad (A5.12)$$

Expression (A5.12) describes how a variation in the augmented terminal constraint, $\delta \psi$, and a variation in the state $\mathbf{x}_n$ at $t = t_0$ influence a change in control history.

2. Extended method

We now derive the expression for $\delta \mathbf{u}(t)$ with the elements of $\mathbf{u}$ bounded. With a technique from the calculus of variations similar to that of the last discussion, we start with Eqs. (5.56), (5.57), and (5.58). First the new functional V^* is minimized:

$$V^* = \sum_i [\delta \mathbf{u}^T\ T_i\ \delta \mathbf{u} - \mu^T\Lambda^T(t_f,t_i)G_i\ \delta \mathbf{u}(t_i)]$$
$$+ \mu^T[\delta \psi - \Lambda^T(t_f,t_0)\ \delta \mathbf{x}(t_0)] \quad (A5.13)$$

where $G_i = G(t_i)$. The first variation of V^* leads to

$$\delta V^* = \sum_i [2\delta \mathbf{u}^T\ T_i - \mu^T\Lambda^T(t_f,t_i)G_i]\ \delta(\delta \mathbf{u}(t_i)) \qquad (A5.14)$$

For an extremum in V^*, $\delta V^* = 0$ for arbitrary variations in $\delta(\delta \mathbf{u}(t_i))$. Each term of the summation in Eq. (A5.14) must vanish, leading to

$$\delta \mathbf{u}(t_i) = \tfrac{1}{2}T_i^{-1}G_i^T\Lambda(t_f,t_i)\mu \qquad\qquad (A5.15)$$

Substituting Eq. (A5.15) into Eq. (5.57) gives

$$\delta \psi = \Lambda^T(t_f,t_0)\ \delta \mathbf{x}(t_0) + \tfrac{1}{2}D(t_0)\ \mu \qquad\qquad (A5.16)$$

with the defining relationship

$$D(t_0) = \sum_i \Lambda^T(t_f,t_i)G_iT_i^{-1}G_i^T\Lambda(t_f,t_i) \qquad\qquad (A5.17)$$

Thus the vector μ may be written, from Eq. (A5.16), as

$$\mu = 2D^{-1}(t_0)\ [\delta \psi - \Lambda^T(t_f,t_0)\ \delta \mathbf{x}(t_0)] \qquad\qquad (A5.18)$$

With Eqs. (A5.15) and (A5.18) we may write an expression for $\delta \mathbf{u}(t)$ for this case:

$$\delta \mathbf{u}(t_i) = T_i^{-1}G_i^T\Lambda(t_f,t_i)\ D^{-1}(t_0)[\delta \psi - \Lambda^T(t_f,t_0)\ \delta \mathbf{x}(t_0)] \qquad (A5.19)$$

Then, by defining an $m \times (p + 1)$ matrix

$$N_1(t_i) \equiv T_i^{-1}G_i^T\Lambda(t_f,t_i) \qquad\qquad (A5.20a)$$

and a $(p + 1) \times n$ matrix

$$N_2(t_0) \equiv D^{-1}(t_0)\Lambda^T(t_f,t_0) \tag{A5.20b}$$

we may write Eq. (A5.19) as

$$\delta \mathbf{u}(t_i) = N_1(t_i) \, D^{-1}(t_0) \, \delta \psi - N_1(t_i)N_2(t_0) \, \delta \mathbf{x}(t_0) \tag{A5.21}$$

Note the similarity between Eqs. (A5.12) and (A5.21). Relationship (A5.21) provides information on how the switching times must be changed from their nominal values $\mathbf{u}_n(t_i)$ before the next iteration is begun.

3. Computational techniques

A computation algorithm is presented here for application of the steepest-descent method to systems with bounds on the control variables.

1. Guess a nominal-control-time history $\mathbf{u}_n(t)$ and integrate the system differential equations forward until t_f is reached, storing the values of $\mathbf{x}_n(t)$ at a set of sufficiently small time intervals.

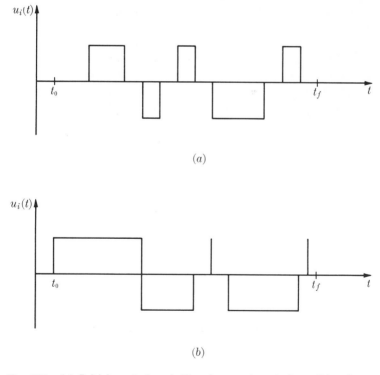

(a)

(b)

Fig. A5.1 (a) Initial control and (b) subsequent control resulting from application of method of steepest-descent.

2. Compute the matrix $\Lambda^T(t_f, t_f)$ [Eq. (5.46)] and integrate the adjoint system of Eq. (5.45) backward in time from t_f, using the stored values of $\mathbf{x}_n$. Compute and store $N_1(t_i)$ at each of the switching times t_i.

3. If desired, set $t = t_0$ and allow t to become a running variable with discrete values; calculate the matrices $D(t_k)$ of Eq. (A5.17), where $t_k = t_0, t_i, \ldots, t_r$ and $t_r < t_f$. In each case the summation $D(t_k)$ is performed over all values of switching times t_i, where $t_k \leq t_i \leq t_f$. Invert the $D(t_k)$ matrices and store the resulting matrices along with the $N_2(t_k)$ matrices.

4. Integrate the equations forward again on the basis of a new control history of switching times $\mathbf{u}(t_i) = \delta\mathbf{u}(t_i) + \mathbf{u}_n(t_i)$, where $\delta\mathbf{u}(t_i)$ is calculated from (A5.21). Again, the variable t_0 may take on discrete values $t_0, t_i, \ldots, t_r$. The $\delta\mathbf{x}(t_k)$ vector is calculated by Eq. (5.35) and the $\delta\psi$ vector is selected as in Eq. (A5.3) for use in Eq. (A5.21). No attempt is made to improve the payoff function until further iterations partially satisfy the terminal constraints. The new values of $\mathbf{x}(t)$, based on the new $\mathbf{u}(t_i)$, which has become $\mathbf{u}_n(t_i)$, are stored as $\mathbf{x}_n(t)$.

This iterative procedure of forward and backward iteration and updating of the control-variable and state-variable nominal histories is continued until convergence to a satisfactory trajectory is achieved.

To simplify the simulation the newly calculated switching times resulting from $\delta\mathbf{u}(t_i)$ and Eq. (5.56) were required to retain their order in time for each component of the control vector, and the t_i were required to satisfy $t_0 \leq t_i \leq t_k$. For example, the set of pulses for the u_i element may be changed from that of Fig. A5.1a to that of Fig. A5.1b. The pulses can expand and contract, and can even collapse.

Index